Consumer Math Success Kit

Second Edition

David E. Newton

WALCH PUBLISHING®

User's Guide
to
Walch Reproducible Books

As part of our general effort to provide educational materials which are as practical and economical as possible, we have designated this publication a "reproducible book." The designation means that purchase of the book includes purchase of the right to limited reproduction of all pages on which this symbol appears:

Here is the basic Walch policy: We grant to individual purchasers of this book the right to make sufficient copies of reproducible pages for use by all students of a single teacher. This permission is limited to a single teacher, and does not apply to entire schools or school systems, so institutions purchasing the book should pass the permission on to a single teacher. Copying of the book or its parts for resale is prohibited.

Any questions regarding this policy or requests to purchase further reproduction rights should be addressed to:

Permissions Editor
J. Weston Walch, Publisher
P. O. Box 658
Portland, Maine 04104-0658

1   2   3   4   5   6   7   8   9   10
ISBN 0-8251-2852-8
Copyright © 1983, 1996 Instructional Horizons
Published by J. Weston Walch, Publisher,
P.O. Box 658, Portland, ME 04104-0658

Contents

Introduction to the Second Edition

Over the last decade, *Consumer Math Success Kit* has been used by more than 100,000 teachers and students. The continuing popularity of the book suggests that no major changes in its format should be attempted. Instead, the focus of this revision has been to correct errors found in the first edition and to bring up to date information, statistics, and other aspects of the book that have become outdated. In particular, interest rates, prices, tax tables, and new nutrition information have been incorporated into the new edition. As always, the author has appreciated input from users of the book and encourages both teachers and students to make us aware of any errors that may remain.

—David E. Newton
Ashland, Oregon
May 1995

Introduction to the First Edition

Buy! Sell! Spend! Save! Invest!

Consumers face many demands in the marketplace today. There seem to be endless ways in which we can use our money. Students need help in facing these demands. They need to understand the terminology of consumer mathematics. They need to understand what their options are in buying, selling, and saving. And, most of all, they need to develop the skills needed for problems in consumer mathematics.

The mathematics of consumerism is actually quite simple. There are few instances in which anything more complex than addition, subtraction, multiplication, and division of whole numbers, fractions, and decimals is involved. Problems in consumer mathematics may seem more difficult than they really are because of the settings in which they occur. Stock transactions, bus and train schedules, and utility bills do not involve advanced mathematics. But the terms that are used and the form in which problems appear may frighten off those not familiar with these fields. One objective of this book is to help students see that they probably already have the mathematical skills needed to be "survivors" in the marketplace.

But that argument works in reverse, too. Some math students never quite see the point of the skills they are asked to master. What need is there for learning how to multiply fractions or divide decimals? As a result, they are not motivated to develop these skills . . . and in some cases they never do! A book like this can show students the practical applications of mathematics which most of us cannot avoid. Mathematics is not a theoretical subject of use only in schoolrooms; it is a vital, everyday necessity. Our second aim, then, is to provide motivation for students to develop essential skills in basic mathematics.

A word about the design of this book. It has been put together in such a way that you may choose those topics on which you want students to work. The topics are arranged in an alphabetic, encyclopedic order. The table of contents allows you to locate any one of 53 topics in consumer mathematics. The particular section you select for your students may be removed from the book and photocopied or reproduced in any other manner.

Each topic consists of three parts. One page provides a brief introduction to the topic and at least one solved example. The introduction is not intended to supply a complete, detailed discussion of the topic. You have probably already done that in class. Or your regular textbook will have done a more thorough job of teaching the subject. The solved example(s) will, however, provide students with a model they can use in solving the

practice problems. You may photocopy and hand out this background page, or you may choose to use it as the basis for your own lecture on the topic.

A second section is entitled "Practice Problems." This is the heart of the book. It contains exercises which illustrate the concepts discussed in the background page and described in the solved example(s). The problems are arranged in order, from simple to more complex.

Finally, there is a page of teacher notes. These mention new vocabulary used in the topic, the type of mathematics required in solving problems of this type, and a few ideas for teaching the topic at hand.

—David E. Newton

CHAPTER ONE

Bank Statements

1. Bank Statements

A bank statement is a record of your checking account with some bank or other financial institution. The statement includes a list of the deposits you have made, the checks you have written, any ATM transactions you have conducted, and any bank charges. The bank statement allows you to compare your own financial records with those of the bank. The process of checking your own records against those of the bank is called **reconciliation**. Reconciling a checking account against a bank statement is sometimes difficult if any of the checks you have written or any of your ATM transactions have not "cleared" the bank. That means that you have written and sent the checks to someone, but they have not been returned to the bank before the statement came out. Or you may have used an ATM to withdraw money from your account just before the statement came out. In either case, the bank does not know that you have conducted a transaction that you already show in your checkbook.

Also, there may be service charges and/or interest payments that need to be recorded in your account. The bank knows what these charges and payments are as soon as they are figured. But you don't know them until you receive your bank statement. At this point, you have to add them to or subtract them from your own records. The solved example below shows how to reconcile a checkbook with a bank statement.

● **Example:**

Robin's checkbook balance as of March 31 is $148.35. Her bank statement shows that her balance is $182.21 The statement also shows interest of $0.31 and charges of $1.75. The following transactions appear in Robin's checkbook but have not yet cleared the bank:

Deposit: $100.00 on March 31. Checks: #872: $19.89; #880: $24.35; #883: $16.06; ATM withdrawal: $75.00.

Solution:

The first calculation is to correct the checkbook balance.

Corrected checkbook balance = Balance shown + Interest − Charges

Corrected balance = $148.35 + $0.31 − $1.75 = $146.91

Next, correct the bank statement balance.

Corrected bank statement balance = Balance shown + Late deposits
                                                            − Outstanding checks − Late ATM withdrawals

Corrected balance   = $182.21 + $100.00 − ($19.89 + $24.35 + $16.06) − $75.00
                              = $182.21 + $100.00 − $135.30 = $146.91

Now, both balances agree with each other and the checkbook and the bank statement have been reconciled.

Name _____ Date _____

1. Bank Statements

1. Lester's checkbook balance as of March 31 was $223.85. The bank statement he received on the same date showed a balance of $227.19. He received $0.79 interest and was charged $2.45 on his account for the month. Lester had one deposit of $25.00 and one check of $30.00 that were not recorded on the statement. Reconcile the checkbook balance with the statement balance.

_____

_____

2. The balance in Thong's checkbook on June 30 was $307.87. The bank statement dated June 28 showed a balance of $304.11. The statement also showed $1.19 interest earned and $3.15 in bank charges. The checks and deposits not shown on the statement are listed below. Reconcile the checkbook balance with the statement balance.

   Outstanding checks: #312: $18.25; #315: $12.45; Unrecorded deposit: $32.50 (June 29).

_____

_____

3. The statement Domenico received today (April 1) showed a balance in his checking account of $282.19. His own checkbook shows a balance of $45.98. He knows that the difference is a result of the fact that some checks he wrote last week and one ATM withdrawal have not yet cleared the bank. Those checks and that ATM transaction are listed below. The bank statement also showed interest of $1.83 and bank charges of $6.05 for the month. From this information, reconcile Domenico's account.

   Outstanding checks: #135: $17.85; #136: $62.00; #138: $44.98; #141: $29.87; #142: $35.85; #143: $49.88. ATM withdrawal: $50.00. Deposit not recorded: $50.00 (March 31).

_____

_____

4. Sylvia's checkbook balance on July 31 is $389.32. The information on her bank statement is given below. The outstanding checks, unrecorded deposits, and unrecorded ATM transactions are listed here also. From this information, reconcile her account for the month.

   Bank statement: $434.30; Interest: $0.79; Service charge: $2.75.
   Outstanding checks: #911: $53.29; #912: $31.16; #913: $20.04; #920: $11.42; #923: $24.50; #925: $16.90; #930: $33.30; #932: $8.70; #933: $10.55. Unrecorded deposits at ATM: 7/30: $183.52; 7/31: $69.40. Unrecorded ATM withdrawals: 7/30: $40.00; 7/31: $50.00.

_____

_____

Bank Statements
Teacher Notes

Mathematical skills required:

addition and subtraction of decimals

New vocabulary:

ATM
balance
bank statement
cleared
reconcile
service charge

Related topics:

Checking Accounts
Interest
Savings Accounts

Teaching suggestions:

1. The teacher or students might bring in bank statements of their own to examine.

2. The teacher may wish to explain some more detailed aspects of bank statements, such as additional bank charges for overdrawn accounts. Most bank statements describe the process of reconciliation and give detailed information about bank charges on the back of the bank statement.

3. The teacher may find it necessary to review with students the concept of ATM machines and explain how both deposits and withdrawals can be made using such machines.

CHAPTER TWO

Borrowing Money

Promissory Notes

Short-term Loans

Collateral Loans

Installment Loans (I)

Installment Loans (II)

Mortgage Loans

2. Promissory Notes

One way to borrow money is with a promissory note. A promissory note is an agreement between two people or between a financial institution and a person. The lender agrees to loan the borrower a certain amount of money for a certain period of time. If interest is charged on the note, it is said to be an **interest-bearing note**. The amount of interest collected on the note can be calculated from the following formula:

$$\text{Interest (i)} = \text{Principal (p)} \times \text{Rate (r)} \times \text{Time (t)}$$

The following examples show how to calculate the interest on a promissory note.

- **Example 1:**

Jane has asked to borrow money from her Aunt Alma. The terms Jane suggests are a loan of $500 for a period of 6 months at 12% interest per year. What total amount of money would Jane have to pay back at the end of the 6-month period? How much of this would be interest?

Solution:

Interest   = Principal × Rate × Time

= $500 × 12% per year × $\frac{1}{2}$ year (6 months)

= $30

Total amount due at end of 6 months = Principal + Interest

= $500 + $30

= $530

- **Example 2:**

Ariadne has received a loan from the Sunbeam National Bank for $2000. The loan is for 18 months and was issued at a rate of 14.8%. What total amount of interest will Ariadne have to pay on this loan?

Solution:

Interest   = Principal × Rate × Time

= $2000 × 14.8% × 1.5 years

= $444

The total amount Ariadne will have to pay back at the end of 18 months is equal to the principal plus the interest, or

Total amount due   = $2000 + $444

= $2444

Name _____ Date _____

2. Promissory Notes

1. Kurt has taken a 6-month loan from his Uncle Dave. The loan is for $1000 and will carry an interest rate of 8%. How much interest will Kurt owe at the end of the 6-month period?

   _____

2. Andrea has agreed to loan her friend Eddie $250 for a period of 18 months at a rate of 10%. How much interest will Eddie have to pay on this loan?

   _____

3. The Acme State Bank is offering personal loans for a period of two years at a rate of 11.4% simple interest. If Mrs. Durrell borrows $500 on this plan, how much interest will she have to pay for the loan?

   _____

   What is the total amount of money she will have to pay the bank at the end of two years?

   _____

4. Diane has taken out a loan for $1500 from the Sunbeam National Bank. The interest rate for the loan is 12.9% and is for a period of 15 months. What is the total amount of money Diane will have to pay back at the end of 15 months?

   _____

5. Simon's loan from the Sunbeam Bank is for $4500 at an interest rate of 1.3% per month. How much will he have to pay back if he retires the loan at the end of 6 months?

   _____

   At the end of 12 months? _____

   At the end of 18 months? _____

6. Listed below are five promissory notes from the Sunbeam Bank. Determine the amount of interest due on each note when it is repaid.

	Amount of Loan	Interest Rate	Time of Loan	
(a)	$1000	8%	1 year	_____
(a)	$2000	9.6%	6 months	_____
(a)	$ 500	11.3%	6 months	_____
(a)	$3000	14.8%	18 months	_____
(a)	$4500	15.1%	18 months	_____

3. Short-term Loans

Banks often loan money for a period of 30, 60, or 90 days. These are called **short-term loans**. Interest on the loan is calculated and deducted from the amount given to the borrower. Thus, a person who borrows $1000 on a short-term loan may actually receive only $960 from the bank. The other $40 would be interest on the loan, deducted in advance. The amount actually received by the borrower ($960 in this example) is called the **proceeds** of the loan. This kind of loan may also be called a **noninterest-bearing loan**.

The following examples show how to solve problems with short-term loans.

● **Example 1:**

Violet received a 60-day short-term loan of $850 from The Women's Bank. The interest on this loan is 12.8% per annum (per year) and is deducted from the face value of the loan. What are the proceeds due Violet on this loan?

Solution:

The proceeds = Face value of loan – Interest

Interest   = Principal × Rate × Time

             = $850 × 12.8% per annum × $^{60}\!/_{360}$ year

             = $18.13

The proceeds = $850.00 – $18.13

             = $831.87

● **Example 2:**

Peter's request for a short-term loan in the amount of $2500 was approved by the Plymouth State Bank. The proceeds for the loan, $2420.62, must be paid back in 90 days. What is the interest rate on this loan?

Solution:

Amount of interest = Face value of loan – Proceeds

                  = $2500.00 – $2420.62

                  = $79.38

Rate of interest $= \dfrac{\text{Interest}}{\text{Principal} \times \text{Time}}$

                  $= \dfrac{\$79.38}{\$2500 \times \frac{1}{4}(90 \text{ days})}$

                  = 12.7%

3. Short-term Loans

1. The Sterling Finance Company offers special commercial loans at the rate of 18.93% per year for 6-, 12-, or 18-month periods. How much interest would be owed on a $1500 loan for each of these three time periods?

   _____

2. The Women's Bank has issued Grant a 90-day short-term loan in the amount of 15.8% interest. The amount of the loan is $4500. Calculate the interest on this loan and the proceeds due Grant.

   _____

3. The Star State Bank issues 30-, 60-, and 90-day notes at a rate of 17.5% interest. What would be the proceeds and the interest on a $500 loan under each of these?

   _____

4. The short-term loan which Grace received from the Women's Bank for $1500 over a 90-day period brought her proceeds of $1449.37. How much interest and what rate of interest did she pay on this loan?

   _____

5. Joella's 60-day loan from the Star State Bank is for $850. The proceeds she received from the loan are $839.30. What is the interest rate on this loan?

   _____

6. The table below shows the amount of interest, proceeds, total loan and/or time of loan for some short-term loans granted by the Star State Bank. Calculate the unknown quantity or quantities in each case.

	Amount of Loan	Proceeds	Interest	Rate of Interest	Time
(a)	$1000	_____	_____	10.5%	30 days
(a)	$2000	_____	_____	17.4%	60 days
(a)	$2500	_____	_____	9.9%	90 days
(a)	$5000	_____	$110.83	_____	60 days
(a)	$2750	$2671.62	_____	_____	90 days

4. Collateral Loans

Loans are sometimes made if a person has something of value to offer as **collateral**. Collateral means that if the loan is not repaid, the bank or lender can keep the property given as collateral. A house, land, stocks, bonds, and insurance are often used as collateral. The term **demand loan** may also be used for collateral loans. The term means that the lender can ask for ("demand") its money back at any time. If the borrower does not return the money, he or she loses the collateral on the loan. The examples below illustrate the mathematics of collateral or demand loans.

● **Example 1:**

The Acme State Bank holds a demand note from Wendell Motley for $4000 dated January 3. Interest on the note is 14.9% per annum (per year). It is due to be paid back on August 14 the same year. How much interest will Wendell have to pay on this note?

Solution:

The first problem here is to find the number of days covered by the loan. From January 3 to August 14 would be:

January	28 days	May	31 days
February	28 days	June	30 days
March	31 days	July	31 days
April	30 days	August	14 days

Total: 223 days

For banking purposes, the **commercial year** is usually taken as having 360 days. So the length of time covered by the loan is $^{223}/_{360}$ year. Then,

Interest   = Principal × Rate × Time

= $4000 × 14.9% per year × $^{223}/_{360}$ year

= $369.19

● **Example 2:**

A second demand note held by the Acme Bank with Wendell was for $3500. It was issued on March 15 and called in on June 15. At that time, Wendell paid back a total of $3636.85. What was the interest rate on this note?

Solution:

From March 15 to June 15 is 92 days, or 92/360 year. So,

$$\text{Interest rate} = \frac{\text{Amount of Interest}}{\text{Principal} \times \text{Time}}$$

$$= \frac{\$136.85 (= \$3636.85 - \$3500.00)}{\$3500 \times \frac{92}{360}}$$

$$= 15.3\%$$

4. Collateral Loans

1. Robert has borrowed $2500 on a demand note from the First National Bank at a rate of 16.7% per annum. The note was approved on March 15 and falls due on September 9. How much interest will Robert have to pay on this note?

   _____

2. The chart below lists the principal and other information about some collateral loans from the Acme State Bank. In each example, calculate the quantity indicated by the blank lines.

	Principal	Date Issued	Date Called In	Interest Rate	Amount of Interest	Total Repaid
(a)	$1000	1/15	2/15	10.0%	_____	_____
(a)	$1000	2/3	4/8	10.8%	_____	_____
(a)	$1500	6/9	9/14	11.5%	_____	_____
(a)	$2250	7/10	10/5	13.8%	_____	_____
(a)	$1750	4/18	10/19	14.1%	_____	_____
(a)	$3500	3/8	11/1	11.9%	_____	_____
(a)	$2000	3/15	11/9	9.8%	_____	_____
(a)	$2000	3/18	11/10	_____	$142.20	_____
(a)	$5000	6/21	11/20	_____	_____	$5282.39
(a)	$2500	7/15	_____	12.3%	_____	$2611.04

5. Installment Loans (I)

Long-term loans are usually not repaid all at once. Instead, the borrower pays back a portion of the loan each month. Money borrowed on a car loan, for example, may be paid back in 24, 36, or 48 monthly payments. Each monthly payment consists of two parts: a payment towards the principal and an interest payment. Principal is the amount of money loaned the borrower. In some kinds of installment loans, the interest is calculated on the unpaid balance due on the loan. In this method, the monthly payment will be different (less) each month. As the amount still owed (the balance remaining on the principal) becomes less, the interest also becomes less. The example below illustrates this method.

● **Example:**

Henry borrows $1250 from the Apple Growers Credit Union at 16.1% per year for a period of six months. Interest is calculated on the unpaid balance of the loan. What are the monthly payments on this loan?

Solution:

The monthly payments will be different each month. But they will all be calculated the same way:

Monthly interest = Unpaid balance × Rate × Time

For the first month, this will be:

Interest, Month 1 $= \$1250 \times 16.1\%$ per year $\times \frac{1}{12}$ year
$= \$16.77$

Payment, Month 1 = One sixth of principal + Interest
$= 1/6 \times \$1250 + \$16.77$
$= \$208.33 + \$16.77$
$= \$225.10$

Now, the balance due for the second month is:
$\$1250.00 - \$208.33 = \$1041.67$

So the interest due for Month 2 is:

Interest $= \$1041.67 \times 16.1\% \times \frac{1}{12}$
$= \$13.98$

And the payment due is:

Amount due $= \$208.33 + \$13.98$
$= \$222.31$

Calculations for the remaining months are made in the same way. The interest payments and total payments for the last four months of the loan are as follows:

Month 3: $208.33 + $11.18 = $219.51

Month 4: $208.33 + $ 8.39 = $216.72

Month 5: $208.33 + $ 5.59 = $213.92

Month 6: $208.33 + $ 2.80 = $211.13

© 1983, 1996 Instructional Horizons. Produced and Distributed by J. Weston Walch, Publisher, Portland, Maine 04104-0658

Consumer Math Success Kit

Name _____   Date _____

5. Installment Loans (I)

1. Bob has received a three-year loan toward the purchase of a new car. The loan is for $3500 at an annual rate of 14.67% interest, with the interest calculated on the unpaid balance of the loan. What will be the monthly payments for the first six months of this loan?

   _____

2. Sybil has applied for a four-year car loan in the amount of $6500. The interest rate would be 15.1% per annum over the four-year period. The interest is calculated on the unpaid balance of the loan. What will be the monthly payments for the first six months of the loan?

   _____

3. The Sharpee Appliance Company arranges financing for the purchase of most items it sells. In all cases, the interest charged on the installment loan is calculated on the unpaid balance of the loan. What would be the first three months' payments for each of the following loans?

   (a) $2500 for 2 years at 9.8% per year. _____

   (a) $1500 for 18 months at 13.1% per year. _____

   (a) $1750 for 15 months at 11.8% per year. _____

   (a) $950 for 12 months at 10.8% per year. _____

   (a) $750 for 9 months at 9.9% per year. _____

4. Abner's loan for his motorcycle is for 18 months, with interest calculated on the unpaid balance of the loan. The loan is for $1250 at an annual rate of 18.1%. What will be his total payments for the first four months of the loan?

   _____

5. The Kar King Used Car Lot is having a special sale this month. It will finance any vehicle purchased with an installment loan on which the interest is calculated on the unpaid balance of the loan. Andrea is interested in an older model selling at $1050. If she takes a two-year installment loan at 15.5%, what will her payments be in the first four months of the loan?

   _____

6. Installment Loans (II)

Many expensive items, like cars, major appliances, and property, are purchased on installment loans. An installment loan is not paid back all at once, as most loans are. Instead, it is paid back in monthly payments called **installments**. The monthly payments can be calculated in different ways. One way is to calculate the interest over the full term of the loan and then add that interest to the principal at the beginning. This total—principal plus total interest—is then divided by the number of months covered by the loan. Every monthly payment is the same, and the loan is called a **level-payment loan**. The first example below shows how the monthly payments are calculated for a level-payment loan. The second example shows how the interest rate for such a loan can be found.

- ### Example 1:

Veronica applies for a 36-month car loan for $3500 from the Barstow National Bank at an annual rate of 15.2%. The interest is calculated and added to the loan principal before determining monthly payments. Calculate Veronica's monthly payments on this loan.

Solution:

The interest on this loan can be calculated as usual:

Interest	= Principal × Rate × Time
	= $3500 × 15.2% per year × 3 years
	= $1596
Total cost of loan	= Principal + Interest
	= $3500 + $1596
	= $5096

Divided among 36 equal monthly payments, each payment would amount to:

$$\$5096 \div 36 = \$141.56$$

- ### Example 2:

Sammy's 24-month car loan costs him $149.80 per month for a car he could have purchased for $2800 cash. How much interest did he pay overall, and what was the interest rate on this loan?

Solution:

Total interest	= Total cost of loan − Purchase price
	= 24 × $149.80 − $2800
	= $3595.20 − $2800.00
	= $795.20

$$\text{Interest rate} = \frac{\text{Total interest}}{\text{Principal} \times \text{Time}}$$

$$= \frac{\$795.20}{\$2800 \times 2}$$

$$= 14.2\%$$

© 1983, 1996 Instructional Horizons. Produced and Distributed by J. Weston Walch, Publisher, Portland, Maine 04104-0658

Consumer Math Success Kit

6. Installment Loans (II)

1. The Kowalski Cycle Shop is offering to finance the sale of motorcycles with 24-month loans at an annual rate of 19.4%. The interest is calculated and added to the loan principal before monthly payments are determined. How much would the monthly payments be for loans of

   (a) $1000? _____ (b) $2500? _____ (c $5000? _____

2. Calculate the amount of interest on each of the following loans and the monthly payment, if the total interest and principal due is divided equally among the number of months shown:

   (a) $1000 @ 12% for one year: _____

   (a) $500 @ 12% for 6 months: _____

   (a) $2000 @ 18% for 6 months: _____

   (a) $3500 @ 17% for one year: _____

   (a) $450 @ 18% for 18 months: _____

   (a) $550 @ 15.5% for one year: _____

   (a) $2000 @ 14.7% for 6 months: _____

   (a) $350 @ 16.2% for 8 months: _____

   (a) $750 @ 14.9% for 15 months: _____

   (a) $1350 @ 11.9% for 48 months: _____

3. Roscoe's 12-month loan on his stereo set costs him $86.67 a month. Had he paid cash, he could have purchased the set for $895. What rate of interest was charged on this loan?

   _____

4. Amy has received a 30-month car loan with monthly payments of $275.00. The purchase price of the car was $6250.00. What rate of interest is she paying on this loan?

   _____

5. Karl, the Kar King, is offering three installment plans for the purchase of late-model cars from his company. The purchase price, length of loan, and monthly payment for three of these plans are given below. What is the interest rate for each of the three purchase plans?

   (a) Purchase price: $9520; 24-month loan; payments of $502.97. _____

   (a) Purchase price: $8875; 36-month loan; payments of $350.81. _____

   (a) Purchase price: $9979; 48-month loan; payments of $298.54. _____

© 1983, 1996 Instructional Horizons. Produced and Distributed
by J. Weston Walch, Publisher, Portland, Maine 04104-0658   18   Consumer Math Success Kit

7. Mortgage Loans

Probably the largest loan most people take is for the purchase of a home. Loans of this kind are installment loans that extend over long periods of time—20, 30, or 40 years, for example. The mathematics of mortgage loans is like that of other installment loans in which the interest is calculated on the balance due on the principal each month. A payment is also made to the principal such that the monthly payment is the same every month. The example below illustrates how these calculations are made.

● **Example:**

Jan and Jerry Henderson have applied for a 30-year home mortgage in the amount of $83,500 (the principal amount of the mortgage). The mortgage carries an interest rate of 14.6% which is applied to the unpaid principal balance each month. Calculate the interest due the first six months of this mortgage. The Hendersons' total monthly payment on this mortgage is $1043.80. How much goes towards paying off the principal each of the first six months?

Solution:

Calculations can be simplified in this problem by arranging them in a table, like the one below. The calculations needed to complete each part of the table are as shown:

(1) Payment to interest = Balance on principal $\times$ Rate $\times$ $^1/_{12}$ year

(2) Payment to principal = Monthly payment – Payment to interest

(3) New balance on principal = Balance on principal – Payment to principal

Month	Balance on Principal	Monthly Payment	Payment to Interest (1)	Payment to Principal (2)	New Balance on Principal (3)
1	$83,500.00	$1043.80	$1015.92	$27.88	$83,472.12
2	$83,472.12	$1043.80	$1015.58	$28.22	$83,443.90
3	$83,443.90	$1043.80	$1015.23	$28.57	$83,415.33
4	$83,415.33	$1043.80	$1014.89	$28.91	$83,386.42
5	$83,386.42	$1043.80	$1014.53	$29.27	$83,357.15
6	$83,357.15	$1043.80	$1014.18	$29.62	$83,327.53

Name _____ Date _____

7. Mortgage Loans

1. Renalda has purchased a condominium and received a mortgage loan in the amount of $50,000 for 25 years. Her monthly payments on this loan are $510.55. In the first three months of this mortgage, how much of this payment goes to interest and how much to principal? The interest rate on this loan is 11.9% per year.

   _____

2. Veronica and Sandy have decided to purchase a cooperative apartment together. They have received a mortgage loan in the amount of $42,500 for a period of 30 years. The interest rate on the mortgage is 16.2%. If their monthly payments are $592.40, how much will they be paying towards interest, and how much towards principal during the first three months of this mortgage loan?

   _____

3. Bruno and Destri are looking into the possibility of a 40-year mortgage loan for $132,000 at an interest rate of 15.7%. Their monthly payments on this loan would be $1742.80. Determine the amount that would go to interest and the amount that would go to principal during the three months of repayments on this loan.

   _____

4. Fidelio has purchased a condominium for $39,750, of which 80% is to be financed by a mortgage. Monthly payments on this mortgage are $395.80, and the interest rate is 14.3%. How much of this monthly payment goes to interest and how much to principal in the first six months the mortgage is in effect?

   _____

5. Dick and Jane Buell have purchased a home for $114,500. They will need to obtain a mortgage for 75% of that amount. The Nearbi State Bank will give them a mortgage for 40 years at 17.3% interest. In the first six months of this mortgage, how much of the $1265.50 monthly payment goes to principal and how much to interest?

   _____

© 1983, 1996 Instructional Horizons. Produced and Distributed
by J. Weston Walch, Publisher, Portland, Maine 04104-0658   20

Borrowing Money

Teacher Notes

Mathematical skills required:

multiplication and division of percentages and decimals

New vocabulary:

collateral
demand loan
installment plan
interest
level-payment loan
mortgage loan
noninterest-bearing loan
per annum
principal
proceeds
promissory note
rate
short-term loan

Related topics:

Credit: Installment Buying
Interest

Teaching suggestions:

1. Ask students to list purchases for which they might require a loan now and purchases for which they might require a loan later in their lives. Mention some nonpurchase reasons for needing a loan (college education, for example).

2. Decide which type of loan would be most suitable for each of the purchases/needs listed above.

3. You might invite a loan officer from a local bank to speak to the class about loan regulations at that bank and criteria the bank applies in deciding about the issuance of loans.

4. Students may be interested in knowing about cosigners on loans. Since they will be too young to qualify for some types of loans, they should know about the possibility of having an older person cosign for a loan with them.

CHAPTER THREE

Budgets

Long-term Budgets
Short-term Budgets

8. Long-term Budgets

Most people have a few very large financial expenses at certain times in their lives. They may want to send a child to college, buy a new house, replace a major appliance, or the like. For very large expenses like these, long-term budgeting can be very helpful. A **long-term budget** is a plan for setting aside enough money to pay a large expense at some time in the future. There is usually some uncertainty in a long-term budget. We may not know exactly how much an item will cost five or ten years from now. But we can make good estimates, and then try to save money on the basis of those estimates. The two examples below show how long-term budgets can be planned.

● **Example 1:**

Andrea is now 14 years old. She expects to enter college in four years. Tuition at the four-year college she plans to attend is $4800 per year. Andrea wants to save one third of her college tuition by the time she enters college. Based on current tuition rates, how much will she have to save each year until she enters college?

Solution:

At current tuition rates, Andrea will have to pay 4 × $4800 or $19,200 for tuition in four years at college. A third of that amount is $6400. If she has four years to save that amount, she will have to save $\frac{\$6400}{4} = \$1600$ each year.

● **Example 2:**

The Wongs want to save enough money to pay cash when their major appliances wear out. The age of their present appliances is given below. Table 1 on page 27 gives the average lifetime and average price of some major appliances. From this information, calculate the amount of money the Wongs should save each year to replace each appliance.

Washing machine:	8 years	Television set:	3 years
Vacuum cleaner:	5 years	Refrigerator:	10 years

Solution:

One way to solve this problem is to make a table like the one shown here. You can calculate the amount to be budgeted each year by dividing the cost of the new appliance by the number of years the Wongs have to save for it.

Item	Present Age	Expected Lifetime	Years to Replacement	Expected Cost	To Be Set Aside Annually	Monthly Budget
Washing machine	8	11	3	$370	$123.33	$10.28
Television set	3	11	8	$625	$ 78.13	$ 6.51
Vacuum cleaner	5	15	10	$180	$ 18.00	$ 1.50
Refrigerator	10	16	6	$580	$ 96.67	$ 8.06

© 1983, 1996 Instructional Horizons. Produced and Distributed by J. Weston Walch, Publisher, Portland, Maine 04104-0658

Consumer Math Success Kit

8. Long-term Budgets

1. Allen is 14 years old. He expects to buy a motorcycle when he is 18. If the one he wants costs $2000, how much will he have to save each year in order to pay cash for the motorcycle? How much will he have to save if he decides to put down only $200 on the vehicle and get a loan for the rest?

   _____

2. Ynez hopes to enter a two-year training program when she is 19 years old. The program will cost about $1300 per year. How much will she have to save each year in order to have enough money to pay for this program? Ynez is now 13.

   _____

3. For the past five years, Nancy has been saving money from gifts, allowance, and her baby-sitting wages to put toward college expenses. She is now 15 and intends to enter a four-year college when she is 18. She has saved $2850 so far and plans on having 30% of her college tuition saved by the time she starts college. If the yearly tuition is $3800, how much more will she have to save each year between now and the time she enters college?

   _____

4. The stereo system that Gerry wants to buy when she is 19 costs $950. Her aunt has promised to give her one fourth of the cost of the system on her 19th birthday. Her parents will pay another 10% of the cost of the system. How much will Gerry have to save each year in order to be able to pay cash for this system? Gerry is now 14 years old.

   _____

5. The Bensons' electric range is now four years old. How much will they have to put aside each year in order to pay cash for a new one? They want to replace their present range when it has reached the average age at which ranges are replaced (see Table 1 on page 27).

   _____

6. Listed in Table 1 on page 27 are the average lifetimes and replacement costs of the major appliances owned by Farley Muxster. How much should Farley budget monthly in order to replace these appliances at the time they are likely to be worn out? The age of Farley's appliances is shown here:

   Washing machine: 4 years _____   Television set: 2 years _____
   Refrigerator: 9 years _____   Electric range: 6 years _____

(continued)

© 1983, 1996 Instructional Horizons. Produced and Distributed by J. Weston Walch, Publisher, Portland, Maine 04104-0658

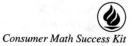

Consumer Math Success Kit

Practice Problems

8. Long-term Budgets *(continued)*

7. The Waltons have decided to start budgeting in order to have enough money to replace their major appliances when they begin to wear out. The present age of their appliances is given here. How much should they set aside each month in order to have enough cash to pay for new appliances when the time arrives?

Refrigerator: 9 years _____   Dryer: 7 years _____

Washing machine: 4 years _____   Sewing machine: 2 years _____

8. The Flaxners hope to build their own home some day. They think they will be able to sell their present home for about $110,000. The new house should cost them about $155,000. They think they can save between $4000 and $7000 a year. What is the longest time they will have to save to get their new house?

_____

The shortest time? _____

TABLE 1: Average Lifetime and Average Cost of Various Major Appliances

Appliance	Lifetime (years)	Cost
Refrigerator	16	$580
Electric range	16	$425
Washing machine	11	$370
Dryer	14	$350
Vacuum cleaner	15	$180
Sewing machine	24	$335
Television set	11	$625

9. Short-term Budgets

Budgeting is a system for keeping track of the way you take in and spend your money. Short-term budgets are plans that extend over a few weeks or a month or two. Two important points need to be made about budgets. First, they are **individual** financial plans. We can say how an average person or an average family is likely to spend money. But your own situation could be quite different from this average. Your own lifestyle and priorities are likely to make your own personal budget somewhat different from the **average** budget.

This means, also, that budgeting must be thought of as a **flexible** process. The first time you make a budget, you may **think** that 25% of your income should go for housing. But after two or three months, you could find that this is not enough. . . or too much. The example below shows how one family uses budgeting in its financial planning.

● **Example:**

The Aronsons have read that an average American family spends its income as shown in Table 2 on page 30. They decide to try living on a budget in which they use exactly the average proportions listed in the table. How much will they spend on each item in their budget for the next month? How much for each week in the month? Betty Aronson takes home $625.99 a month as a bus driver while her husband Bruce is currently working as a volunteer for a community service agency.

Solution:

The amount the Aronsons should budget for each item can be found by multiplying their monthly income by the percentage for that item in Table 2 on page 30. The weekly amount is one fourth of the monthly amount. Using these relationships, the amount to be budgeted in each category is:

Food:	21% × $625.99 = $131.46 per month;	$32.87 per week
Housing:	25% × $625.99 = $156.50 per month;	$39.12 per week
Clothing:	7% × $625.99 = $ 43.82 per month;	$10.95 per week
Personal care:	2% × $625.99 = $ 12.52 per month;	$3.13 per week
Medical care:	5% × $625.99 = $ 31.30 per month;	$7.82 per week
Automobile expenses:	12% × $625.99 = $ 75.12 per month;	$18.78 per week
Recreation:	4% × $625.99 = $ 25.04 per month;	$6.26 per week
Gifts:	3% × $625.99 = $ 18.78 per month;	$4.69 per week
Insurance:	5% × $625.99 = $ 31.30 per month;	$7.82 per week
Taxes:	9% × $625.99 = $ 56.34 per month;	$14.08 per week
Savings:	3% × $625.99 = $ 18.78 per month;	$4.69 per week
Others:	4% × $625.99 = $ 25.04 per month;	$6.26 per week

Name _____   Date _____

9. Short-term Budgets

1. Vonda and Rhea have decided to try budgeting their expenses for the next few months. Vonda takes
    home $1003.89 a month and Rhea, $956.78. If they combine their incomes, how much should they
    budget for each of the following items? Assume that they should budget the same percentage of their
    income as an average American family (see Table 2 on page 30). Items to be budgeted:

    Food: _____

    Clothing: _____

    Housing: _____

    Automobile expenses: _____

2. Arnell lives alone, but thinks she can use the average American family percentages to work out a budget
    for her money. She brings home $1568.90 each month. How much should she set aside for each item
    shown in the budget on page 30?

Food:	_____	Recreation:	_____
Housing:	_____	Gifts:	_____
Clothing:	_____	Insurance:	_____
Personal care:	_____	Taxes:	_____
Medical care:	_____	Savings:	_____
Automobile expenses:	_____	Others:	_____

3. During the month of April, the Fu family spent the following amounts of money for each of the items
    listed. On which items did they spend **more** than the average amount shown on page 30? On which did
    they spend less? Given their total income of $2457.68 per month, how much **should** they budget for
    each item according to these percentages?

Food: $466.96	_____	Recreation: $147.46	_____
Housing: $540.69	_____	Gifts: $196.61	_____
Clothing: $172.04	_____	Insurance: $73.73	_____
Personal care: $98.31	_____	Taxes: $221.19	_____
Medical care: $49.15	_____	Savings: $122.88	_____
Automobile expenses: $344.08	_____	Others: $24.58	_____

4. Harry and Jolinda want to try budgeting their income and expenses, but they think the table shown
    on page 30 is not right for them. They think that personal care should get three times as much in their
    budget as is shown for the average family. They would also increase recreation by 4%, taxes by 1%, and

    (continued)

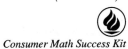
Consumer Math Success Kit

9. Short-term Budgets (continued)

savings by 2%. They would cut automobile expenses in half and reduce housing by 5%. With these percentages, what amounts should Harry and Jolinda budget in each of the following categories? Harry takes home $15,896.93 each year and Jolinda $15,698.66.

Food: _____   Recreation: _____

Housing: _____   Gifts: _____

Clothing: _____   Insurance: _____

Personal care: _____   Taxes: _____

Medical care: _____   Savings: _____

Automobile expenses: _____   Others: _____

5. Bob Gilbert and Ralph Sweeney have decided to start their own lawn care business. A friend has outlined for them the income they can expect and the probable expenses the first few months. The following data summarize this information. Use these data to prepare a budget for the first month. Use high, low, and average income estimates to develop three different budgets.

Income (projected):	$8 per hour per person

	Reasonable maximum:	60-hour week
	Reasonable minimum:	40-hour week
	Reasonable average:	50-hour week

Expenses (projected):	Purchase of equipment: 18%	Taxes: 12%
	Purchase of supplies: 22%	Other expenses: 6%
	Repairs: 15%	Profit: 17%
	Advertising: 10%	

Table 2: Percentages Spent by Average Family on Various Items

Item	Percentage
Food	21%
Housing	25%
Clothing	7%
Personal care	2%
Medical care	5%
Automobile expenses	12%
Recreation	4%
Gifts and contributions	3%
Insurance	5%
Taxes	9%
Savings	3%
Other expenses	4%

Budgets

Teacher Notes

Mathematical skills required:

>multiplication and division with percentages and decimals
>addition and subtraction of decimals

New vocabulary:

>budget
>long-term budget
>short-term budget

Related topics:

>Savings Accounts
>Vacation Planning

Teaching suggestions:

1. Ask students to list items or events for which they might need to make long-term budgets. This might include later education, purchase of a car, down payment on a house, or the like. For each item they list, have them make their own long-term budget.

2. Review with students the advantages of developing and using short-term budgets. Have students develop a short-term budget of their own for a period of a few weeks or a month. Ask them to evaluate how, if at all, having the budget affected their consumer habits.

3. Discuss some factors which might make an individual person's short-term budget ratios different from those listed in Table 2 on page 30. Factors such as lifestyle and income level may increase or decrease the proportion of one's income spent on food, housing, taxes, etc. Explain why this is so.

CHAPTER FOUR

Checking Accounts

10. Checking Accounts

Most people today have a checking account. This provides them with a safe, simple, convenient way to pay bills without handling a lot of cash. Many kinds of checking accounts are now available. They differ from each other in two important ways: (1) fees that may be charged for the account, and (2) interest you can earn on the account. The examples below illustrate only two of the many kinds of accounts available.

● **Example 1:**

Aaron has a checking account at the Algorithm Federal Bank that charges 15¢ for each check written and 12¢ for each deposit made. Shown below is the activity in Aaron's account this month. If Aaron's balance on February 27 was $142.69, what was his balance on March 31?

Deposits: March 1: $100.00; March 11: $225.00; March 18: $37.75;
March 24: $225.00; March 31: $40.00

Checks: #48: $22.95; #49: $63.40; #50: $105.35; #51: $6.95; #52: $14.45;
#53: $81.80; #54: $36.69

Solution:

Balance on 3/31	= Balance on 2/27 + Deposits − Checks − Charges
Total of deposits	= $627.75; Total of checks = $331.59
Bank charges	= 7 checks @ 15¢ + 5 deposits @ 12¢ = $1.65
Balance on 3/31	= $142.69 + $627.75 − $331.59 − $1.65
	= $437.20

● **Example 2:**

Ardella's checking account at the Salem Dime Bank pays $5\frac{1}{4}\%$ annual interest on the lowest balance in her account at any time during the month. It charges a $3.00 service charge per month. Ardella's deposits and withdrawals during the month of June are shown below. If her balance on May 31 was $89.33, what was her balance on June 30?

Deposits: 6/9: $150.00; 6/15: $375.50; 6/18: $189.90

Checks: 6/2: $35.78; 6/10: $79.90; 6/19: $408.80; 6/25: $96.95

Solution:

To solve this problem, we need to know Ardella's balance after each transaction. The table below shows that information.

Date	Transaction	Balance	Date	Transaction	Balance
6/1		$89.33	6/15	+ $375.50	$499.15
6/2	− $35.78	$53.55	6/18	+ $189.90	$689.05
6/9	+ $150.00	$203.55	6/19	− $408.80	$280.25
6/10	− $79.90	$123.65	6/25	− $96.95	$183.30

The lowest balance for the month was on June 2 ($53.55). The interest on this balance would be:
$5\frac{1}{4}\% \times \$53.55 \times \frac{1}{12} = \$0.23$. So Ardella's final balance would be: $183.30 + $0.23 = $183.53.

© 1983, 1996 Instructional Horizons. Produced and Distributed
by J. Weston Walch, Publisher, Portland, Maine 04104-0658

Consumer Math Success Kit

Name _____ Date _____

10. Checking Accounts

The Algorithm Federal Bank charges 15¢ for each check written and 12¢ for each deposit made. Use this information in each of the problems that follow.

1. Phoenicia has had the following activity in her checking account at the Algorithm Federal Bank last month:

   Deposits: August 4: $100.00; August 15: $250.00; August 28: $300.00
   Checks:

   #85 Wilson's Clothing Store: $35.00   #88 Corner Bookstore: $9.50
   #86 Johnson's Beauty Parlor: $50.00   #89 Harry's Musicworld: $20.10
   #87 Mr. Amos Tattler, Landlord: $115.00

   If Phoenicia's balance on July 31 was $184.91, what was her
   closing balance on August 31?   _____

2. Brian has a checking account at the same bank as Phoenicia. What would be his closing balance on December 31, given the following information on his account?

   Deposits: 12/1: $50.00; 12/15: $32.89; 12/27: $483.67
   Checks:

   #106 Bartley's Sporting Goods: $45.89   #109 Harry's Musicworld: $103.59
   #107 Meekheimer's Auto Repair Shop: $89.35   #110 Deidra Folsum (loan repaid): $17.82
   #108 Marsh and Meyer's Clothing: $114.39   #111 Bartley's Sporting Goods: $79.05

   Balance as of 11/30: $284.71   _____

3. Arvel also has a checking account at the Algorithm Federal Bank. Listed below are his deposits and withdrawals for the month of August. If his balance on July 31 was $135.87, what was his closing balance on August 31?

   Deposits: 8/8: $150.00; 8/13: $325.76
   Checks:

   #133 Patty's Pet Shoppe: $35.00   #136 Viva's Ford (auto loan): $101.95
   #134 Marsh and Meyer's Clothing: $87.20   #137 Will's Burger Spot: $13.89
   #135 Meekheimer's Auto Repair Shop: $152.50 #138 Van Eerden's Shoe Emporium: $42.40

                                                                          _____

4. The transactions against Veronica's checking account at the Algorithm Federal Bank are listed below. Find her balance on July 31 if her balance on June 30 was $248.45.

   Deposits: 7/9: $232.45; 7/19: $142.67; 7/28: $54.00
   Checks:

   #333 Winifred's Style Shoppe: $48.00   #336 Benson's Moped and Cycle Shop: $114.35
   #334 The Book Corner: $92.50   #337 West Farnsworth School District: $99.05
   #335 Alfredo's Restaurant: $68.93   #338 Will's Burger Spot: $27.42

                                                                          _____

© 1983, 1996 Instructional Horizons. Produced and Distributed
by J. Weston Walch, Publisher, Portland, Maine 04104-0658   *36*   *Consumer Math Success Kit*

Name _____ Date _____

10. Checking Accounts

The Salem Dime Bank pays $5\frac{1}{4}\%$ interest on the lowest balance in a checking account at any time during the month. It also charges a $3.00 service charge on all accounts every month. Use this information in each of the problems that follow.

1. Cleo's transactions for the month of March are listed below. Find her balance as of March 31.

    Deposits: 3/5: $45.00; 3/17: $50.00
    Checks: #18 Wimpy's Hamburgers: $20.00 (3/8)
                #19 Sunshine Markets: $25.00 (3/10)
                #20 Wester's Dry Cleaning Service: $9.50 (3/20)

    Balance, 3/1: $150.90   _____

2. Doreen also has an account at the Salem Dime Bank. Her balance on May 1 was $85.80. Her transactions for the month are listed below. Find her balance as of June 1.

    Deposits: 5/4: $200.00; 5/8: $150.00; 5/20: $200.00
    Checks: #87 Veronica's Hair Salon: $15.50 (5/5)
                #88 Sunshine Markets: $50.00 (5/9)
                #89 Packy's Auto Service: $21.25 (5/23)   _____

3. Karl's account at the Salem Dime Bank showed a balance of $45.55 on March 31. His transactions for the month of April are listed below. From this information, find his balance as of April 30.

    Deposits: 4/2: $139.63; 4/5: $200.01; 4/26: $284.15
    Checks:

    #138 Benson's Radio Store: $35.89 (4/1)   #143 Ottawa Track and Field Club: $25.39 (4/18)
    #139 Sunshine Markets: $75.00 (4/4)   #144 Henken's Bakery: $4.58 (4/25)
    #140 Bucky Franklin: $8.96 (4/4)   #145 Vreesma's Auto Body Shop: $156.79 (4/28)
    #141 True-Bright Paint Factory: $90.50 (4/11) #146 State of Wyoming (taxes): $64.00 (4/28)
    #142 Vander Meer's Clothing: $30.15 (4/18)   _____

4. On August 1, Wendy's balance at the Salem Dime Bank was $86.58. During the month of August, she completed the transactions shown below. What was the balance in her account on August 31?

    Deposits: 8/4: $78.63; 8/5: $293.68; 8/6: $309.58; 8/9: $400.00
    Checks:

    #209 Diversey Street Trust: $75.00 (8/1)   #214 Franklin Ave. Service Station: $80.52 (8/10)
    #210 Helena's House of Fashion: $32.06 (8/5)   #215 Serendipity Wallpapers: $52.36 (8/10)
    #211 Town of Duxbury (taxes): $40.00 (8/5)   #216 Andrew B. Molson: $195.41 (8/18)
    #212 Veronica Welbeen: $5.68 (8/5)   #217 The Plant Shoppe: $95.78 (8/18)
    #213 Estelle's: $103.65 (8/10)   _____

Name _____ Date _____

10. Checking Accounts

The Pallindrome State Bank's Gold Checking account permits free checking (deposits and checks) as long as one's balance does not fall below $500 at any time during the month. If the balance is reduced to less than $500, a flat fee of $15 is charged. If the balance drops to less than $100, additional fees of 12¢ per check and 9¢ per deposit are charged. Use this information in each of the following problems.

1. Samantha's balance as of December 1 was $1582.83. Listed below are her transactions for December. Find her balance on January 1.

   Deposits: 12/2: $25.00; 12/18: $200.00; 12/20: $50.00
   Checks: #145 Harry's Musicworld: $75.00 (12/4)
                #146 D'Alessandro's Misses Shoppe: $45.78 (12/8)
                #147 MasterCard of Delaware: $108.97 (12/15)
                #148 Francesco's Hair Styling: $38.90 (12/24)
                #149 Boudreau's Furniture: $68.98 (12/27)

   _____

2. Darcy's account at the Pallindrome Bank showed a balance of $1582.83 on June 30. Her deposits and checks for the month of July are shown below. Find her balance as of July 31.

   Deposits: 7/3: $864.33; 7/9: $143.98; 7/12: $1042.69
   Checks: #308 Pallindrome State Bank (Savings): $750.00 (7/2)
                #309 Dr. Johnathan H. Hennessey: $1366.48 (7/10)
                #310 West Cisco Real Estate Company: $909.90 (7/15)

   _____

3. Mr. Anthony's account at the Pallindrome Bank showed a balance of $567.35 on September 30. His deposits and checks are shown below. What was his balance on October 31?

   Deposits: 10/8: $359.75; 10/15: $209.57; 10/24: $118.52; 10/26: $1068.45; 10/30: $454.00
   Checks: #355 Westwood Cement and Gravel Co.: $205.50 (10/6)
                #356 Johannson Carpenters: $253.25 (10/9)
                #357 Town of Canton (fees): $300.00 (10/14)
                #358 Kent County (fees): $150.00 (10/20)
                #359 Louisa's Restaurant: $45.68 (10/20)
                #360 Frankie and Johnny's Musicland: $89.20 (10/20)
                #361 Texas State Licensing Board: $15.00 (10/20)
                #362 Van Buren and Van Aiken, Inc.: $68.75 (10/20)
                #363 Dr. Georgia I. Stickley: $96.78 (10/25)

   _____

© 1983, 1996 Instructional Horizons. Produced and Distributed
by J. Weston Walch, Publisher, Portland, Maine 04104-0658   *38*

Checking Accounts

Teacher Notes

Mathematical skills required:

addition, subtraction, multiplication, and division of decimals

New vocabulary:

deposit
transaction
withdrawal

Related topics:

Bank Statements
Electronic Funds Transfer Systems
Interest

Teaching suggestions:

1. A local bank may be willing to give you a set of sample or voided checks. Use these with students to give them practice in writing checks and maintaining a check ledger.

2. Obtain from a local bank a brochure describing the variety of checking accounts available at the bank. Most banks offer more than one kind of checking account, each paying different amounts of interest and assessing different service charges. Discuss with students the situations for which each type of checking account would be most appropriate.

3. You or a representative of the bank might discuss proper methods of writing checks to avoid alteration or cashing by someone other than the intended payee.

CHAPTER FIVE

Credit

Retail Store Charge Accounts
Installment Buying
Budget Accounts
Credit, Charge, and Bank
    Cards

11. Retail Store Charge Accounts

Many retail stores allow customers to make purchases on credit through their own charge accounts. These charge accounts are of two types: **regular** and **revolving**. In a regular charge account, you are allowed one month to pay for anything you buy. You take home your purchase, the store sends you a bill, and you pay the bill within 30 days. There is no charge for this service.

A revolving charge account is a variation of the regular charge account. You make your purchase, take it home, and are billed, as with a regular charge account. You then have the choice of paying the full amount of the bill or some minimum payment. If you pay the full amount, there is no credit charge. If you pay the minimum amount, a credit charge is added to your next bill. The example below shows how revolving charge accounts work.

● **Example:**

Evie Blackstone made the purchases listed below at the Sel-E-Z Department Store last month. The company requires a minimum payment of (a) 15% of the total amount due or (b) a minimum payment of $20.00, whichever is larger. The store charges 1.5% interest per month on any unpaid balance. What is Evie's minimum payment and her new balance on this account?

Previous Balance: $143.85
Payments: $50.00
Charges this month: $38.28; $114.40; $57.75; $88.66; $100.00

Solution:

The balance due this month is equal to:

Balance due = Previous balance – Payments + Finance charge + New charges

Previous balance – Payments = $143.85 – $50.00 = $93.85

Finance charge = 1.5% × $93.85 = $1.41

New charges this month = $38.28 + $114.40 + $57.75 + $88.66 + $100.00 = $399.09

New balance = $93.85 + $1.41 + $399.09 = $494.35

Minimum payment due on this amount = 15% × $494.35 = $74.15

Since this is greater than $20, the minimum payment is $74.15.

11. Retail Store Charge Accounts

The Sel-E-Z Department Store offers customers a revolving charge account for making purchases. The conditions of the account are (1) a minimum payment of (a) 15% of the present month's balance or (b) $20.00, whichever is larger, and (2) an 18% annual finance charge on any unpaid balance. Use this information in each of the following problems.

1. During the month of January, Sandra made the following purchases and payments. From this information, calculate her new monthly balance and the minimum payment due this month. Her balance on January 1 was $140.41.

Payments:	1/25:	$50.00	
Charges:	1/3:	Small electrical appliances	$53.81
	1/8:	Junior sportswear	$70.99
	1/8:	Housewares	$10.76
	1/8:	Towels, rugs, bath	$10.50

2. Rodney also has a revolving charge account at the Sel-E-Z Department Store. Listed below are his charges and payments for the month of February. If his balance on January 31 was $237.83, what was his balance on March 1?

Payments:	2/20:	$40.00	
Charges:	2/15:	Cosmetics, toiletries	$32.50
	2/15:	Notions	$50.25
	2/15:	Housewares	$13.60

3. Francine's charge account record for the month of April is shown below. Her balance on March 31 was $376.10. What was her balance on April 30?

Payments:	4/23:	$43.50	
	4/25:	$50.00	
Charges:	4/8:	Stationery	$25.50
	4/8:	Stationery	$13.95
	4/19:	Cosmetics, toiletries	$25.85
	4/19:	Girls and subteens	$56.25

(continued)

Consumer Math Success Kit

11. Retail Store Charge Accounts
(continued)

4. Feodora's charges and payments for the month of June on his account at the Sel-E-Z Department Store are shown below. If his balance on May 31 was $429.67, what was his balance on June 30?

Payments:	6/21:	$50.00	
Charges:	6/13:	Men's sportswear	$114.58
	6/13:	Automotive	$ 25.00
	6/13:	Gloves	$ 13.95
	6/20:	Men's sportswear	$ 65.45

5. On July 31, lsadora's balance on her Sel-E-Z charge account was $506.37. During the month of August, she made the charges and payments shown below. Calculate her balance on August 31.

Payments:	8/25:	$150.00	
Charges:	8/4:	Towels, rugs, bath	$ 18.00
	8/4:	Towels, rugs, bath	$ 22.50
	8/7:	Girls and subteens	$ 35.76
	8/7:	Girls and subteens	$ 57.95
	8/18:	Cosmetics, toiletries	$ 29.50
	8/20:	Books	$ 24.60

12. Installment Buying

Installment purchases are a common way of buying large appliances such as washers, dryers, and refrigerators. Here is how an installment purchase works. A buyer agrees to make a **down payment** on the purchase price of an item. The buyer may take the item home, but the seller still owns the item legally. The buyer also agrees to pay the remaining balance due on the item over a certain number of months. These payments include not only the balance due on the original purchase price, but also the interest charges for the privilege of using installment credit. In many cases, you may want to calculate the rate of interest on an installment purchase. The second example below shows how to do that.

● **Example 1:**

Arthur wants to buy a "home entertainment center." The cash price for this item is $2850. It can also be purchased in 24 monthly payments of $140 each, with a down payment of $250. How much interest would he be paying if he purchased the item on the installment plan?

Solution:

The total price paid = Down payment + Total of monthly payments

$$= \$250 + (24 \times \$140)$$
$$= \$250 + \$3360$$
$$= \$3610$$

Amount of interest = Total amount paid – Cash price

$$= \$3610 - \$2850$$
$$= \$760$$

● **Example 2:**

What rate of interest would Arthur be paying on the installment plan described in Example 1?

Solution:

$$\text{The rate of interest} = \frac{\text{Amount of interest paid}}{\text{Amount of money borrowed} \times \text{Time of loan}}$$

The amount of interest paid = Full installment price – Cash price

$$= \$3610 - \$2850$$
$$= \$760$$

Amount of money borrowed = Full installment price – Down payment

$$= \$3610 - \$250$$
$$= \$3360$$

$$\text{So, rate of interest} = \frac{\$760}{\$3360 \times 2 \text{ years}}$$

$$= 11.3\%$$

                        Consumer Math Success Kit

12. Installment Buying

1. Frankie wants to buy a new stereo that sells for $600. He will make a down payment of $75 and then six monthly payments of $100. What is the full installment price and the annual interest rate?

   _____

2. Jolene's new chair would have cost $500 if she had paid cash for it. On the installment plan, she will pay down $45 and then complete the purchase with six monthly payments of $84.17 each. What is the full installment price and the annual interest rate for this chair?

   _____

3. A kitchen table-and-chair set that normally sells for a cash price of $485 can be purchased on the installment plan for $45 down and eight monthly payments. The full installment price is $520. What is the amount of each monthly payment and the annual interest rate for this set?

   _____

4. Jack's new sport coat will cost him $250 if he pays cash and $300 if he pays by installments. If the down payment is $60 on this coat, how much will he pay in each of 12 monthly payments?

   What is the annual interest rate on this purchase? _____

5. A new living room rug can be purchased for $375 cash or on the installment plan for $50 down with six monthly payments of $60. What is the full installment price and the annual interest rate for this rug?

   _____

6. Rick could buy a new canoe at the cash price of $895 or with a down payment of $75 and eight monthly payments. The full installment price would come to $960. What would the annual interest rate and the monthly payments be for the installment purchase?

   _____

7. Andrea can buy a set of four tires for her car on the installment plan by putting down $50 and making 12 monthly payments of $30.46. Under the installment plan, what would be the full installment price and the annual interest rate for this purchase? The cash price for the tires is $375.

   _____

8. The Bickersons have decided to buy a new home entertainment center which lists for $895. They can buy the center on an installment plan by placing down $75 and then making 18 monthly payments of $48.06. What is the annual interest rate and the full installment price under these terms?

   _____

13. Budget Accounts

Budget accounts are a variation of credit buying that lie between regular charge accounts and installment buying. Many retail stores allow customers to spread out their payments on a purchase over a short period of time (usually three months). In exchange, the customer pays a small service fee on top of the purchase price of the item. Budget purchases are often used for items of moderate price (about $100). The two examples below show how to determine the cost, total interest, and interest rate for budget accounts.

- **Example 1:**

Karol's Klassy Klothes Korner charges a monthly interest rate of $\frac{1}{2}\%$ for budget purchases carried over a three-month period. What would be the total price and total interest charge on a coat with a cash price of $125 purchased on this budget plan?

Solution:

The total price	= Cash price + Interest charges
Interest charges	= Cash price × Interest rate × Number of months
	= $125 × 0.5% × 3 months
	= $1.88
Total price	= $125 + $1.88
	= $126.88

- **Example 2:**

Connie has decided to buy a clock radio on a budget plan. The radio lists for $89.95 and the budget payments amount to $32 a month for three months. What is the total interest paid and the annual and monthly interest rate on this plan?

Solution:

The interest paid	= Total price paid – Cash price
	= Monthly payment × Number of months – Cash price
	= $32 × 3 – $89.95
	= $96 – $89.95
	= $6.05

$$\text{Monthly interest rate} = \frac{\text{Interest paid}}{\text{Cash price} \times \text{Number of months}}$$

$$= \frac{\$6.05}{\$89.95 \times 3}$$

$$= \$2.2\%$$

Annual interest rate	= Monthly interest rate × 12
	= 2.2% × 12
	= 26.4%

Name _____   Date _____

13. Budget Accounts

1. Sylvia has purchased a new coat that normally sells for $100. She buys the coat on a budget account for which the monthly interest is 1.5%. If she pays for the coat in three months, what is her monthly payment?

   _____

2. The desk Taylor wants to buy normally sells for $200. He can buy the same desk over a period of three months on a budget account on which the annual rate of interest is 18%. What will be his monthly payments on the budget purchase?

   _____

3. Charley has chosen to buy a new stereo set on a three-month budget purchase plan on which the annual rate of interest is 12%. The set sells for $250 cash. How much will his monthly payments be?

   _____

4. The set of encyclopedias that Buster wants to buy sells for $299.95 cash. He can buy the set over a period of three months by paying 15% annual interest on the purchase price. What will be his monthly payments under this plan?

   _____

5. Edgar's new suit would cost him $325 if he paid cash for it. But he has decided to purchase the suit on a three-month budget plan on which the annual interest is 15.8%. What will be his monthly payments under this plan?

   _____

6. Patty has decided to buy an FM stereo clock radio for which the cash price is $95.95. Her monthly payments over a four-month period are $25.00. What are the monthly and annual interest rates on this plan?

   _____

7. The bookcase Lou has purchased on a six-month budget plan will cost him $26.86 per month. The cash price for the bookcase was $150. What are the monthly and annual rates of interest under this plan?

   _____

8. Lonnie can't decide whether to buy a new radio/cassette/CD player for cash or on a three-month budget plan. The cash price for the radio is $149.95, while the monthly payments under the budget plan would be $51.82. How much total interest would he be paying, and what are the annual and monthly interest rates under the budget plan?

   _____

14. Credit, Charge, and Bank Cards

The three terms used here—**credit**, **charge**, and **bank cards** all describe similar systems of credit. A consumer purchases an object and pays for it with a credit card rather than with cash. The credit card company pays the store and then bills the customer. The differences among various types of credit cards are not great. Today, most companies offering credit cards charge an annual fee for their use. Some companies require payment in full at the end of each month. Most other companies expect the consumer to pay **either** the full amount due or some minimum balance on this amount. If the full amount is not paid, a finance charge is added to the bill. The example below explains the mathematics of credit card finances.

● **Example:**

Listed below is the information on Yolanda Figueroa's most recent credit card bill. From this information, calculate the total amount due this month, the finance charge, and the minimum payment due this month. This company charges 18% annual interest (finance charge) on its accounts and requires a minimum payment equal to 15.345% of the new balance.

Previous balance:	$286.19
Payments:	$100.00
New charges:	$175.25
	$ 10.45
	$ 45.90
	$ 15.00
	$ 29.19

Solution:

This month's balance = Previous balance – Payments + Finance charge + New charges

Finance charge = 1.5% (18% per year ÷ 12) × ($286.19 – $100.00)

= 1.5% × $186.19

= $2.79

New charges = $175.25 + $10.45 + $45.90 + $15.00 + $29.19

= $275.79

New balance = $286.19 – $100.00 + $2.79 + $275.79

= $464.77

Minimum balance due = 15.345% × $464.77

= $71.32

50   *Consumer Math Success Kit*

Name _____   Date _____

14. Credit, Charge, and Bank Cards

In each of the following problems, a finance charge (FC) of 18% per year is charged on the unpaid balance. The finance charge is computed and added each month. In addition, a minimum payment equal to 5.345% of the new balance *or* $20, whichever is larger, is required each month.

1. Listed below are the payments and charges made by Andrea on her credit card for the month of February. From the information given above, calculate the FC, new balance, and payment due on this account.

   Previous Balance: $47.89   *Payments:* $ 15.00
   Purchases:
   Earl's Record Shop: $ 42.35
   Willie's Sleep Emporium: $ 40.00
   Susan's Hair Today: $ 55.00

   _____

2. Tom has a credit card with the company whose policies are described above. His transactions for the month are shown below. Calculate the FC, new balance, and payment due on Tom's account for March.

   Previous Balance: $170.73   *Payments:* $ 20.00
   Purchases:
   Earl's Record Shop: $ 55.78
   Maple Street Service: $ 18.57
   Sammy's Quik-Snak: $ 23.80

   _____

3. Shown below are the payments and purchases made on Earl's credit card this month. The FC and minimum payment due are calculated as shown above. Find the new balance and the payment due.

   Previous Balance: $251.14   *Payments:* $ 20.00
   Purchases:
   World's Best Auto Repair: $182.50
   Sammy's Quik-Snak: $ 29.58
   Earl's Record Shop: $ 55.69
   Stage One Summer Theater: $ 85.00
   Maple Street Service: $ 20.68

   _____

(continued)

© 1983, 1996 Instructional Horizons. Produced and Distributed
by J. Weston Walch, Publisher, Portland, Maine 04104-0658   51   Consumer Math Success Kit

14. Credit, Charge, and Bank Cards
(continued)

4. The credit card statement Willie received for July contained the charges and payments shown below. Use the information given previously to calculate the FC, new balance, and minimum payment due.

Previous Balance: $1517.11

Payments: $100.00
$ 15.13

Purchases:

Maple Street Service:	$ 21.69
Corner Drugs:	$ 34.50
Chet's Lock Shop:	$ 45.00
Bare Hill Kennels:	$ 55.78
Sammy's Quik-Snak:	$ 25.75
Samson's Books, Inc.:	$187.68
Chet's Lock Shop:	$ 45.00
Ku Fung Defense League:	$ 95.00

         Consumer Math Success Kit

Credit

Teacher Notes

Mathematical skills required:

addition, subtraction, multiplication, and division of decimals

New vocabulary:

bank card
budget account
charge card
credit
credit card
down payment
finance charge
installment buying
minimum payment due
regular charge account
revolving charge account
unpaid balance

Related topics:

Borrowing Money: Installment Loans
Interest
Savings Accounts

Teaching suggestions:

1. Make extensive use of the daily newspaper. Look for ads for installment purchases that can be used as additional practice problems of the type given in this section.

2. Sellers are required by law to state the rate of interest on installment purchases. In some cases, they neglect to do so or print the interest rate in very small type. Have students calculate the interest rate or finance charge on purchases for which this information is not clearly given.

3. Obtain information from various retail stores on the budget or other charge plans they offer. Have students compare the cost of various items in which they might be interested if purchased either for cash or on a delayed payment plan.

4. Conduct a class discussion on some of the advantages and disadvantages of using credit/charge/bank cards in making purchases.

CHAPTER SIX

Eating Out

15. Eating Out

Finding the price of a meal in a restaurant or fast-food shop may require as many as three steps. First, you have to find out the total cost of all items purchased. This usually means simply adding up the cost of the items. Second, you may have to calculate and add on the state tax. Not every state charges a tax on meals eaten in restaurants. For those states that do, you have to multiply the cost of the food by the tax rate and then add that total to the cost of the food. Finally, you may want to add a tip for the person who waited on you. There is no set amount that you should tip. But 15% is considered about right for good service. The example below shows how to calculate the cost of eating out when all these factors must be included.

● **Example:**

The menu at Buster's Diner is shown on page 58. What is the cost of the meal listed below and the change left from a $20 bill? The state tax here is 4% and the tip to be left is 15%.

    2 hamburgers
    1 Sr. Busterburger
    1 Jr. Busterburger
    1 ham and cheese sandwich
    2 coffees
    1 iced tea
    1 milk

Solution:

The cost of the food is as follows:

2 hamburgers @ $1.65	= $ 3.30
1 Sr. Busterburger	= $ 2.95
1 Jr. Busterburger	= $ 1.95
1 ham and cheese	= $ 2.45
2 coffees @ $.45	= $ .90
1 iced tea	= $ .75
1 milk	= $ .60
Total of food	= $12.90
Tax on food	= 4% × $12.90
	= $.52
Food + Tax	= $12.90 + $.52
	= $13.42
Tip	= 15% × $12.90
	= $1.94
Change	= Amount tendered – Total bill
	= $20.00 – $13.42
	= $6.58

 Consumer Math Success Kit

15. Eating Out

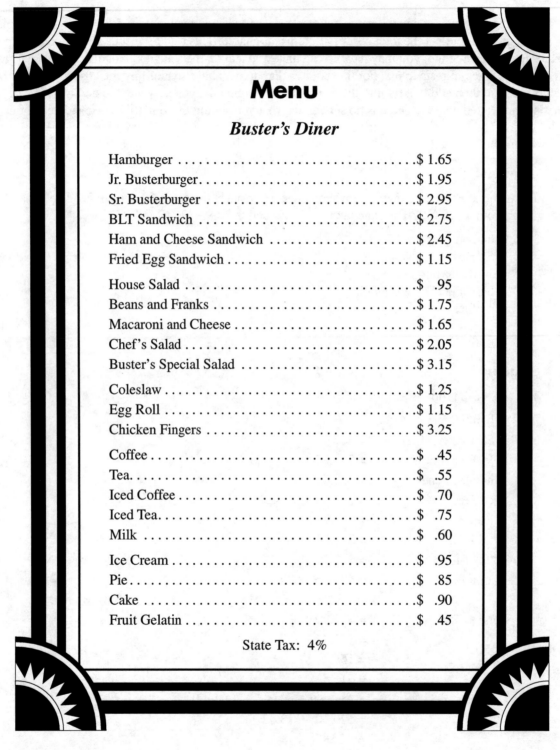

Menu

Buster's Diner

Hamburger	$ 1.65
Jr. Busterburger	$ 1.95
Sr. Busterburger	$ 2.95
BLT Sandwich	$ 2.75
Ham and Cheese Sandwich	$ 2.45
Fried Egg Sandwich	$ 1.15
House Salad	$ .95
Beans and Franks	$ 1.75
Macaroni and Cheese	$ 1.65
Chef's Salad	$ 2.05
Buster's Special Salad	$ 3.15
Coleslaw	$ 1.25
Egg Roll	$ 1.15
Chicken Fingers	$ 3.25
Coffee	$ .45
Tea	$ .55
Iced Coffee	$ .70
Iced Tea	$ .75
Milk	$ .60
Ice Cream	$ .95
Pie	$ .85
Cake	$ .90
Fruit Gelatin	$ .45

State Tax: 4%

© 1983, 1996 Instructional Horizons. Produced and Distributed
by J. Weston Walch, Publisher, Portland, Maine 04104-0658

Consumer Math Success Kit

Name _____ Date _____

15. Eating Out

The prices needed to solve the problems below are listed on the menu for Buster's Diner on page 58.

1. Pamela's lunch at Buster's consists of 2 hamburgers, coffee, and a piece of pie. What is the cost of the food (without tax or tip)?

   _____

2. Heidi, Rod, and Sandra have the items listed below for supper at Buster's. Calculate the cost of this meal for all three: 2 hamburgers; 1 BLT sandwich; 1 coffee; 2 milks. Calculate also the tax on the meal, and the total cost without the tip.

   _____

3. The LaScola family has dinner at Buster's and orders the items listed below. What is the total cost of this meal for the whole family, not counting the tip? 1 Sr. Busterburger; 1 Jr. Busterburger; 2 Buster Special Salads; 3 cakes; 2 teas; 1 coffee.

   _____

4. Alyre and Joseph have decided to treat their friends to a complete meal at Buster's. The meal consists of the items listed below. What is the total cost of this meal, without the tip? 2 ham and cheese sandwiches; 1 fried egg sandwich; 2 house salads; 4 egg rolls; 2 pieces of pie; 2 milks; 2 coffees.

   _____

5. The Farwell family decides to go to Buster's Diner for Saturday night dinner. The meal they order is listed below. Mr. Farwell leaves a tip of 20%, and there is a sales tax of 5.5% on meals in this state. From this information, calculate the complete cost of the meal plus tax and tip for the Farwell family: 3 Sr. Busterburgers; 2 Buster's Special Salads; 3 coleslaws; 1 egg roll; 1 beans and franks; 3 cakes; 1 ice cream; 5 coffees.

   _____

6. Armand and his friends stop by Buster's for a late night snack and order the food listed below. Since the service was slow, they decide to leave a 10% tip. The sales tax on meals in this state is 5%. The party decides to divide the check evenly among all five people. What is the total cost of the meal, including tax and tip, and what is the cost to each person? 3 chef's salads; 2 Buster's Special Salads; 1 macaroni and cheese; 2 chicken fingers; 3 cakes; 1 pie; 2 coffees; 2 teas.

   _____

Consumer Math Success Kit

Eating Out

Teacher Notes

Mathematical skills required:

addition and multiplication of percents and decimals

New vocabulary:

amount tendered
gratuity
subtotal
tax

Related topics:

Estimating Answers
Sales Tax

Teaching suggestions:

1. Students might be asked to select meals of their own choice from the menu given on page 58, and then asked to calculate the subtotal, tax (if any), total, tip, and change due from a $20 bill for the meal.

2. The whole sequence of mathematical operations required for the problems in this topic can be carried through in a continuous series of operations on many hand calculators. Ask students to see if they can complete this series of calculations without writing down any partial answers along the way.

3. Ask students to bring in menus from other restaurants with which they are familiar in order to calculate the cost of meals at these restaurants.

CHAPTER SEVEN

Electronic Funds Transfer Systems (EFTS)

16. Electronic Funds Transfer Systems (EFTS)

Some financial institutions now have systems that allow you to make deposits and pay bills by means of a telephone call. You call a given telephone number and then make transactions either by voice or by punching information into a push-button phone. In many cases, you can enter a deposit or payment into your account, with instructions to complete the transaction up to 30 days in the future. These electronic transfers are handled in the same way that regular deposits and checks are handled in your checking account. The following example illustrates how electronic funds transfer works.

● **Example:**

Marjorie will be out of the city for the whole month of August. She has decided to prepay all her bills through her electronic funds transfer system. Since these are her only transactions for the month of August, you can determine her September 1 balance knowing the following facts about her checking account.

1. The account pays 6.2% interest on the lowest balance in her account during the month.

2. She is charged $3 a month to maintain her checking account and $1 a month for her EFTS service.

3. Her account balance on August 1 was $498.88.

Here are her EFTS transactions, called in on July 21:

8/3	pay	$ 100.00
8/3	pay	$ 238.50
8/5	deposit	$2458.38
8/7	pay	$ 38.67
8/7	pay	$ 62.14
8/7	pay	$ 8.99
8/15	pay	$ 350.00
8/18	pay	$ 125.00
8/18	pay	$ 107.73
8/18	pay	$ 64.99
8/20	pay	$ 133.34
8/20	pay	$ 150.00

Solution:

Final balance = Beginning balance + Deposits − Payments − Charges + Interest

Charges = $3.00 + $1.00 = $4.00

Interest = 6.2% on lowest balance; lowest balance was on 8/3: $160.38

$= 6.2\% \times \$160.38 \times \frac{1}{12}$

= $ .83

Final balance = $498.88 + $2458.38 − $1379.36 − $4.00 + $ .83

= $1574.73

Consumer Math Success Kit

Name _____ Date _____

16. Electronic Funds Transfer Systems (EFTS)

The Farmer's Bank offers an electronic funds transfer system known as Push-n-Pay. There is a charge of 6¢ for each Push-n-Pay payment, and a fee of $3.00 is assessed any time a person's checking account balance falls below $100 during the month. The bank also pays a 6.2% interest rate (annual) on the lowest balance in a checking account each month.

1. The transactions in Van's checking account at the Farmer's Bank are listed below. From this information and the regulations given above, determine the final balance in Van's account for the month of March.

   Previous balance: $409.72   *Deposits:* $ 50.00 (3/15)
   Push-n-Pay: G & B Sporting Goods: $100.00 (3/7)
   Checks: #182: Wilson's Quick Shop: $ 25.00 (3/22)_____

2. Cindy's account at the Farmer's Bank has shown the transactions listed below for the month of April. From the information given above, find her balance at the end of the month.

   Previous balance: $336.26   *Deposits:* $250.00 (4/20)
   Push-n-Pay: Z & Z Service Station: $100.00 (4/9)
   Push-n-Pay: SpinOff Records: $ 50.00 (4/16)_____

3. Shown below are the transactions in Fernando's account at the Farmer's Bank for the month of May. Remember the information given above on bank charges. What is the balance in Fernando's account on May 31?

   Previous balance: $437.10   *Deposits:* $125.00 (5/1)
   Push-n-Pay: Elvira's Pet Corner: $ 75.00 (5/11)
   Push-n-Pay: Wilamette Luggage: $ 50.00 (5/13)
   Checks: #183: Dundee High School Boosters: $ 15.00 (5/15)_____

4. Sandy's statement for June from the Farmer's Bank is shown below. Refer to the bank charges given above. What is Sandy's balance at the end of June?

   Previous balance: $424.16   *Deposits:* $100.00 (6/27)
   Push-n-Pay: Wilson's Quick Shop: $ 75.00 (6/8)
   Push-n-Pay: City of Beloit: $ 25.00 (6/24)
   Push-n-Pay: Brite-Lamp Shop: $ 12.50 (6/26)
   Checks: #208: Postmaster, Bellevue: $ 32.50 (6/10)
           #209: Mrs. Harold Anderson: $ 15.75 (6/10)
           #210: Benson's BookShelf: $ 39.68 (6/10)_____

© 1983, 1996 Instructional Horizons. Produced and Distributed
by J. Weston Walch, Publisher, Portland, Maine 04104-0658   64   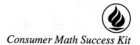 Consumer Math Success Kit

Electronic Funds Transfer Systems (EFTS)

Teacher Notes

Mathematical skills required:

addition, subtraction, multiplication, and division of decimals

New vocabulary:

electronic funds transfer systems
delayed payment

Related topics:

Bank Statements
Checking Accounts
Interest

Teaching suggestions:

1. Discuss with students the advantages and disadvantages of having an EFTS service in place of or in addition to a regular checking account.

2. It seems likely that the availability of home computers will change the character of many other aspects of consumer mathematics. Discuss with students some other applications of computers to consumer math. This might include such things as grocery shopping or purchase of other consumer items by means of the computer terminal in a person's home. What would be the advantages and disadvantages of this kind of change?

CHAPTER EIGHT

Estimating Answers

17. Estimating Answers

The art of estimating answers can be very useful in consumer mathematics. Many times, it is not necessary to know an answer exactly. It is enough to have only a general idea as to approximately what an answer will be. For example, suppose you have to figure a tip in a restaurant. The bill comes to $7.97. You could take out your calculator and find 15% of $7.97. But there is an easier way. You could notice that $7.97 is about $8. Then, you could find 15% of $8 in your head (15% × $8 = $1.20). This would be a fast way to figure the tip. And you don't need to have an exact answer here anyway. The examples below illustrate some ways of estimating answers.

● **Example 1:**

What is the cost of three shirts priced at $7.95 each?

Solution:

Round off the price to the nearest whole dollar:

$$\$7.95 \approx \$8$$

(A wavy equals sign means "is approximately equal to.")

Then, the cost of three shirts $\approx 3 \times \$8$

$\approx \$24$

● **Example 2:**

A restaurant meal consisted of the items listed below. What is the cost of the meal and the correct tip (figured at 15% of the bill)?

    2 hamburgers @ $1.29
    2 milks @ 45¢
    2 french fries @ 49¢
    2 apple pies @ 69¢

Solution:

Round off all prices to the nearest whole number or most convenient price to use:

hamburgers: $2 \times \$1.29 \approx 2 \times \$1.30 \approx \$2.60$
french fries: $2 \times 49¢ \approx 2 \times 50 \approx \$1.00$
apple pies: $2 \times 69¢ \approx 2 \times 70¢ \approx \$1.40$
milks: $2 \times 45¢ = \$.90$ (no estimate needed)

Then, estimated bill $\approx \$2.60 + \$1.00 + \$1.40 + \$.90 \approx \$5.90$

tip $= 15\% \times$ bill
    $= 15\% \times \$6.00$
    $= \$1.00$ (exact number: $0.90)

69   *Consumer Math Success Kit*

17. Estimating Answers

1. Suzanne wants to buy two cassette tapes at $6.99 each. Estimate the total cost of this purchase. Estimate the change she should receive from a $50 bill. _____

2. Felix has chosen three cassette tapes selling at $5.89 each. Estimate the total cost of these tapes and the change to be expected from a $20 bill. _____

3. For dinner Toni and Tony have ordered the items listed below. Estimate the size of their bill for this meal: 3 hamburgers @ 99¢ each; 2 french fries @ 49¢ each; 2 milks @ 50¢ each. _____

4. Andrea wants to know how much water she will need to fill her aquarium, whose dimensions are 1.8 m long, 1.1 m wide, and 0.9 m high. Estimate the volume of water in this aquarium. _____

5. The items which Donald has selected at the clothing store are listed below. Estimate the total bill for these purchases: 2 shirts @ $13.99; 2 pairs of trousers @ $14.99. _____

6. Helena has chosen three cassette tapes, selling at $9.79 each, and three CD's, selling at $11.95 each, to buy. Estimate the total cost of this purchase and the tax, if the sales tax in this state is 5.9%. _____

7. Estimate the change that Rosamond should get from $15.00 for the meal listed below: 3 Superburgers @ $2.49 each; 2 salads @ 69¢ each; 2 french fries @ 47¢ each; 3 coffees @ 26¢ each. _____

8. For his cookout, Gerald has bought five pounds of hamburger @ $1.89 a pound and two dozen buns @ 79¢ for a package of 6. Estimate his total bill for this food. _____

9. Estimate the total area Mr. Larson has to paint on the tennis court if the dimensions of the court are 13.8 m by 7.2 m. How much will the paint cost for this job (estimate) if one can of paint covers 50 m^2 and costs $23.95 per can? _____

10. Nicole is going to pay for the following purchases with a check for $100 given to her by her aunt for the holiday season. How much change should she get back on this purchase? 2 dresses @ $12.89 each; 2 jackets @ $18.99 each; 3 blouses @ $9.79 each. _____

Estimating Answers

Teacher Notes

Mathematical skills required:

addition and multiplication of decimals
rounding off numbers

New vocabulary:

Related topics:

This topic is applicable to almost all other topics in this book. In particular, it can be applied in the areas of:

Eating Out
Grocery Shopping (all areas)
Heating Costs
Home Care (all areas)
Recipes
Sales Tax
Telephone Bills
Travel (all areas)
Vacation Planning

Teaching suggestions:

1. Examine newspaper advertisements for grocery prices. Use these prices to estimate the cost of purchasing various combinations of items.

2. Point out the importance of using estimation since so many consumer items are listed as odd figures: 99¢; $5.99; $1.95; etc. Point out the reason that prices are listed in such a way (i.e., to make prices seem less than they really are).

3. Make a special effort to apply the principles of estimation to all other topics in this book.

4. Obtain menus from one or more restaurants in the area, and have students estimate the cost of meals, the tax, and the tip for various meals from these restaurants.

CHAPTER NINE

Excise Tax

18. Excise Tax

An excise tax is another kind of sales tax. Although its name is different, an excise tax is assessed in the same way as any other sales tax. Most excise taxes are charged by the federal government on items such as tires and on services such as airplane tickets and telephone calls.

● **Example 1:**

The federal excise tax (FET) charged on tires is a flat rate based on the weight of a tire. For this example, assume that the FET rate schedule shown below is currently in effect. Use this schedule to determine the total price of four new tires costing $35.85 each. Each tire weighs 26.4 pounds.

Federal Excise Tax on Tires

Weight of Tire	Tax
22 lbs	$2.30
26.4 lbs	$2.73
27.6 lbs	$2.93

Solution:

The cost of each tire is equal to the list price plus the excise tax.

Cost	= Price + Excise tax
(per tire)	= $35.85 + $2.73
	= $38.58
Cost of four tires	= 4 × $38.58
	= $154.32

● **Example 2:**

Collette notices that a federal tax of $26.36 has been added to the cost of her airline ticket from Detroit to Omaha. If the total cost of the ticket is $290.00, what is the federal excise tax rate for an airline ticket?

Solution:

Total price of ticket	= Cost of flight + Federal tax
or, cost of flight	= Total price of ticket – Federal tax
	= $290 – $26.36
	= $263.64

$$\text{Tax rate} = \frac{\text{Amount of tax}}{\text{Cost of flight}} \times 100\%$$

$$= \frac{\$26.36}{\$263.64} \times 100\%$$

$$= 10.0\%$$

Consumer Math Success Kit

Name _____   Date _____

18. Excise Tax

The federal excise tax table for new tire purchases is shown on page 77. Use this table in solving problems 1 through 5.

1. Andy is buying two new tires for his car. The tires are listed at $33.74 each. What is the total cost of this purchase?   _____

2. Robin wants to borrow enough money to buy two new R89/138 tires for her car. How much will she need to borrow?   _____

3. Elvira has saved $200 to buy tires for her car. Will she have enough to buy four R89/139 tires, including the excise tax?   _____

4. Gary's truck requires T47/266 tires. How much will three new tires for the truck cost, excise tax included?

    _____

5. The Roundee Tire Store has just ordered 12 tires of each of the following types: R89/135; R89/140; T47/267; T47/269. What will be the total excise tax the store must collect when it sells all of these tires?

    _____

6. Linda plans to fly from Boston to New York City. The fare is $72.72 with a 10% excise tax. What is the total cost of the ticket?   _____

7. A one-way ticket from Atlanta to Lansing costs $214.55. What is the total cost of this ticket when the 10% excise tax has been added?   _____

8. Ronnie is flying from Friday Harbor to visit his aunt in Burbank. What is the total cost of the ticket if the one-way fare is $304.55 and the excise tax is 10%?   _____

9. Evelyn has saved $400.00 to fly from New York City to Hot Springs. If the one-way fare for this trip is $159.09, does she have enough for a round-trip ticket? Don't forget the 10% excise tax.

    _____

10. How much is the total telephone bill on charges of $36.45 with a 3% excise tax?

    _____

11. David's telephone bill this month is $29.93. How much tax must be added if the excise rate is 3%?

    _____

12. A new tax law raises the telephone excise tax from 3% to 5%. What would the old and new tax be on a bill of $40.38?

    _____

18. Excise Tax

You may use the following table for problems involving excise tax on tires.

Table 3: Federal Excise Tax Schedule

Tire	Price	FET
R89/135	$33.74	$1.67
R89/136	$41.99	$2.01
R89/137	$43.49	$2.08
R89/138	$44.24	$2.26
R89/139	$46.49	$2.42
R89/140	$49.49	$2.45
R89/141	$50.24	$2.66
T47/266	$85.59	$2.87
T47/267	$92.79	$2.93
T47/269	$103.54	$3.08

Excise Tax

Teacher Notes

Mathematical skills required:

addition and multiplication of decimals

New vocabulary:

excise tax
list price

Related topics:

Estimating Answers
Sales Tax

Teaching suggestions:

1. Federal excise taxes are often seen as temporary taxes. However, they have a way of hanging on for a long time. The temporary excise tax on tires, for example, seems likely to have become a permanent tax. The excise tax on telephone calls was scheduled to be phased out, but instead has been extended. You may want to check with travel agents and your local telephone company to be sure that the tax rates mentioned in this section are still correct.

2. Newspaper ads for tires often list the federal excise tax (FET) as part of the tire prices. Use these ads as the source of additional problems in this area.

3. Students may be interested in knowing that the federal excise tax on airline tickets is always built right into the ticket price. For example, if a person is quoted a price of $39.00 for an airline ticket, the FET has been prefigured into that price. The true breakdown would be: $37.14 + $1.86 = $39.00. Thus, all airline fares are listed as whole-dollar amounts.

CHAPTER TEN

Grocery Shopping

Finding the Cost
Unit Pricing
Discount Food Stores
Sales
Discount Coupons

19. Finding the Cost

The mathematics of grocery shopping is usually simple. Here are the steps you may have to follow.

1. Multiply the cost of each item by the number of items of that kind chosen. For example, 3 oranges @ 29¢ will cost

$$3 \times \$.29 = \$.87$$

2. Special prices may be available for buying more than one kind of item. You may have to take this into consideration in doing step #1. For example, suppose you buy 5 oranges that sell at a special price of 3 for 69¢. Then:

3 oranges for 69¢ = 1 orange for 23¢
5 oranges   = 5 × 23¢ = $1.15

3. Add the total of all kinds of groceries.

4. Calculate the tax (if any) of the cost of the groceries.

5. Add the tax to the cost of the groceries.

6. Subtract the total bill from the amount tendered.

The following example illustrates these steps for one grocery list.

● **Example:**

What is the total cost of the following groceries and the change from a $20 bill? The cost of these groceries is given on pages 92–93. The shopping was done at the P&Q Supermarket. The tax in this state is 4.5%.

$\frac{1}{2}$ gallon milk	one 16-oz package of cottage cheese
1 lb green beans	2 lbs bacon
1 dz oranges	3 lbs butter

Solution:

The cost for each item is listed below.

milk:		$ 1.39
green beans:		$ .49
oranges:		$ 1.69
cottage cheese:	$.89 ÷ 2 =	$ .45
bacon:	2 × $1.75 =	$ 3.50
butter:	3 × $1.59 =	$ 4.77

Total cost = $1.39 + $.49 + $1.69 + $.45 + $3.50 + $4.77 = $12.29

Tax   = 4.5% × $12.29 = $.55

Total bill = $12.29 + $.55 = $12.84

Change   = $20.00 − $12.84 = $7.16

                   Consumer Math Success Kit

..

Name _____   Date _____

19. Finding the Cost

The prices needed to solve these problems are listed on pages 92–93.

1. Elrod has purchased the items listed below at Martin's Store. He pays for his purchases with a $5 bill. There is no sales tax in this state. How much change does he receive? One 1-lb box club crackers; $\frac{1}{2}$ gal milk; 1 lb butter.

   _____

2. Maria pays for the groceries listed below with $15. How much change does she receive? There is no sales tax in this state. The groceries were purchased at the P&Q Supermarket. 2 lbs hamburger; 1 box facial tissues; one 12-oz pkg American cheese; one 16-oz pkg of fig bars; 1 gal orange juice.

   _____

3. Winnie makes the purchases listed below at Martin's Store and pays with a $20 bill. How much change does she receive? The sales tax in this state is 2%. 1 lb bacon; 16 oz sour cream; one 16-oz pkg mushrooms; 2 dz eggs; 3 cucumbers; two 6-oz jars olives; 5 lbs sugar.

   _____

4. Yuri has $25 to pay for the following groceries purchased at the Happy World Discount Store. Will this be enough for the groceries? The tax in this state is 5%. 2 lbs fresh ham; 3 lbs turkey; three 3-oz pkgs Parmesan cheese; 1 gal milk; 1/2 gal ice cream; one 16-oz pkg instant rice; 5 cucumbers; 1 lb green beans; $1\frac{1}{2}$ dz oranges; one 32-oz bottle dishwashing detergent.

   _____

5. Denise calculates the cost of her groceries at the P&Q Supermarket from its advertised prices. How much should she take to the store to pay for the groceries listed below? The sales tax in this state is 3%. 2 lbs lamb chops; 3 lbs margarine; $2\frac{1}{2}$ lbs potatoes; 1 dz eggs; 1 lb asparagus; two 10-oz boxes strawberries; 9 ears of corn; three 8-oz cans peas; one 8-oz bottle hair shampoo; one 46-oz can pineapple juice; two 12-oz tubes of toothpaste.

   _____

6. Ozzie purchases the following items at the Happy World Store and pays $30.00. How much change should he receive? The sales tax is 5%. 2 lbs smoked ham; 10 lbs potatoes; 6 cucumbers; four 3-oz pkg Parmesan cheese; 1 lb scrod; one 16-oz carton sour cream; six 8-oz cans sweet peas; 1 dz ears of corn; 4 lbs margarine; two 10-oz pkg frozen broccoli; one 12-oz pkg macaroni; 3 lbs canned ham.

   _____

20. Unit Pricing

Intelligent shopping involves comparisons of various brands with each other. This can be difficult when companies produce the same product in different sizes or different amounts. For example, is it more economical to buy 12 ounces of Mrs. Kasparsik's egg noodles at 79¢, 16 ounces of Rondolini's egg noodles at 99¢, or generic egg noodles at $1.89 for two pounds? At one time, consumers had to make these calculations themselves. Now, many states require that stores show the unit price of the things they sell. For example, in this case, a store might be required to show the following "unit cost" for each kind of egg noodles:

Mrs. Kasparsik's egg noodles:	6.6¢ per oz
Rondolini's egg noodles:	6.2¢ per oz
Generic egg noodles:	5.9¢ per oz

If this information is not listed by the store, you can calculate the unit cost easily. Here is the procedure to use:

Unit price of an item = cost of item ÷ total weight or total amount.

In the example above, the cost of three kinds of egg noodles can be found by:

Mrs. Kasparsik's	= $ .79 ÷ 12 oz = 6.6¢ per oz
Rondolini's	= $ .99 ÷ 16 oz = 6.2¢ per oz
Generic	= $1.89 ÷ 32 oz = 5.9¢ per oz

The following example shows another case in which you can use unit pricing to compare the cost of an item.

● **Example:**

Which of the following would be the least expensive way to purchase oranges?

   (a) 1 dz for $1.39

   (b) 50   for $4.69

   (c) 10   for $1.10

   (d) 30   for $3.19

Solution:

The unit price for all four cases would be:

Unit cost = Total cost ÷ Number of oranges

For each case, then, the unit cost would be:

   (a) $1.39 ÷ 12 = 11.6¢ per orange

   (b) $4.69 ÷ 50 = 9.4¢ per orange

   (c) $1.10 ÷ 10 = 11.0¢ per orange

   (d) $3.19 ÷ 30 = 10.6¢ per orange

The offer labeled "b" would be the least expensive way to buy oranges in this example.

Name _____   Date _____

20. Unit Pricing

1. Jeff notices that the price of hamburger is 2 lbs for $4.00. What is the price of the hamburger per pound?

   _____

2. In his shopping, Marco finds that 2 boxes of cereal cost $2.50. What is the unit price of the cereal (cost per box)? _____

3. Mr. Latini advertises his chicken at 3 lbs for $5.00. What is the unit price (price per pound) for the chicken?

4. At the Burkhardt Farm Stand, a dozen apples sell for $2.50. What is the price of a single apple (the unit price of the apples)? _____

5. Two weeks later, the Burkhardt Farm Stand has changed its price to 3 lbs for $1.20. Two other farm stands in the area sell their apples at 5 lbs for $2.00 and at 10 lbs for $4.50. At which stand(s) is the unit price of apples the least? _____

6. Last month, hamburger was on sale at Martin's Store, the P&Q Supermarket, and the Happy World Discount Store at 2 lbs for $3.00, 3 lbs for $4.20, and 5 lbs for $6.00, respectively. At which of the three stores was the unit price of hamburger the lowest? _____

7. In shopping around, Gertrude finds canned peas offered for sale at 3 cans for $1.00 in one store, 5 cans for $1.50 in a second, and 8 cans for $2.25 in a third. In which store is the unit price the least?

   _____

8. The price of cookies at Smedling's Bakery is $.85 for a half pound. At the P&Q, the same cookies sell for $1.50 per pound. At Martin's, the price is 2 lbs for $2.80. What is the unit price for the cookies in each of these stores? _____

9. The P&Q Supermarket carries three types of washing soap. The prices for the three kinds are: 28 oz for $2.30; 35 oz for $3.05; and 56 oz for $5.00. Which of the three kinds of washing soap is the best buy on the basis of price alone? _____

10. Nancy finds that she can buy rice in three stores at three different prices: 89¢ for 500 g; $1.79 for 1.5 kg; and 3.2 kg for $2.98. For which of these is the unit price the lowest? _____

11. Exactly the same type of salt can be bought at Martin's for the following prices: 79¢ for 250 g; $1.57 for 500 g; or 2.5 kg for $2.09. Which of these is the best buy? _____

12. Find the unit price for honey when it is sold in each of the following ways: 6 oz for $1.46; 8.2 oz for $1.79; and 13.7 oz for $2.45. _____

Consumer Math Success Kit

21. Discount Food Stores

There are many ways to save money when you are grocery shopping. One of those ways is to shop at discount stores. A discount grocery store sells nearly all products at less than "standard" competitors. The Happy World Discount Store, whose prices are included on pages 92–93, is an example of this kind of store. The extra services (check cashing, for example) may be fewer than those at a standard store. But you can almost always save money by shopping at a store like this. The example below allows you to calculate the prices of groceries purchased at each of three kinds of stores.

● **Example:**

Compare the cost of the following list of groceries purchased at each of the three stores listed on pages 92–93. There is no tax on groceries in this state.

3 lbs potatoes	2 boxes frozen strawberries
2 lbs hamburger	3 boxes macaroni
1 dz oranges	5 lbs sugar

Solution:

Refer to the prices shown on pages 92–93. At Martin's Store, the prices would be:

potatoes:	3 lbs @ 35¢ per lb	= $ 1.05
hamburger:	2 lbs @ $1.89 per lb	= $ 3.78
strawberries:	2 boxes @ $1.69 ea.	= $ 3.38
macaroni:	3 boxes @ 99¢ ea.	= $ 2.97
oranges:	12 @ $2.09 a dz	= $ 2.09
sugar:	5 lbs @ 69¢ per lb	= $ 3.45
	Total	= $ 16.72

At the P&Q Supermarket, the prices would be:

potatoes:	3lbs @ $1.49 for 5 lbs	= $ .89
hamburger:	2 lbs @ $1.79 per lb	= $ 3.58
strawberries:	2 boxes @ $1.45 ea.	= $ 2.90
macaroni:	3 boxes @ 99¢ per lb	= $ 2.97
oranges:	12 @ $1.69 a dz	= $ 1.69
sugar:	5 lbs @ 59¢ per lb	= $ 2.95
	Total	= $ 14.98

At the Happy World Discount Store, the prices would be:

potatoes:	3 lbs @ 89¢ for 5 lbs	= $ .53
hamburger:	2 lbs @ $1.59 per lb	= $ 3.18
strawberries:	2 boxes @ $1.29 ea.	= $ 2.58
macaroni:	3 boxes @ 79¢ ea.	= $ 2.37
oranges:	12 @ $1.79 a dz	= $ 1.79
sugar:	5 lbs @ $2.49 for 5 lbs	= $ 2.49
	Total	= $ 12.94

21. Discount Food Stores

Price information needed for all of the problems below can be found on pages 92–93.

1. Scott's grocery list is shown below. How much will these groceries cost at Martin's Store, the P&Q Supermarket, and the Happy World Discount Store? There is no sales tax in this state. One 16-oz pkg mushrooms; 1 lb green beans; 1 lb club crackers.

_____

2. The items Gwyneth expects to purchase at the store today are listed below. What will be the cost of these groceries at each of the three stores? There is no sales tax in this state. 3 lbs hamburger; 2 cantaloupes; 2 lbs butter; 1 dz oranges; 3 lbs pears.

_____

3. Garabet is trying to find the best place to shop for the following grocery list. What will these groceries cost in each of the three stores? The sales tax in this state is 5%. 2 lbs bacon; 3 lbs lamb chops; 1 dz eggs; 5 lbs sugar; one 10-oz box frozen strawberries; one 6-oz jar artichoke hearts.

_____

4. Laura wants to know the cost of the groceries listed below at each of the three stores. What will be the cost if the state sales tax here is 6%? 1 box facial tissues; six 8-oz cans sweet peas; 2.5 lbs beef brisket; two 16-oz pkgs mushrooms; one 32-oz bottle dishwashing detergent; $\frac{1}{2}$ gal ice cream; one 6-oz jar olives.

_____

5. Find the cost of the following groceries at each of the three stores listed on pages 92–93. The sales tax to be applied in each case is 4%. 3 lbs asparagus; 5 lbs sugar; one 12-oz pkg American cheese; 2 lbs butter; 3 lbs bacon; one 8-oz bottle hair shampoo; 1 jar olives; 2 half gals ice cream.

_____

6. Stephen wants to know how much he can save by shopping at the least expensive store for the groceries listed here. Be sure to include the state tax of 4.7% in these calculations. One 3-lb canned ham; 2 lbs butter; 2 half gals ice cream; six 8-oz cans sweet peas; two 40-oz jars honey; 6 boxes facial tissue; three 16-oz pkgs fig bars; one 12-oz tube toothpaste.

_____

22. Sales

Food stores often try to attract customers by having "sales." This means that certain items in the store are being sold for less than their usual price. Sometimes this makes grocery shopping at a store like Martin's or the P&Q (see pages 92–93) less expensive than shopping at a discount store like Happy World, and sometimes not. The following example shows how to calculate food prices when sales are held at a store. Refer to pages 92–93 for the prices at all three stores.

● **Example:**

Both Martin's and the P&Q are having sales on certain products this week. The products on sale are listed below. Keeping these prices in mind, what is the total cost of the groceries listed below at all three stores?

3 lbs asparagus	3 lbs bacon
5 lbs sugar	one 8-oz bottle hair shampoo
one 12-oz pkg American cheese	one 6-oz jar olives
2 lbs butter	2 half gals ice cream

Sale Prices	Martin's	P&Q
asparagus	$1.29 per lb	$1.19 per lb
bacon	$1.65 per lb	$1.39 per lb
American cheese	$1.49 per 12 oz	$1.35 per 12 oz
orange juice	$1.23 per ½ gal	$1.29 per ½ gal
butter	(not on sale)	$1.49 per lb
fresh ham	$3.09 per lb	(not on sale)
ice cream	$1.59 per ½ gal	(not on sale)
olives	(not on sale)	79¢ per 6-oz jar

Solution:

From the prices on pages 92–93, the cost of groceries would be:

At Martin's:

asparagus: 3 lbs @ $1.29	= $ 3.87	sugar: 5 lbs @ 69¢	= $ 3.45
cheese: 1 pkg @ $1.49	= $ 1.49	butter: 2 lbs @ $1.69	= $ 3.38
bacon: 3 lbs @ $1.65	= $ 4.95	shampoo: 1 bottle @ $1.99	= $ 1.89
olives: 1 jar @ 89¢	= $ .89	ice cream: 2 half gals @ $1.59	= $ 3.18

Total cost = $23.10

At P&Q:

asparagus: 3 lbs @ $1.19	= $ 3.57	sugar: 5 lbs @ 59¢	= $ 2.95
cheese: 1 pkg @ $1.35	= $ 1.35	butter: 2 lbs @ $1.49	= $ 2.98
shampoo: 1 bottle @ $1.38	= $ 1.38	bacon: 3 lbs @ $1.39	= $ 4.17
olives: 1 jar @ 79¢	= $ .79	ice cream: 2 half gals @ $1.89	= $ 3.78

Total cost = $20.97

At Happy World:

asparagus: 3 lbs @ $1.29	= $ 3.87	sugar: 5 lbs @ 5 lbs for $2.49	= $ 2.49
cheese: 1 pkg @ $1.69	= $ 1.69	butter: 2 lbs @ $1.39	= $ 2.78
shampoo: 1 bottle @ $1.05	= $ 1.05	bacon: 3 lbs @ $1.49	= $ 4.47
olives: 1 jar @ 59¢	= $ .59	ice cream: 2 half gals @ $1.98	= $ 3.96

Total cost = $20.90

Name _____ Date _____

22. Sales

For the following problems, refer to the price list on pages 92–93. Both Martin's and the P&Q Supermarket are having sales this week on certain items, listed below. Keep these prices in mind as you find the cost of groceries in each of the following problems.

Sale Prices	Martin's	P&Q
asparagus	$1.29 per lb	$1.19 per lb
bacon	$1.65 per lb	$1.39 per lb
American cheese	$1.49 per 12 oz	$1.35 per 12 oz
orange juice	$1.23 per ½ gal	$1.29 per ½ gal
butter	(not on sale)	$1.49 per lb
fresh ham	$3.09 per lb	(not on sale)
ice cream	$1.59 per ½ gal	(not on sale)
olives	(not on sale)	79¢ per 6-oz jar

1. Cecil is trying to decide which of the three stores is the cheapest place to shop for the groceries listed here. Which store do you recommend? There is no sales tax in this state. 2 lbs asparagus; 4.7 lbs fresh ham; 1 lb sugar; 1 lb green beans. _____

2. Thierry's grocery list is given below. Find the cost of these groceries at each of the three stores when the above sales are in effect. There is no sales tax here. 3 half gals ice cream; 3 lbs butter; one 16-oz pkg mushrooms; 2 lbs margarine. _____

3. Milton could buy the items listed below at any one of the three stores. When the above sales are in effect, at which store would the groceries be cheapest? The sales tax in this state is 4%. 3.5 lbs lamb chops; 4.8 lbs hamburger; 2 lbs butter; 2 half gals orange juice. _____

4. Ann Marie usually does her shopping at the Happy World Store because prices are cheaper there. Is that still true for the following list of groceries when the above sales are in effect? The state sales tax here is 5%. 2 dz oranges; 3 dz eggs; 3 lbs margarine; 2 lbs bacon; 4.6 lbs fresh ham; 2 lbs sugar. _____

5. Leo's grocery list is shown here. What will be the cost of these groceries at each of the three stores while the above sale prices are in effect? The sales tax here is 6%. 5 lbs potatoes; 6 oranges; 2 lbs butter;
3 half gals milk; 3.2 lbs hamburger; three 12-oz pkgs American cheese. _____

6. Everett is guessing that the cost of the groceries listed below will be less at the P&Q store during the special sale listed above. Is he correct? The sales tax on these items is 4.5%. 2 cartons sour cream; 1.8 lbs fresh ham; 4 half gals orange juice; 2 dz eggs; one 16-oz pkg mushrooms; 3 lbs bacon.

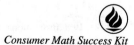

Consumer Math Success Kit

23. Discount Coupons

One way to save money shopping for groceries is with discount coupons. These are special offers made by the companies that manufacture, process, and package foods. They are usually "cents off" coupons, meaning that the consumer can subtract a few cents for the food item mentioned on the coupon. The example below shows how the use of food coupons can reduce the cost of groceries.

● **Example:**

Listed below are some coupons that appeared in local newspapers last week. These coupons are redeemed at face value at Happy World and Martin's, but at double value at P&Q. With this in mind, calculate the cost of the grocery list below.

Coupons: 25¢ off any canned ham (limit: 1 ham)
15¢ off each half gallon of ice cream (no limit)
10¢ off each can of sweet peas (limit: 6 cans)
75¢ off each jar of honey (limit: 2 jars)
One box of facial tissues free with each two boxes purchased
    at regular price (no limit)
35¢ off each package of fig bars (limit: 3 packages)

Grocery list: one 3-lb canned ham
2 lbs butter
2 half gals ice cream
six 8-oz cans sweet peas
two 40-oz jars honey
6 boxes facial tissues
three 16-oz pkgs fig bars
one 12-oz tube toothpaste

Solution:

Prices quoted below are taken from pages 92–93.

At Martin's:

ham: $6.29 – 25¢	= $ 6.04
butter: 2 lbs @ $1.69	= $ 3.38
ice cream: 2 half gals @ $2.19 – (2 × 15¢)	= $ 4.08
peas: 6 cans @ 45¢ – (6 × 10¢)	= $ 2.10
honey: 2 jars @ $3.49 – (2 × 75¢)	= $ 5.48
tissues: 4 boxes @ 99¢ (gives 2 free)	= $ 3.96
fig bars: 3 pkgs @ $1.50 – (3 × 35¢)	= $ 3.45
toothpaste:	= $ 1.59

Total cost = $30.08

(continued)

© 1983, 1996 Instructional Horizons. Produced and Distributed
by J. Weston Walch, Publisher, Portland, Maine 04104-0658   *Consumer Math Success Kit*

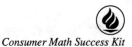

23. Discount Coupons
(continued)

At P&Q:

ham: $5.99 – 2 × 25¢	= $ 5.49
butter: 2 lbs @ $1.59	= $ 3.18
ice cream: 2 half gals @ $1.89 – (2 × 2 × 15¢)	= $ 3.18
peas: 6 cans @ 3 for $1.00 – (6 × 2 × 10¢)	= $ .80
honey: 2 jars @ $2.99 – (2 × 2 × 75¢)	= $ 2.98
tissues: 4 boxes @ 69¢ (gives 4 free)	= $ 2.76
fig bars: 3 pkgs @ $1.35 – (2 × 3 × 35¢)	= $ 1.95
toothpaste: 1 tube @ $1.59	= $ 1.59

Total cost = $21.93

At Happy World:

ham: $5.59 – 25¢	= $ 5.34
butter: 2 lbs @ $1.39	= $ 2.78
ice cream: 2 half gals @ $1.98 – (2 × 15¢)	= $ 3.66
peas: 6 cans @ 4 for $1.00 – (6 × 10¢)	= $ .90
honey: 2 jars @ $3.19 – (2 × 75¢)	= $ 4.88
tissues: 4 boxes @ 59¢ (gives 2 free)	= $ 2.36
fig bars: 3 pkgs @ $1.15 – (3 × 35¢)	= $ 2.40
toothpaste: 1 tube @ $1.09	= $ 1.09

Total cost = $23.41

Name _____ Date _____

23. Discount Coupons

The prices needed to solve the following problems are given on pages 92–93. The coupons listed below can be used for purchases made this week at Martin's and Happy World. P&Q gives double credit for each coupon.

25¢ off any canned ham (limit: 1 ham)
15¢ off each half gallon of ice cream (no limit)
10¢ off each 8-oz can of sweet peas (limit: 6 cans)
75¢ off each 40-oz jar of honey (limit: 2 jars)
One box of facial tissues free with each two boxes purchased at regular price (no limit)
35¢ off each 16-oz package of fig bars (limit: 3 packages)

1. Terry's grocery list today contains the items shown below. What will be her cost if she uses coupons on her purchases at each of the three stores? There is no sales tax here. 1 canned ham; 3 lbs bacon; six 8-oz cans sweet peas. _____

2. How much will Bernard pay for the groceries listed below at each of the three stores, provided he uses coupons wherever possible? There is no sales tax in this state. 2 half gals ice cream; three 40-oz jars honey; 4 lbs hamburger. _____

3. Betty normally shops at Happy World, but wants to know if she can save money because of coupons this week. Find the total cost of her groceries listed below at each of the three stores. No sales tax here. Six 8-oz cans sweet peas; one 16-oz pkg fig bars; 3 lbs sugar. _____

4. Sebastian calculates the cost of his groceries at each of three stores from their newspaper advertisements and the coupon discounts shown above. How much do these groceries cost at each store if there is a 4% sales tax in this state? Two 40-oz jars honey; six 8-oz cans sweet peas; 2 canned hams; 1 half gal ice cream; 1 lb butter. _____

5. Find the cost of Sheila's groceries, shown below, at each of three stores, from prices shown on pages 92–93 and discount coupons listed above. The state sales tax here is 5.8%. 2 cartons cottage cheese; 3 half gals milk; three 40-oz jars honey; 3 canned hams; one 1-lb box club crackers; 3.7 lbs lamb chops.

6. The Burnetts' shopping list for today includes two boxes of facial tissues, three 16-oz pkgs of fig bars, 2 lbs of sugar, four 40-oz jars of honey, 2 lbs of green beans, and six 8-oz cans of sweet peas. How much will these groceries cost at Martin's, the P&Q, and Happy World, using the discount coupons listed above? The sales tax in this state is 5%. _____

Table 4: Prices of Groceries at Three Kinds of Stores

Item	Amount	Martin's Store	P&Q Supermarket	Happy World Discount Store
American Cheese	12-oz pkg	$1.69	$1.69	$1.69
Apples	1 lb	$ .79	$ .69	$ .59
Artichoke Hearts	6-oz jar	$1.35	$1.09	$1.25
Asparagus	1 lb	$1.49	$1.39	$1.29
Bacon	1 lb	$1.85	$1.75	$1.49
Bagels	12-oz pkg	$ .69	$ .63	$ .59
Beef Brisket	1 lb	$1.85	$1.78	$1.89
Butter	1 lb	$1.69	$1.59	$1.39
Canned Ham	3 lbs	$6.29	$5.99	$5.59
Cantaloupes	each	$1.39	$1.19	$1.15
Club Crackers	1-lb box	$1.29	$1.09	$ .99
Corn	1 dz	$2.09	6 for $.89	$1.19
Cottage Cheese	16-oz carton	$ .59	2 for $.89	3 for $.99
Cucumbers	each	$ .19	8 for $.69	10 for $1.19
Dishwashing Detergent	32-oz bottle	$1.89	$1.59	$1.39
Eggs	1 dz	$1.09	$ .89	$ .79
Facial Tissues	200-count box	$ .99	$ .69	$ .59
Fig Bars	16-oz pkg	$1.50	$1.35	$1.15
Fresh Ham	1 lb	$3.29	$3.09	$2.99
Frozen Apple Juice	12-oz can	$ .89	$ .79	$ .69
Frozen Broccoli	10-oz pkg	$ .59	$ .59	$ .59
Frozen Lasagna	12-oz pkg	$1.59	$1.39	$1.19
Frozen Strawberries	10-oz box	$1.69	$1.45	$1.29
Green Beans	1 lb	$ .69	$ .49	$ .45

(continued)

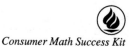

Consumer Math Success Kit

Table 4: Prices of Groceries at Three Kinds of Stores (continued)

Item	Amount	Martin's Store	P&Q Supermarket	Happy World Discount Store
Hair Shampoo	8-oz bottle	$1.89	$1.38	$1.05
Hamburger	1 lb	$1.89	$1.79	$1.59
Honey	40-oz jar	$3.49	$2.99	$3.19
Ice Cream	½ gal	$2.19	$1.89	$1.98
Lamb Chops	1 lb	$3.79	$3.29	$3.19
Macaroni	12-oz pkg	$ .99	$ .99	$ .79
Margarine	1 lb	$ .59	2 for $1.00	3 for $1.25
Milk	½ gal	$1.59	$1.39	$1.19
Mushrooms	16-oz pkg	$1.89	$1.69	$1.59
Olives	6-oz jar	$ .89	$ .89	$ .59
Orange Juice	1/2 gal	$1.39	$1.39	$1.19
Oranges	1 dz	$2.09	$1.69	$1.79
Parmesan Cheese	3-oz pkg	$ .99	$ .99	$ .99
Pears	1 lb	$ .89	$ .69	$ .69
Pineapple Juice	46-oz can	$1.18	$1.08	$ .98
Potatoes	1 lb	$ .35	$1.49 for 5 lbs	$.89 for 5 lbs
Pound Cake	10.7-oz pkg	$1.98	$1.72	$1.65
Rice, Instant	16-oz pkg	$1.19	$ .89	$ .79
Scrod	1 lb	$3.99	$3.59	$3.29
Smoked Ham	1 lb	$1.19	$ .88	$ .99
Sour Cream	16-oz carton	$1.39	$1.13	$1.09
Sugar	1-lb pkg	$ .69	$ .59	5 lbs for $2.49
Sweet Peas	8-oz can	$ .45	3 for $1.00	4 for $1.00
Toothpaste	12-oz tube	$1.59	$1.59	$1.09
Turkey	1 lb	$ .98	$ .88	$ .79

© 1983, 1996 Instructional Horizons. Produced and Distributed by J. Weston Walch, Publisher, Portland, Maine 04104-0658

Consumer Math Success Kit

Grocery Shopping

Teacher Notes

Mathematical skills required:

addition, subtraction, multiplication, and division of decimals and fractions

New vocabulary:

discount coupons
discount food store
sale
unit pricing

Related topics:

Budgets: Short-term
Estimating Answers
Nutrition
Recipes
Sales Tax

Teaching suggestions:

1. Point out to students that prices may not be the only factor to consider in choosing a store to shop at. For example, a discount store may offer fewer services (such as free bags and check cashing) than a regular store. Also, the travel costs in shopping at a discount store a greater distance from one's home may more than make up for the money saved in shopping at that store.

2. Most states now require that unit prices be listed on store shelves. As admirable as this requirement may be, it is sometimes not as helpful as it is designed to be. Items may be moved about on shelves, the prices may be outdated, or new items may have been added. Students should see how easy it is to calculate unit prices using hand calculators. They probably will not want to do this on every item they buy, but for some basic food items, knowing the unit price can result in a considerable savings.

3. Point out to students that for smaller families, it may be more economical to pay a higher unit price and purchase smaller quantities to avoid loss through spoilage or waste from large, unusable quantities.

4. The wide availability of food prices, discount coupons, sale information, etc., from daily newspaper ads makes this section one that can be made very current in your own classroom.

Chapter Eleven

Heating Costs

24. Heating Costs

For many people, heating has become the second largest housing expense after rent or mortgage payments. The most common methods of heating are (1) electricity, (2) natural gas, and (3) fuel oil. Costs of the first two of these would show up on regular electric or gas meter readings. Determining the cost of heating with oil is slightly different.

Heating oil is usually delivered by and pumped from large oil trucks. A gauge on the truck records the amount of oil delivered to a house. Then the oil company determines the charge for the oil by multiplying the amount of oil delivered times the price of the oil per gallon (or per liter).

Cost of oil = Number of gallons × Price per gallon

or   = Number of liters × Price per liter

● **Example 1:**

The Do-Glo Heating Oil Company delivered 228 gallons of oil to the Humphreys' house on October 28. The oil costs 89¢ per gallon. What is the charge for this delivery?

Solution:

Cost of oil = Number of gallons × Price per gallon

= 228 gallons × $0.89 per gallon

= $202.92

● **Example 2:**

The following month, the Humphreys received a delivery of 248.5 gallons. The price of the oil had gone up to 94¢ per gallon. What was the total cost of this delivery?

Solution:

Cost of oil = Number of gallons × Price per gallon

= 248.5 gallons × $0.94 per gallon

= $233.59

● **Example 3:**

Sunrise Oil Company is now registering its deliveries of oil in liters. The posted price for oil is 22.7¢ per liter. At this rate, what is the cost of a delivery of 783.5 liters of oil?

Solution:

Cost of oil = Number of liters × Price per liter

= 783.5 liters × $0.227 per liter

= $177.85

© 1983, 1996 Instructional Horizons. Produced and Distributed
by J. Weston Walch, Publisher, Portland, Maine 04104-0658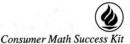

Consumer Math Success Kit

Name _____   Date _____

24. Heating Costs

The cost of heating oil in each of the following problems is $89\frac{9}{10}$¢ per gallon or 22.7¢ per liter.

1. The Foukal family received an oil shipment on October 15 of 188.9 gallons. What was the cost of that oil? _____

2. On October 30, the Quinn family received a delivery of 206.9 gallons. How much did this oil cost them? _____

3. On a recent oil delivery to Phillip Mazza's house, the initial reading on the oil tank gauge was 106.3 gallons, and the final reading was 329.3 gallons. What was the total cost of this oil delivery? _____

4. Lloyd watches as oil is being delivered to his parents' house. He notices that the initial reading on the delivery gauge is 698.3 gallons, and the final reading is 933.2 gallons. What will be the cost of this oil shipment? _____

5. During the month of May, the Austins received two shipments of oil. The first was 264.7 gallons and the second, 188.9 gallons. What was the Austins' oil bill for the month? _____

6. Murphy's Oil Company is now measuring its delivery of oil in liters. One month it made shipments of 899.5 liters, 1064.6 liters, and 950.3 liters to the Murtaugh home. What is the cost of oil for the Murtaughs this month? _____

7. The Sevinors received an oil bill for the month showing the beginning and ending meter readings for each oil delivery. But the total amount delivered and the total cost had been omitted. From the readings below, calculate their bill for the month. (All readings in gallons.)

Jan 4:	467.3	603.8
Jan 11:	389.3	623.8
Jan 19:	559.1	782.4
Jan 26:	407.8	612.7 _____

8. Lynda's job at the oil company is to calculate the oil bills for customers in the Wilshire area of town. Here are the deliveries for one customer for the month. What is the total bill for the month for this customer? (All readings in liters.)

2/1:	385.7	1487.9
2/9:	497.8	1392.9
2/18:	105.8	1187.9
2/26:	549.2	1676.3 _____

© 1983, 1996 Instructional Horizons. Produced and Distributed
by J. Weston Walch, Publisher, Portland, Maine 04104-0658   98   *Consumer Math Success Kit*

Heating Costs
Teacher Notes

Mathematical skills required:

subtraction and multiplication of decimals

New vocabulary:

meter reading
price per gallon
price per liter

Related topics:

Budgets: Short-term
Estimating Answers
Utility Bills: Gas, Electric, and Water

Teaching suggestions:

1. You should be able to get from your local heating oil, gas, or electric company a sample of the forms used in delivering and billing for oil deliveries, gas, or electricity use. Make photocopies of these bills, insert numerical values of your own choosing, and have students use these values in calculating the cost of heating by oil, gas, or electricity.

2. Discuss some of the advantages and disadvantages of using each of these three energy sources as a way of heating a home.

3. Find out if the heating oil companies in your area have yet converted or are considering converting to metric units. What are the advantages and disadvantages in making this conversion?

CHAPTER TWELVE

Home Care

Painting
Wallpapering
Yard Work
Patios and Driveways
Carpentry

25. Painting

Many people prefer to do the work of painting their own homes, inside and outside. Besides requiring painting skills, this type of home improvement also demands certain mathematical skills. Finding the amount and cost of paint needed for a job involves three steps.

1. What is the area to be painted? This can be calculated from formulas for various geometric figures.

2. How much paint is needed to cover this area? The area covered by one can of paint is usually given on the label.

3. What is the cost of painting this area? The cost can be found by multiplying the number of cans needed by the cost per can.

The examples below illustrate how these steps are to be followed in finding the amount of paint needed and the cost of painting an area.

● **Example 1:**

Carmen has decided to paint the ceiling of his bedroom. The room measures 8 ft 6 in high, 10 ft long, and 8 ft wide. One pint of the paint he will use covers 30 sq ft. How much paint should he buy?

Solution:

Look back at the steps to be followed in solving this kind of problem:

Step 1:   Area of space   = length × width
                         = 10 ft × 8 ft = 80 sq ft

Step 2:   Number of cans needed   = 80 sq ft ÷ 30 sq ft per can
                                 = 2.67 cans (buy 3 cans)

● **Example 2:**

Sarah wants to paint all four walls in her den. The dimensions of the room are 8 ft wide by 12 ft long by 8 ft high. The paint she will use covers 100 sq ft per quart and costs $9.95 per quart. What will be the cost of this job?

Solution:

Step 1:   Area to be covered   = 2 walls (8 ft × 8 ft) and 2 walls (12 ft × 8 ft)
                             = 2 × 8 ft × 8 ft + 2 × 12 ft × 8 ft
                             = 128 sq ft + 192 sq ft = 320 sq ft

Step 2:   Paint needed   = 320 sq ft ÷ 100 sq ft per can
                       = 3.2 cans (buy 4 cans)

Step 3:   Cost   = 4 cans × $9.95 per can
                 = $39.80

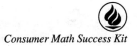
Consumer Math Success Kit

25. Painting

Diagram 1

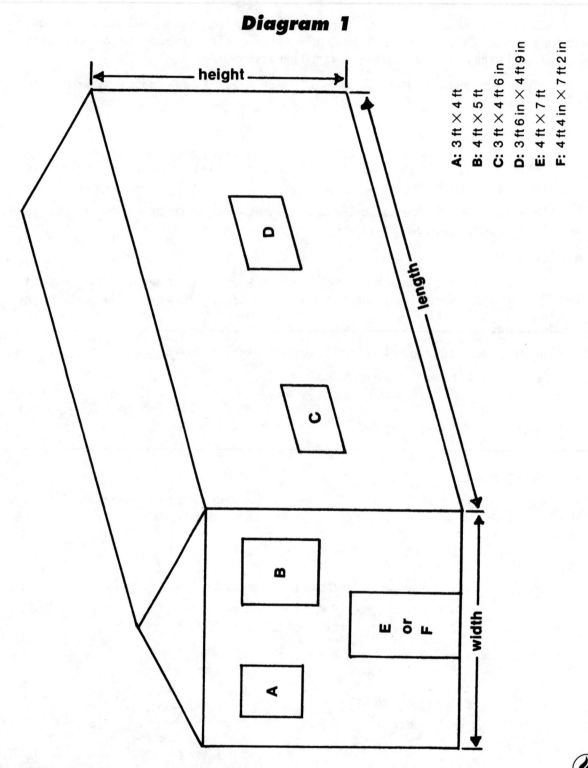

A: 3 ft × 4 ft
B: 4 ft × 5 ft
C: 3 ft × 4 ft 6 in
D: 3 ft 6 in × 4 ft 9 in
E: 4 ft × 7 ft
F: 4 ft 4 in × 7 ft 2 in

Consumer Math Success Kit

25. Painting

Diagram 2

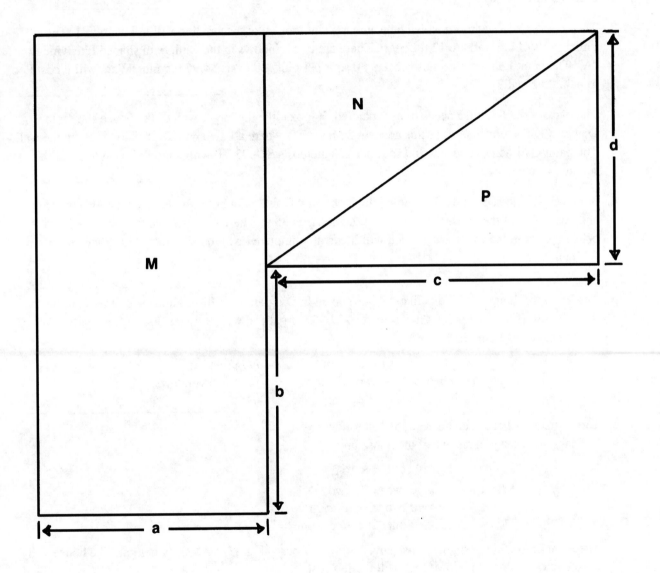

25. Painting

Areas referred to in the following problems are shown in the diagrams on pages 104 and 105.

1. Denise wants to paint a wall in her office that has the shape of Figure M in Diagram 2. The dimensions of the wall are 8 ft by 10 ft. One pint of the paint she wants to use will cover 50 square feet. How many pints should she buy?

   _____

2. The wall in Leo's bedroom which he wants to paint looks like the smaller wall in Diagram 1. The dimensions of the wall are 12 ft by 9 ft. There are two windows in the wall, both shaped like window "A." The paint Leo intends to use covers 50 sq ft per pint and costs $4.95 per pint. What will it cost Leo to paint this wall?

   _____

3. The back of Gail's house needs to be repainted. It looks like the larger wall of the house shown in Diagram 1. The dimensions of this area are 22 ft by 9 ft. There are two windows of style "B" in the wall. The paint Gail will use covers 300 sq ft per gal and costs $18.95. How much will it cost to paint this section of the house?

   _____

4. Suppose Gail decides to do the whole job (Problem #3) and paint not only the back but also the front and both sides of the house. The length of the house is 35 ft. There are six more "B" windows and one "E" door in the walls. How much will it cost to complete this job using the paint described in Problem #3?

   _____

5. The Verranos' house also looks like the one shown in Diagram 1. Its dimensions and other features are listed below. If they use a paint that sells for $24.95 per gal and which covers 300 sq ft per gal, what will be the cost of painting the house?

length: 46 ft	*width:* 28 ft	*height:* 15 ft
eight "B" windows	two "E" doors	four "C" windows

   _____

6. Tom Burstow's house can be described as follows:
   In Diagram 1, the dimensions of the house are:

   $$38 \text{ ft} \times 26 \text{ ft} \times 16 \text{ ft}$$

   Windows: *Sides:* two "C"; two "D";
              Front: two "C"; *Back:* two "D"
   Doors: *Front:* one "F"; *Back:* one "F"

   The paint Tom will use on the house covers 400 sq ft per gal and costs $21.79 per gal. The house will need two coats of paint. How much will the job cost?

   _____

(continued)

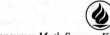

25. Painting *(continued)*

7. Listed below are the dimensions of six walls. Tell what the cost of painting each wall would be using paint that covers 65 sq ft per can and sells at $11.95 per can. Also give the area of each wall.

    (a) 8 ft by 14 ft

    (a) 10 ft by 15 ft

    (a) 12 ft 6 in by 9 ft

    (a) 9 ft 9 in by 11 ft

    (a) 8 ft 4 in by 9 ft

    (a) 11 ft by 13 ft 8 in

8. Listed below are the dimensions of four floors. Tell what the cost of shellacking each floor would be with shellac that covers 125 sq ft per can and sells at $23.75 per can.

    (a) 9 ft 10 in by 18 ft

    (a) 12 ft 7 in by 60 ft 6 in

    (a) 14 ft 3 in by 10 ft 8 in

    (a) 22 ft 4 in by 18 ft 8 in

26. Wallpapering

Wallpapering is often a more difficult job than painting. Making paper fit around corners and in narrow places is usually more difficult than painting those areas. The mathematics of wallpapering is also more difficult. If the wallpaper has a pattern, you will need to make the pattern on one strip match the pattern on the adjoining strip. Some companies publish formulas that tell you how to calculate the amount of wallpaper needed for a job. But you can get a good idea simply by using mathematics too. Here are the steps to follow:

1. Calculate the area of the surface to be papered.

2. Allow one roll of wallpaper for each 30 sq ft to be papered.

3. Multiply the cost of one roll of paper by the number of rolls needed for the job. This will give you the cost of papering the whole surface.

The following example shows how to use these steps in determining the cost of papering a room.

● **Example:**

Mark intends to wallpaper a room that is 12 ft long, 9 ft wide, and 8 ft high. The room contains 1 "E" door and 4 "A" windows (see page 104). One roll of wallpaper to be used in the job covers 30 sq ft and costs $12 per roll. What will the job cost?

Solution:

Step 1:	Area to be papered	= Area of 4 walls – Area of one door – Area of 4 windows
	Area of 4 walls	= Area of 2 end walls + Area of 2 side walls
	Area of end wall	= 9 ft × 8 ft = 72 sq ft
	Area of side wall	= 12 ft × 8 ft = 96 sq ft
	Area to be papered	= 2 × 72 sq ft + (2 × 96 sq ft) – 28 sq ft – (4 × 12 sq ft)
		= 144 sq ft + 192 sq ft – 28 sq ft – 48 sq ft
		= 260 sq ft to be papered
Step 2:	Rolls of wallpaper	= 260 sq ft ÷ 30 sq ft per roll
		= 8.67 rolls (buy 9 rolls)
Step 3:	Cost of wallpaper	= 9 rolls × $12.00 per roll
		= $108.00

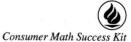

26. Wallpapering

Areas referred to in the following problems are shown in the diagrams on pages 104 and 105.

1. Rhena has decided to wallpaper one long wall in her study with a paper that costs $15.95 per roll. One roll covers 30 square feet. The wall she will be working on has the shape of Figure M in Diagram 2. The dimensions of the wall are 32 ft by 10 ft. How much will this job cost?

   _____

2. If Rhena decides to wallpaper the other three walls in the room with the same paper, here are the dimensions of the walls she will have to use:

   opposite wall: 32 ft × 10 ft; contains two "A" windows

   end walls: 10 ft × 10 ft; contain one "E" door

   What would be the cost of papering the remaining three walls?   _____

3. The room that Paul has converted to his office has three walls that need to be wallpapered. Two have the shape of Figure N + P and one the shape of Figure M in Diagram 2. The dimensions of these walls are as follows: M: 18 ft × 9 ft;   N + P: 13 ft × 9 ft

   There is one "E" door in an "N + P" wall. There are no windows in any of the walls. The wallpaper Paul has selected covers 30 sq ft per roll and sells for $17.95 per roll. What will be the cost of papering this room?   _____

4. Alonzo's bedroom looks like the figure shown in Diagram 1. The room is 15 ft long, 9 ft wide, and 8 ft high. There are two "C" windows in one wall and one "F" door in another wall. Alonzo will wallpaper this room with paper that covers 35 sq ft per roll and costs $19.99 per roll. What will be the cost of papering this room?   _____

5. The den in Renata's house looks like the figure shown in Diagram 1. The room is 18 ft long, 12 ft wide, and 10 ft high. There are three "B" windows in one wall, two "C" windows in a second wall, and one "E" door in a third wall. The wallpaper she wants to use costs $15.99 a roll and covers 30 sq ft per roll. How much will it cost to paper this room?   _____

6. Given below are the dimensions for five rooms that need to be wallpapered. In each case, assume that one roll of wallpaper covers 30 sq ft. The cost of the paper is given in each case. What is the cost of papering each room?

   (a) 12 ft long by 8 ft wide by 8 ft high; 1 "E" door; $13.95   _____

   (a) 10 ft long by 9 ft wide by 8 ft high; 1 "E" door; 2 "A" windows; $9.95   _____

   (a) 12 ft long by 10 ft wide by 8 ft high; 1 "F" door; $15.95   _____

   (a) 10 ft long by 9 ft 6 in wide by 8 ft high, 1 "F" door; 2 "A" windows; $16.95   _____

   (a) 14 ft long by 8 ft 6 in wide by 8 ft 6 in high; 1 "F" door; 2 "C" windows; $22.95   _____

                   Consumer Math Success Kit

27. Yard Work

Most people don't think of fertilizing and seeding the lawn as an exercise in mathematics. Yet, mathematical problems are involved in keeping the yard looking good. You may have to calculate the amount of grass seed, weed killer, and/or fertilizer to use on your yard and the cost of these materials. Here are the steps involved in these calculations.

Step 1: Calculate the total area to be seeded or fertilized.

Step 2: Find out how many bags of grass seed or fertilizer will be needed to cover this area. The area covered by one bag is usually given on the label.

Step 3: Find out the cost of the job. Multiply the number of bags you need by the cost of one bag.

The sample problem below shows how to follow these steps in calculating the cost of fertilizing a lawn.

● **Example:**

Sharon wants to fertilize her lawn. The lawn has the shape of Figure M + N + P in Diagram 2 on page 105. The fertilizer she uses will cover 800 sq ft of lawn and costs $26.95 per bag. What will be the total cost of fertilizing the lawn? The dimensions of the figure in Diagram 2 are:

$$a = 40 \text{ feet} \quad b = 30 \text{ feet} \quad c = 20 \text{ feet} \quad d = 10 \text{ feet}$$

Solution:

Step 1: The area of the total lawn is equal to the area of two rectangles, M and N + P. The dimensions of rectangle M are 40 ft wide (= a) and 40 ft long (= b + d). The dimensions of rectangle N + P are 20 feet long (= c) and 10 feet wide (= d). So the area of the lawn is:

Area of M $= 40 \text{ ft} \times 40 \text{ ft}$
$= 1600 \text{ sq ft}$

Area of N + P $= 20 \text{ ft} \times 10 \text{ ft}$
$= 200 \text{ sq ft}$

Total area $= 1600 \text{ sq ft} + 200 \text{ sq ft}$
$= 1800 \text{ sq ft}$

Step 2: Number of bags needed $= \dfrac{\text{Total area to be covered}}{\text{Area covered by one bag}}$

$= \dfrac{1800 \text{ sq ft}}{800 \text{ sq ft per bag}}$

$= 2.25 \text{ bags (buy 3 bags)}$

Step 3: The total cost of the job $= \text{Cost per bag} \times \text{Number of bags}$

$= \$26.95 \text{ per bag} \times 3 \text{ bags}$

$= \$80.85$

Consumer Math Success Kit

27. Yard Work

The diagram referred to in the following problems is found on page 105.

1. The front lawn at the Bensons' house has the shape of Figure M in Diagram 2. The dimensions of the lawn are 80 ft by 40 ft. A box of the fertilizer they use on this lawn covers 400 sq ft. At a price of $13.95 per box, what will it cost to fertilize this lawn? _____

2. At Plum Hill Farm, a new area that has the shape of Figure M + N + P in Diagram 2 is to be seeded with grass seed. The dimensions of this area are:

$$a = 40 \text{ ft} \quad b = 60 \text{ ft} \quad c = 80 \text{ ft} \quad d = 30 \text{ ft}$$

The grass seed used in this job comes in boxes that cover 600 sq ft of area and cost $26.95 per box. What will be the cost of seeding this area? _____

3. Randy was told by his father to fertilize their side yard, which has the shape of Figure M in Diagram 2. The dimensions of the yard are 35 ft 8 in long and 22 ft 6 in wide. The fertilizer Randy is to use sells at $19.99 per box and covers 300 sq ft of grass. How much will the job cost? _____

4. The street, driveway, and house line around the Dobronskis' home gives them a lawn area that looks like Figure M + P in Diagram 2. The weed killer they want to use on this lawn will cover 250 sq ft of lawn at a price of $15.95 per bottle. The dimensions of the lawn are as follows:

$$a = 15 \text{ ft} \quad b = 32 \text{ ft } 6 \text{ in} \quad c = 19 \text{ ft} \quad d = 10 \text{ ft } 8 \text{ in}$$

What will be the price of using weed killer on this section of the lawn? _____

5. Listed below are lawn areas of different dimensions. Find the cost of (a) fertilizing and (b) adding weed killer to each of these areas, given the following costs:

Fertilizer: 1 bag covers 300 sq ft and costs $26.95 per bag
Weed killer: 1 bag covers 1200 sq ft and costs $37.25 per bag

Shape	Dimensions
(a) M	a = 10 ft; b = 6 ft; d = 28 ft
(a) N	c = 80 ft; d = 30 ft
(a) N + M	a = 15 ft; b = 12 ft; c = 18 ft; d = 20 ft
(a) M	a = 24 ft 6 in; b = 18 ft 3 in; d = 26 ft 5 in
(a) M + N + P	a = 20 ft; b = 14 ft 5 in; c = 30 ft 8 in; d = 16 ft 7 in

28. Patios and Driveways

The consumer can do many construction and repair jobs outside the house. The most common of these jobs might be building a new patio or driveway, or repairing an existing area used for one of these purposes. The mathematics required in this kind of work usually involves these three steps:

Step 1:   Calculate the area of the patio, driveway, or other area you want to work on.

Step 2:   Find out how many bricks, how much concrete, or the amount of some other materials you will need to use in the job.

Step 3:   From the cost per brick, per sack of concrete, or per container of other material, calculate the total cost of the job.

The following example will show a typical calculation of this kind.

● **Example:**

Jasper is going to build a new concrete patio in a section of his backyard that has the shape of Figure M + N in Diagram 2 on page 105. The dimensions of that piece of land are as follows:

$$a = 8 \text{ m} \qquad b = 7 \text{ m} \qquad c = 3 \text{ m} \qquad d = 2 \text{ m}$$

The concrete he buys will pour an area of 20 sq m, 5 cm thick. A bag of concrete costs $13.95. What will be the total cost of this job for the concrete?

Solution:

The total area to be covered consists of a rectangle, M, and a triangle, N. The areas of each can be found as follows:

Step 1: Area of M $= \text{Length} \times \text{Width}$
$= 9 \text{ m (b + d)} \times 8 \text{ m (a)}$
$= 72 \text{ m}^2$

Area of N $= \frac{1}{2} \text{ Base} \times \text{Height}$
$= \frac{1}{2} \times 3 \text{ m (= c)} \times 2 \text{ m (= d)}$
$= 3 \text{ m}^2$

Total area of section $= 72 \text{ m}^2 + 3 \text{ m}^2$
$= 75 \text{ m}^2$

Step 2: If Jasper pours his slab of concrete 5 cm thick, the amount of concrete he will have to buy is:

Number of bags needed $= \dfrac{\text{Total area to be covered}}{\text{Area covered by one bag}}$

$= \dfrac{75 \text{ m}^2}{20 \text{ m}^2}$

$= 3.75 \text{ bags (buy 4 bags)}$

Step 3: Total cost of job $= \text{Price per bag} \times \text{Number of bags}$
$= \$13.95 \text{ per bag} \times 4 \text{ bags}$
$= \$55.80$

© 1983, 1996 Instructional Horizons. Produced and Distributed
by J. Weston Walch, Publisher, Portland, Maine 04104-0658   *112*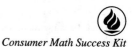

Name _____   Date _____

28. Patios and Driveways

The figures referred to in these problems are shown in Diagram 2 on page 105.

1. The Wongs' backyard has the shape of Figure M + N + P in Diagram 2. The Wongs plan on covering the area with a concrete slab that will be 6 in thick. The dimensions of this area are given below. The concrete they intend to use for this job will cover 350 sq ft in a layer 6 in thick and costs $18.50 per bag. What will be the cost of concrete for this job?

    a = 35 ft   b = 40 ft   c = 10 ft   d = 6 ft

    _____

2. Ellie van Eerden wants to know how much it will cost to remove a section of her side yard and replace it with a brick patio. The area has the shape of Figure M in Diagram 2 with the dimensions given below. The bricks she wants to use are 4 in by 8 in and sell for 28¢ each. What will be the cost of the bricks alone for this job?   a = 8 ft   b = 10 ft   d = 4 ft

    _____

3. The same area could be covered by ceramic patio blocks that are 9 in wide and 16 in long. These sell for 49¢ each. What would be the cost of covering the area with these blocks rather than with bricks? (Refer to Problem 2.)

    _____

4. Whether she uses bricks *or* patio blocks, Ellie will have to buy sand to use as a foundation for the patio. The sand is laid 6 in deep beneath the bricks or patio blocks. She can buy a bag of sand that covers 30 cu ft for $8.57. How much will it cost for the sand needed in either of these jobs? (Refer to Problems 2 and 3.)

    _____

5. The Ficellis will cover an unused part of their yard that has the shape of Figure M + N in Diagram 2 with the patio blocks described in Problem 3. The dimensions of this area are given below. What will be the total cost of patio blocks and sand (see Problem 4) needed for this job?

    a = 8 ft 6 in   b = 9 ft 6 in   c = 10 ft 4 in   d = 3 ft 6 in

    _____

6. The driveway and garage area in the Daltons' house has the general shape of Figure M + N + P in Diagram 2. The dimensions of this area are given below. What would be the cost of covering the driveway with each of the materials listed below?

    a = 3 m   b = 26.5 m   c = 10.4 m   d = 2.7 m
    Blacktop: 1 can covers 30 m^2; cost = $32.99 per can
    Bricks: 1 brick = 12 cm × 25 cm; cost = 35¢ per brick*
    Concrete: 1 bag covers 25 m^2 to proper depth; cost = $25.85 per bag

    _____

* *Ignore cost of sand.*

 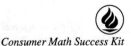

28. Patios and Driveways

The figures referred to in these problems are shown in Diagram 2 on page 105.

1. The driveway leading to Maxine's house has the shape of a stretched-out Figure M in Diagram 2. The dimensions of that driveway are:

$$a = 10 \text{ ft} \qquad b = 35 \text{ ft} \qquad d = 35 \text{ ft}$$

Maxine intends to blacktop the driveway with a material that costs $24.50 per can. One can covers 325 sq ft of driveway. What will be the cost of blacktopping the driveway?

_____

2. The area in front of Maxine's garage has the shape of Figure N + P in Diagram 2. The dimensions of that area are:

$$c = 35 \text{ ft} \qquad d = 18 \text{ ft } 6 \text{ in}$$

What will be the cost of blacktopping this area also (see Problem 1 for material)?

_____

3. Quentin plans on covering the concrete patio in his backyard with artificial turf. This plastic, grasslike material comes in rolls 6 in wide and 30 ft long. Find out how much he will need to cover the patio, which has a shape like that of Figure P in Diagram 2, if the dimensions of the area are:

$$c = 14 \text{ ft} \qquad d = 9 \text{ ft } 6 \text{ in}$$

At $63.99 per roll, what will the job cost?

_____

4. If he likes the appearance of this area (Problem 3), Quentin then intends to cover another section of the yard that has the shape of Figure M + N in Diagram 2. The dimensions of that area are as follows:

$$a = 8 \text{ ft } 4 \text{ in} \qquad b = 10 \text{ ft } 6 \text{ in}$$

What would be the cost of covering this area with the same material as that described in Problem 3?

_____

5. The new tennis courts at the high school will be covered with a plasticlike material and then painted. The dimensions of one tennis court are given below. The cost of the material and paint are also given. What will be the cost of treating all six courts at the school with this method?

Dimensions (Figure M): $20 \text{ m} \times 62.4 \text{ m}$

Cost of material: $29.95 per can; each can covers 150 m^2

Cost of paint: $32.50 per can; each can covers 450 m^2

29. Carpentry

Skill in woodworking can be a great help to the consumer. Many small jobs around the house or apartment can be taken care of without calling in a professional carpenter. Being good with a hammer and a saw does not by itself make someone a good carpenter, however. One also has to know the mathematics of woodworking. In most cases, the calculations you need to make in carpentry are fairly simple. Three steps are involved:

Step 1: Determine the area of the object to be built.

Step 2: Calculate the amount of wood needed to build this area. Sometimes you need to think about the thickness of the wood you will be using. But this is usually not much of a problem.

Step 3: Find out the cost of the wood you need by multiplying the amount of wood required by the cost per unit of the wood. Wood is sometimes measured in **board feet** (a board foot is a piece of lumber one foot square and one inch thick), but you may not have to use that unit of measure.

The example below shows how these calculations may be applied in a specific problem.

● **Example:**

Ruby wants to build a new wall across the middle of her attic. The wall will be 10 ft 6 in long and 8 ft 4 in high. There will be one "F" door in the wall (see page 104). The lumber she will use sells for $3.73 per board foot. How much will the job cost her?

Solution:

Step 1: Area of wall = Total area – Area of one "F" door

Total area   = Length × Height (of wall)

= 10 ft 6 in × 8 ft 4 in

= $10 \frac{1}{2}$ ft × $8 \frac{1}{3}$ ft

= 87.5 sq ft

Area of one "F" door   = Width × Height

= 4 ft 4 in × 7 ft 2 in

= $4 \frac{1}{3}$ ft × $7 \frac{1}{6}$ in

= 31.1 sq ft

Amount of lumber needed   = 87.5 sq ft – 31.1 sq ft

= 56.4 sq ft

Step 2: If Ruby buys lumber 1 inch thick, she will need 56.4 board feet of lumber for this job.

Step 3: Cost of lumber = Price per board foot × Number of board feet

= $3.73 per board foot × 56.4 sq ft

= $210.37

Consumer Math Success Kit

Name _____   Date _____

29. Carpentry

The figures and dimensions needed for these problems are shown in Diagrams 1 and 2 on pages 104 and 105. A board foot is the amount of wood contained in a board 1 foot square and 1 inch thick.

1. A storage chest that Frieda wants to build consists of a top, a bottom, and two sides all having the shape of Figure M in Diagram 2. The end pieces will have the shape of Figure N + P. Here are the dimensions of these pieces:

    a = 2 ft   b = 3 ft   c = 2 ft   d = 2 ft

    The wood Frieda will use for this chest sells at $1.09 per board foot. What will be the cost of the wood alone needed to build the chest?   _____

2. Bruno's idea for a modernistic doghouse for his beagle Beastie can be constructed from the following pieces of wood:

    Two of shape N: c = 3 ft 6 in; d = 4 ft
    Two of shape N + P
    Three of shape M: 6 ft × 6 ft
    One of shape M: 4 ft × 6 ft
    One of shape M: 3 ft 6 in × 6 ft

    The wood Bruno plans on using sells for $.79 per board foot. What will be the cost of the wood needed for the doghouse? You may ignore the doorway in the house.   _____

3. Mr. Xenios wants to install a new wall halfway down the length of the attic of his house. The place he intends to install this wall looks like Diagram 1. The dimensions of that space are:

    length = 42 ft 8 in   width = 20 ft 6 in   height = 10 ft 8 in

    There will be one doorway in the wall with the shape of door "F." The wood needed for this job costs $1.17 per board foot. What will be the total cost of the wood for the new wall?   _____

4. The following problems concern storage chests of the type described in Problem 1 above. The dimensions of the chests are given, and the cost of the wood to be used in building them is also listed. Calculate the cost of building each of these chests.

    (a) *Sides:* a = 3 ft; b = 2 ft; d = 4 ft
        Top and bottom: a = 3 ft; b = 2 ft; d = 4 ft
        Ends: c = 3 ft; d = 3 ft   Cost = $4.05 per board foot

        _____

(continued)

Consumer Math Success Kit

29. Carpentry *(continued)*

(b) *Sides:* a = 2 ft; b = 2 ft; d = 7 ft
   Top and bottom: a = 4 ft; b = 2 ft; d = 7 ft
   Ends: c = 2 ft; d = 4 ft   Cost = $2.89 per board foot

   _____

(c) *Sides:* a = 3 ft 6 in; b = 3 ft 4 in; d = 2 ft 8 in
   Top and bottom: a = 2 ft; b = 3 ft 4 in; d = 2 ft 8 in
   Ends: c = 3 ft 6 in; d = 2 ft   Cost = $3.17 per board foot

   _____

(d) *Sides:* a = 2 ft 4 in; b = 4 ft 4 in; d = 2 ft 6 in
   Top and bottom: a = 3 ft 8 in; b = 4 ft 4 in; d = 2 ft 6 in
   Ends: c = 2 ft 4 in; d = 3 ft 8 in   Cost = $3.58 per board foot

   _____

Home Care

Teacher Notes

Mathematical skills required:

addition, subtraction, multiplication, and division of whole numbers, fractions, and decimals

New vocabulary:

area (total)
area covered per (can, roll, bag, brick, etc.)
board foot
cost per (can, roll, bag, brick, etc.)
dimensions

Related topics:

Estimating Answers
Sales Tax

Teaching suggestions:

1. The exercises in all problems in this section are obviously fictitious. There are abundant opportunities to relate this topic to students' everyday lives, however. For example, they might be asked to measure the walls in a room in their own home which they would like to have painted or papered. This information could be used to calculate the total cost of painting or papering this area. The information they need about cost of paint, wallpaper, and other materials can easily be obtained from local paint and wallpaper stores.

2. The same is true for other areas included in this topic: carpentry, patio and yard work, and the like.

3. Students may be interested in comparing the cost of doing the kind of repair and refurbishing work outlined in this section on one's own versus having it done by a professional. Try to have a professional painter, wallpaper, carpenter or the like visit the classroom and describe to students the way he or she estimates the cost of doing his or her type of work. Perhaps your guest speaker can actually estimate the cost of doing one of the jobs given in the solved examples or practice problems.

4. Knowledge of geometric formulas is very helpful in solving some of the problems in this section. You may want to review the most familiar of these and provide some review drill on the most important of these formulas (square, rectangle, triangle, trapezoid, etc.).

CHAPTER THIRTEEN
<u>Housing</u>

30. Housing

Your housing costs are determined by whether you (1) own a home or a condominium or (2) rent a house or an apartment. The mathematics of rentals is somewhat simpler. You simply pay a monthly fee (the rent) to occupy a place. Sometimes you have to pay something extra in order to move in. This may include a security deposit (to guarantee that you will take good care of the place), first month's rent, and last month's rent. Different rental agencies have different rules.

Purchasing a home is more complicated. Most people do not pay cash for a house or condominium. They have to borrow money from a bank. This loan is also called a **mortgage**. In order to buy the house, you normally have to pay a certain part of the price—usually about 20%—yourself. Then you can get a mortgage loan for the other 80% of the price. You may also have to pay certain **closing costs** (lawyer's fees, unpaid taxes, title searches, etc.) when you buy the house. The examples below illustrate the mathematics of renting and buying.

● **Example 1:**

Lawrence and Daniel have found an apartment they want to rent together. The owner requires a payment of the first and last month's rent and a security deposit of $150 before they can move in. How much will each man have to pay before they can move in? The monthly rent is $325.

Solution:

The cost of the first and last month's rent will be equal to: $2 \times \$325 = \$650$. In addition, the security deposit will be another $150. So the total due for the first month will be: $\$650 + \$150 = \$800$. The amount owed by each man will be: $\$800 \div 2 = \$400$.

● **Example 2:**

The Mareks have found a house they want to buy. The price is $94,570. They must have a 20% down payment for the house, and closing costs will be $687.59. How much cash will they need to buy the house? How large a mortgage will they have to get for the remaining cost of the house?

Solution:

$$\begin{aligned}
\text{Down payment} \ &= 20\% \times \text{Cost of house} \\
&= 20\% \times \$94{,}570 \\
&= \$18{,}914
\end{aligned}$$

$$\begin{aligned}
\text{Total cost needed to purchase} \ &= \text{Down payment} + \text{Closing costs} \\
&= \$18{,}914 + \$687.59 \\
&= \$19{,}601.59
\end{aligned}$$

$$\begin{aligned}
\text{Mortgage amount} \ &= \text{Cost of house} - \text{Down payment} \\
&= \$94{,}570 - \$18{,}914 \\
&= \$75{,}656
\end{aligned}$$

© 1983, 1996 Instructional Horizons. Produced and Distributed by J. Weston Walch, Publisher, Portland, Maine 04104-0658

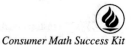

Consumer Math Success Kit

30. Housing

1. Jim and Dan are planning to rent an apartment for $375 per month. In order to move in, they will have to pay the first and last month's rent. How much will each man have to pay when they move in? How much will each pay towards the rent each month?

   _____

2. Agnes, Kathy, and Joanne want to share an apartment for which the monthly rent is $350. In order to move in, they have to pay the first and last month's rent plus a security deposit of $250. How much will each woman have to pay in order to move in? How much will each have to pay towards the rent each month?

   _____

3. Ollie, Harvey, and Brooks have decided to rent an apartment for which the monthly rent is $349.50. To move in, they must pay the first and last month's rent plus a security deposit equal to 75% of one month's rent. How much will each one have to pay in order to move in? How much is each one's share of the monthly rent?

   _____

4. Margie and Delores share an apartment for which the monthly expenses are shown below. How much does each one owe toward the monthly expenses of the apartment?

   Rent: $425   Electric: $49.12   Gas: $19.93   Telephone: $28.65

   _____

5. The Sandersons are looking at a house that is for sale at $132,500. They will need a down payment of 20%, and closing costs will be $808.50. How much cash will they need to buy the house, and how much of a mortgage will they need?

   _____

6. A house at 15 Green Street is listed for sale at $264,000. In order to buy the house, the Mulligans will need a down payment of 20%, and closing costs will be $1450.00. How much cash will the Mulligans need to buy the house, and how much of a mortgage will they have to get from the bank?

   _____

7. The Rando family is looking at a house for sale at $141,750. In order to buy the house, they will need a down payment of 15%. Closing costs will be $375.50. How much cash will they need to buy this house, and what size mortgage will they have to get from the bank to finance the purchase?

   _____

Housing

Teacher Notes

Mathematical skills required:

addition, multiplication, and division of decimals
multiplication of percents

New vocabulary:

closing costs
down payment
monthly expenses
mortgage
rent
security deposit

Related topics:

Borrowing Money: Mortgage Loans
Budgets: Short-term Budgets
Budgets: Long-term Budgets
Estimating Answers
Heating Costs
Insurance: Homeowner's
Property Taxes
Telephone Bills
Utility Bills: Gas, Electric, and Water

Teaching Suggestions:

1. Students may be unfamiliar with the legal and financial aspects of renting an apartment. Try to find a real estate agent who will talk to the class about these considerations. Compare the advantages and disadvantages of renting with a lease versus being a tenant-at-will.

2. Describe cooperative and condominium apartments, and explain the way these may differ from other rental apartments.

3. The classified section of the newspaper may carry advertisements for many types of rental units. These can be used as practice exercises in which students calculate the cost of living alone or with others in certain of these rental units.

CHAPTER FOURTEEN

Income

Wages
Salaries
Commissions

31. Wages

The pay that some people get for their work is determined on an **hourly rate**. This kind of pay is known as a **wage**. A plumber's wage, for example, might be $35.00 per hour. Most people who work for wages are paid once a week, once every two weeks, or once a month. Their paycheck is determined by multiplying the number of hours they have worked times their hourly rate:

Weekly pay (employee on wages) = Hourly rate × Hours worked

Sometimes, an employee is paid extra for working more than a set number of hours. That employee then receives additional pay for his or her work known as **overtime pay**.

The total amount of money a person earns is called the **gross pay**. Almost no one actually receives the gross pay earned. Various **deductions** are subtracted from a person's gross pay before a paycheck is issued. Some typical deductions are federal income, Social Security, and Medicare taxes (all required by law), state income tax (required in some states), payments to private retirement plans, deposits and payments to credit unions, contributions to charitable organizations, and union dues. The amount left from a person's gross pay after taxes and other deductions are subtracted is the **net pay**. The example below shows how to figure a wage earner's net pay.

● **Example:**

Edna Aronson earns $17.42 per hour as a court reporter. She has the following deductions taken from her paycheck in addition to federal income, Social Security, and Medicare taxes:

Otherfund contributions:	$ 18.50 per week
Savings account:	$ 25.00 per week
Health insurance:	$ 19.94 per week

Edna is single and claims one exemption. Calculate Edna's weekly pay in a week during which she worked 40 hours.

Solution:

Gross pay = Hourly rate × Hours worked

= $17.42 × 40

= $696.80

You can use the Withholding Tables on pages 133–140 to figure a person's federal income tax (FIT). As of 1995, Social Security and Medicare taxes (called F.I.C.A. deductions) were 6.2% and 1.45% respectively, for a total deduction of 7.65%.

From Withholding Tables, FIT= $112.00

F.I.C.A.   = 7.65% × $696.80

= $53.31

Total of other deductions   = $18.50 + $25.00 + $19.94 = $63.44

Net Pay = Gross pay – Taxes – Other deductions

= $696.80 – $112.00 – $53.31 – $63.44

= $468.05

31. Wages

(*Note:* In doing problems 2–5, be sure to figure in the F.I.C.A. deduction of 7.65%. In doing problems 3–5, be sure to figure the *weekly* health insurance deduction—multiply the monthly premium given by 12, then divide by 52 to get the weekly premium.)

1. Bonnie works at Healthworks four nights a week after school. She earns $6.50 an hour for a normal 16-hour week. What is her gross monthly pay for the weeks shown here:

    Week 1: 16 hours; Week 2: 16 hours; Week 3: 14 hours; Week 4: 16 hours

   _____

2. Tim earns an hourly wage of $8.25 at the Deebs Visual Aids Company. What is his gross and net weekly pay for a week in which he worked 40 hours? Tim is single, claims zero exemptions, and has union dues of $9.65 per week and health insurance of $6.57 per week deducted from his pay.

   _____

3. Leona also works at Deebs and earns $7.75 per hour. She is married and claims two exemptions. Her only other payroll deduction is $32.40 per month for health insurance. What is her gross and net pay for a week in which she worked 40 hours?

   _____

4. Barry works for the city recreation department and earns $10.75 per hour. In addition, he earns 160% of this amount for any hours worked over 40 in one week. Barry is married and claims three exemptions from his paycheck. What is his gross pay for a week in which he worked 50 hours? Calculate his net pay if he also has the following deductions: union dues: $3.82 per week; health insurance: $58.60 per month; credit union: $10.00 per week; IRA account: $15.00 per week.

   _____

5. Mr. Masterson earns an hourly wage of $20.85 with overtime of 150% of his regular wage. Overtime begins after 40 hours of work in any week. He is married and claims four exemptions. His regular deductions include $85.56 per month for health insurance, $15.00 a week for credit union, and $2.50 a week for Otherfund contribution. In a week in which Mr. Masterson worked 52 hours, what would be his gross and net pay?

   _____

© 1983, 1996 Instructional Horizons. Produced and Distributed by J. Weston Walch, Publisher, Portland, Maine 04104-0658

Consumer Math Success Kit

32. Salaries

Some people earn a certain amount of money each year, regardless of how many hours they worked. This kind of income is known as a salary. A person who earns a salary of $34,500 a year may work 40 hours in one week, 30 hours in another, and 55 hours in a third week. But that person is guaranteed an income of $34,500 a year regardless of the number of hours worked. A person on salary may be paid every week, every two weeks, or every month. That person's paycheck is determined by dividing the annual salary by the number of pay periods in the year. For example, the weekly paycheck would be found by dividing the annual salary by 52:

$$\text{Weekly paycheck} = \text{Annual salary} \div 52$$

The pay calculated by this method is called the **gross pay**. Almost no one actually receives the gross pay earned. Various **deductions** are subtracted from a person's gross pay before a paycheck is issued. Some typical deductions are federal income, Social Security, and Medicare taxes (all required by law), state income tax (required in some states), payments to private retirement plans, deposits and payments to credit unions, contributions to charitable organizations, and union dues. The amount left from a person's gross pay after taxes and other deductions are subtracted is the **net pay**. The example below shows how to figure a salary earner's net pay.

● **Example:**

Harvey Winston earns $35,542 per year as a teacher in the Dansville School District. Determine Harvey's weekly net pay from the additional information given below. Also refer to the Withholding Tables on pages 133–140.

> *Exemptions claimed:* 3
> *Married*
> *Union dues:* $428 per year
> *Credit union deposit:* $25 per week
> *Credit union loan payment:* $42.32 per week

Solution:

$$\text{Gross weekly pay} = \text{Annual salary} \div 52 \text{ weeks}$$
$$= \$35,542 \div 52 = \$683.50$$

From Withholding Tables, FIT = $63.00
F.I.C.A. $= 7.65\% \times \$683.50$
$= \$52.29$
Union dues = $428.00 \div 52 = \$8.23$
Total of other deductions = $8.23 + $25.00 + $42.32 = $75.55

$$\text{Net pay} = \text{Gross pay} - \text{Taxes} - \text{Other deductions}$$
$$= \$683.50 - \$63.00 - \$52.29 - \$75.55$$
$$= \$492.66$$

32. Salaries

(*Note:* In doing these problems, be sure to figure in the F.I.C.A. deduction of 7.65% of gross wages. Also, be sure to figure the *weekly* health insurance deduction—multiply the monthly premium by 12, then divide by 52 to get the weekly premium.)

1. Mr. Radewicz earns an annual salary of $41,000. He is single and claims one exemption from his paycheck. The deductions from his weekly paycheck also include union dues of $10.50 and a credit union payment of $15.00. What is his net weekly paycheck?

   _____

2. Ms. Jimenez is paid an annual salary of $36,500 and has $12.50 a week taken out for her Otherfund contribution. In addition, she has to pay $52.97 a month for health insurance, which is also taken out of her weekly paycheck. She is single and claims one exemption. What is her gross and net pay each week?

   _____

3. Malinda Farmer has just accepted a job for which her annual salary will be $45,584. She is married and claims three exemptions. She has asked that union dues of $38.50 per week and health insurance payments of $129.95 per month be deducted from her weekly paycheck. What weekly pay (gross and net) can she expect on this job?

   _____

4. Mr. Hofstra receives an annual salary of $60,958.88 as principal of the Darling School. He is married and claims five exemptions from his pay. His monthly health insurance deduction is $132.40. He also has the following deductions taken out of his weekly paycheck: IRA account: $27.50; credit union: $35.00; Otherfund: $13.50. What is Mr. Hofstra's average weekly gross pay and net pay?

   _____

5. Mrs. McEleney has just been promoted to a job in which she will be paid $39,792.32 annual salary. She is married and claims two exemptions. She has asked that the following deductions be made from her weekly paycheck: health insurance: $64.72 per month; Otherfund: $17.50 per week; credit union: $12.50 per week; IRA account: $7.50 per week. What will be her weekly gross and net pay?

   _____

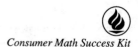

33. Commissions

Some people earn money by working on commission. A commission is a certain percentage of the profit on each item sold. A person who sells cars, for example, might receive 5% of the price on every car she or he sells. Real estate agents often receive a commission on every house or piece of property they sell. People who work on commission may also receive a **draw**. This means the company will pay them a certain amount of money every week or month, whether they have made any commission or not. If the amount of the commissions a person earns in one month is less than the draw received, that person owes the company the difference. The company expects the person to do better in the future and to pay back what he or she owes.

The amount of pay—commission or draw—a person earns in a week or a month is called the **gross pay**. Almost no one actually receives the gross pay earned. Various **deductions** are subtracted from a person's gross pay before a paycheck is issued. Some typical deductions are federal income, Social Security, and Medicare taxes (all required by law), state income tax (required in some states), payments to private retirement plans, deposits and payments to credit unions, contributions to charitable organizations, and union dues. The amount left from a person's gross pay after taxes and other deductions are subtracted is the **net pay**. The example below shows how to figure the net pay for someone who works on commission.

● **Example:**

Antonio receives a 12% commission on each haircut he gives at the Razor's Edge Salon. During the month of August, the profit from his haircuts was $5950. The company promises a draw of $700 to every employee each month. How much commission did Antonio earn in August? Will he have to receive a draw? If he has only tax deductions, what will be his net pay for the month? Antonio is single and claims only one exemption.

Solution:

$$\text{Commission earned} = \text{Rate of commission} \times \text{Sales}$$
$$= 12\% \times \$5950$$
$$= \$714.00$$

Since this is more than the draw, Antonio will not have to take any draw this month.

For federal income tax, see pages 133–140. From these Withholding Tables, the amount withheld for Antonio is $41.00. His Social Security and Medicare tax is $714.00 \times 7.65\% = \$54.62$. Then,

$$\text{Net pay} = \text{Gross pay} - \text{Tax deductions}$$
$$= \$714.00 - \$41.00 - \$54.62$$
$$= \$618.38$$

33. Commissions

1. Emmet has taken a job selling encyclopedias. He will make 5% commission on all sales he makes. What commission should he expect if he sells $4000 worth of encyclopedias in the first month?

    _____

2. Suppose Emmet sells $8795.50 worth of encyclopedias in the second month. How much is his commission in this case? _____

3. The company for which Emmet works increases his commission to 7.2% for all sales over $5000 in any one month. Suppose that Emmet sells $5398.50 worth of encyclopedias in a month. What would be his commission in that month? _____

4. Harvey has gotten a job selling cars at his father's company. The company pays a commission of 4.8% on all new cars sold. If Harvey sells three cars worth a total of $19,558.44 in one month, how much would his commission be? What would his net pay be if Harvey is married with two exemptions?

    _____

5. The company for which Harvey works also pays a commission of 5.5% for all trucks sold and 3.4% for all used cars sold. How much commission would he receive in a month for which his sales included two new cars for $25,885.23, two new trucks for $38,509.93, and two used cars for $6389.00?

    _____

6. Harvey is guaranteed a draw of $800 a month in his job as a car salesman. Would he need to take his draw in either of the months described in Problems 4 and 5? _____

7. In her job as hairdresser at the Quick Clip Salon, Bernice receives a commission of 12.5% on each haircut she does. In a month in which she took in $4585.00, what would her commission be? What would be her net pay if Bernice is single with one exemption? _____

8. Henrietta receives a commission of 5.0% on all books she sells each month, 6.5% on all records, and 3.8% on other items sold in the store where she works. Last month, her sales were as follows:

    | Books: | $ 1435.89 |
    | Records: | $ 2774.51 |
    | Other: | $ 402.35 |

    What would be her commission for this month? _____

© 1983, 1996 Instructional Horizons. Produced and Distributed
by J. Weston Walch, Publisher, Portland, Maine 04104-0658   132   *Consumer Math Success Kit*

Withholding Tables

SINGLE Persons—WEEKLY Payroll Period

(For Wages Paid in 1995)

If the wages are—		And the number of withholding allowances claimed is—										
At least	But less than	0	1	2	3	4	5	6	7	8	9	10
		The amount of income tax to be withheld is—										
$0	$55	0	0	0	0	0	0	0	0	0	0	0
55	60	1	0	0	0	0	0	0	0	0	0	0
60	65	2	0	0	0	0	0	0	0	0	0	0
65	70	3	0	0	0	0	0	0	0	0	0	0
70	75	3	0	0	0	0	0	0	0	0	0	0
75	80	4	0	0	0	0	0	0	0	0	0	0
80	85	5	0	0	0	0	0	0	0	0	0	0
85	90	6	0	0	0	0	0	0	0	0	0	0
90	95	6	0	0	0	0	0	0	0	0	0	0
95	100	7	0	0	0	0	0	0	0	0	0	0
100	105	8	1	0	0	0	0	0	0	0	0	0
105	110	9	1	0	0	0	0	0	0	0	0	0
110	115	9	2	0	0	0	0	0	0	0	0	0
115	120	10	3	0	0	0	0	0	0	0	0	0
120	125	11	4	0	0	0	0	0	0	0	0	0
125	130	12	4	0	0	0	0	0	0	0	0	0
130	135	12	5	0	0	0	0	0	0	0	0	0
135	140	13	6	0	0	0	0	0	0	0	0	0
140	145	14	7	0	0	0	0	0	0	0	0	0
145	150	15	7	0	0	0	0	0	0	0	0	0
150	155	15	8	1	0	0	0	0	0	0	0	0
155	160	16	9	2	0	0	0	0	0	0	0	0
160	165	17	10	2	0	0	0	0	0	0	0	0
165	170	18	10	3	0	0	0	0	0	0	0	0
170	175	18	11	4	0	0	0	0	0	0	0	0
175	180	19	12	5	0	0	0	0	0	0	0	0
180	185	20	13	5	0	0	0	0	0	0	0	0
185	190	21	13	6	0	0	0	0	0	0	0	0
190	195	21	14	7	0	0	0	0	0	0	0	0
195	200	22	15	8	0	0	0	0	0	0	0	0
200	210	23	16	9	2	0	0	0	0	0	0	0
210	220	25	18	10	3	0	0	0	0	0	0	0
220	230	26	19	12	5	0	0	0	0	0	0	0
230	240	28	21	13	6	0	0	0	0	0	0	0
240	250	29	22	15	8	0	0	0	0	0	0	0
250	260	31	24	16	9	2	0	0	0	0	0	0
260	270	32	25	18	11	3	0	0	0	0	0	0
270	280	34	27	19	12	5	0	0	0	0	0	0
280	290	35	28	21	14	6	0	0	0	0	0	0
290	300	37	30	22	15	8	1	0	0	0	0	0
300	310	38	31	24	17	9	2	0	0	0	0	0
310	320	40	33	25	18	11	4	0	0	0	0	0
320	330	41	34	27	20	12	5	0	0	0	0	0
330	340	43	36	28	21	14	7	0	0	0	0	0
340	350	44	37	30	23	15	8	1	0	0	0	0
350	360	46	39	31	24	17	10	2	0	0	0	0
360	370	47	40	33	26	18	11	4	0	0	0	0
370	380	49	42	34	27	20	13	5	0	0	0	0
380	390	50	43	36	29	21	14	7	0	0	0	0
390	400	52	45	37	30	23	16	8	1	0	0	0
400	410	53	46	39	32	24	17	10	3	0	0	0
410	420	55	48	40	33	26	19	11	4	0	0	0
420	430	56	49	42	35	27	20	13	6	0	0	0
430	440	58	51	43	36	29	22	14	7	0	0	0
440	450	59	52	45	38	30	23	16	9	2	0	0
450	460	61	54	46	39	32	25	17	10	3	0	0
460	470	62	55	48	41	33	26	19	12	5	0	0
470	480	64	57	49	42	35	28	20	13	6	0	0
480	490	66	58	51	44	36	29	22	15	8	0	0
490	500	69	60	52	45	38	31	23	16	9	2	0
500	510	72	61	54	47	39	32	25	18	11	3	0
510	520	75	63	55	48	41	34	26	19	12	5	0
520	530	78	64	57	50	42	35	28	21	14	6	0
530	540	80	67	58	51	44	37	29	22	15	8	1
540	550	83	70	60	53	45	38	31	24	17	9	2
550	560	86	73	61	54	47	40	32	25	18	11	4
560	570	89	75	63	56	48	41	34	27	20	12	5
570	580	92	78	65	57	50	43	35	28	21	14	7
580	590	94	81	68	59	51	44	37	30	23	15	8
590	600	97	84	70	60	53	46	38	31	24	17	10

© 1983, 1996 Instructional Horizons. Produced and Distributed by J. Weston Walch, Publisher, Portland, Maine 04104-0658

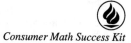

Consumer Math Success Kit

Withholding Tables

SINGLE Persons—WEEKLY Payroll Period
(For Wages Paid in 1995)

If the wages are—		And the number of withholding allowances claimed is—										
At least	But less than	0	1	2	3	4	5	6	7	8	9	10
		The amount of income tax to be withheld is—										
$600	$610	100	87	73	62	54	47	40	33	26	18	11
610	620	103	89	76	63	56	49	41	34	27	20	13
620	630	106	92	79	65	57	50	43	36	29	21	14
630	640	108	95	82	68	59	52	44	37	30	23	16
640	650	111	98	84	71	60	53	46	39	32	24	17
650	660	114	101	87	74	62	55	47	40	33	26	19
660	670	117	103	90	76	63	56	49	42	35	27	20
670	680	120	106	93	79	66	58	50	43	36	29	22
680	690	122	109	96	82	69	59	52	45	38	30	23
690	700	125	112	98	85	71	61	53	46	39	32	25
700	710	128	115	101	88	74	62	55	48	41	33	26
710	720	131	117	104	90	77	64	56	49	42	35	28
720	730	134	120	107	93	80	66	58	51	44	36	29
730	740	136	123	110	96	83	69	59	52	45	38	31
740	750	139	126	112	99	85	72	61	54	47	39	32
750	760	142	129	115	102	88	75	62	55	48	41	34
760	770	145	131	118	104	91	78	64	57	50	42	35
770	780	148	134	121	107	94	80	67	58	51	44	37
780	790	150	137	124	110	97	83	70	60	53	45	38
790	800	153	140	126	113	99	86	72	61	54	47	40
800	810	156	143	129	116	102	89	75	63	56	48	41
810	820	159	145	132	118	105	92	78	65	57	50	43
820	830	162	148	135	121	108	94	81	67	59	51	44
830	840	164	151	138	124	111	97	84	70	60	53	46
840	850	167	154	140	127	113	100	86	73	62	54	47
850	860	170	157	143	130	116	103	89	76	63	56	49
860	870	173	159	146	132	119	106	92	79	65	57	50
870	880	176	162	149	135	122	108	95	81	68	59	52
880	890	178	165	152	138	125	111	98	84	71	60	53
890	900	181	168	154	141	127	114	100	87	74	62	55
900	910	184	171	157	144	130	117	103	90	76	63	56
910	920	187	173	160	146	133	120	106	93	79	66	58
920	930	190	176	163	149	136	122	109	95	82	68	59
930	940	192	179	166	152	139	125	112	98	85	71	61
940	950	195	182	168	155	141	128	114	101	88	74	62
950	960	198	185	171	158	144	131	117	104	90	77	64
960	970	201	187	174	160	147	134	120	107	93	80	66
970	980	204	190	177	163	150	136	123	109	96	82	69
980	990	206	193	180	166	153	139	126	112	99	85	72
990	1,000	209	196	182	169	155	142	128	115	102	88	75
1,000	1,010	212	199	185	172	158	145	131	118	104	91	77
1,010	1,020	215	201	188	174	161	148	134	121	107	94	80
1,020	1,030	218	204	191	177	164	150	137	123	110	96	83
1,030	1,040	222	207	194	180	167	153	140	126	113	99	86
1,040	1,050	225	210	196	183	169	156	142	129	116	102	89
1,050	1,060	228	213	199	186	172	159	145	132	118	105	91
1,060	1,070	231	216	202	188	175	162	148	135	121	108	94
1,070	1,080	234	219	205	191	178	164	151	137	124	110	97
1,080	1,090	237	222	208	194	181	167	154	140	127	113	100
1,090	1,100	240	225	210	197	183	170	156	143	130	116	103
1,100	1,110	243	228	213	200	186	173	159	146	132	119	105
1,110	1,120	246	231	216	202	189	176	162	149	135	122	108
1,120	1,130	249	235	220	205	192	178	165	151	138	124	111
1,130	1,140	253	238	223	208	195	181	168	154	141	127	114
1,140	1,150	256	241	226	211	197	184	170	157	144	130	117
1,150	1,160	259	244	229	214	200	187	173	160	146	133	119
1,160	1,170	262	247	232	217	203	190	176	163	149	136	122
1,170	1,180	265	250	235	220	206	192	179	165	152	138	125
1,180	1,190	268	253	238	223	209	195	182	168	155	141	128
1,190	1,200	271	256	241	226	211	198	184	171	158	144	131
1,200	1,210	274	259	244	229	215	201	187	174	160	147	133
1,210	1,220	277	262	247	233	218	204	190	177	163	150	136
1,220	1,230	280	266	251	236	221	206	193	179	166	152	139
1,230	1,240	284	269	254	239	224	209	196	182	169	155	142
1,240	1,250	287	272	257	242	227	212	198	185	172	158	145

$1,250 and over   Use Table 1(a) for a **SINGLE person** on page 32 Also see the instructions on page 30

© 1983, 1996 Instructional Horizons. Produced and Distributed
by J. Weston Walch, Publisher, Portland, Maine 04104-0658   134   *Consumer Math Success Kit*

Withholding Tables

MARRIED Persons—WEEKLY Payroll Period

(For Wages Paid in 1995)

If the wages are—		And the number of withholding allowances claimed is—										
At least	But less than	0	1	2	3	4	5	6	7	8	9	10
		The amount of income tax to be withheld is—										
$0	$125	0	0	0	0	0	0	0	0	0	0	0
125	130	1	0	0	0	0	0	0	0	0	0	0
130	135	1	0	0	0	0	0	0	0	0	0	0
135	140	2	0	0	0	0	0	0	0	0	0	0
140	145	3	0	0	0	0	0	0	0	0	0	0
145	150	4	0	0	0	0	0	0	0	0	0	0
150	155	4	0	0	0	0	0	0	0	0	0	0
155	160	5	0	0	0	0	0	0	0	0	0	0
160	165	6	0	0	0	0	0	0	0	0	0	0
165	170	7	0	0	0	0	0	0	0	0	0	0
170	175	7	0	0	0	0	0	0	0	0	0	0
175	180	8	1	0	0	0	0	0	0	0	0	0
180	185	9	2	0	0	0	0	0	0	0	0	0
185	190	10	2	0	0	0	0	0	0	0	0	0
190	195	10	3	0	0	0	0	0	0	0	0	0
195	200	11	4	0	0	0	0	0	0	0	0	0
200	210	12	5	0	0	0	0	0	0	0	0	0
210	220	14	7	0	0	0	0	0	0	0	0	0
220	230	15	8	1	0	0	0	0	0	0	0	0
230	240	17	10	2	0	0	0	0	0	0	0	0
240	250	18	11	4	0	0	0	0	0	0	0	0
250	260	20	13	5	0	0	0	0	0	0	0	0
260	270	21	14	7	0	0	0	0	0	0	0	0
270	280	23	16	8	1	0	0	0	0	0	0	0
280	290	24	17	10	3	0	0	0	0	0	0	0
290	300	26	19	11	4	0	0	0	0	0	0	0
300	310	27	20	13	6	0	0	0	0	0	0	0
310	320	29	22	14	7	0	0	0	0	0	0	0
320	330	30	23	16	9	1	0	0	0	0	0	0
330	340	32	25	17	10	3	0	0	0	0	0	0
340	350	33	26	19	12	4	0	0	0	0	0	0
350	360	35	28	20	13	6	0	0	0	0	0	0
360	370	36	29	22	15	7	0	0	0	0	0	0
370	380	38	31	23	16	9	2	0	0	0	0	0
380	390	39	32	25	18	10	3	0	0	0	0	0
390	400	41	34	26	19	12	5	0	0	0	0	0
400	410	42	35	28	21	13	6	0	0	0	0	0
410	420	44	37	29	22	15	8	1	0	0	0	0
420	430	45	38	31	24	16	9	2	0	0	0	0
430	440	47	40	32	25	18	11	4	0	0	0	0
440	450	48	41	34	27	19	12	5	0	0	0	0
450	460	50	43	35	28	21	14	7	0	0	0	0
460	470	51	44	37	30	22	15	8	1	0	0	0
470	480	53	46	38	31	24	17	10	2	0	0	0
480	490	54	47	40	33	25	18	11	4	0	0	0
490	500	56	49	41	34	27	20	13	5	0	0	0
500	510	57	50	43	36	28	21	14	7	0	0	0
510	520	59	52	44	37	30	23	16	8	1	0	0
520	530	60	53	46	39	31	24	17	10	3	0	0
530	540	62	55	47	40	33	26	19	11	4	0	0
540	550	63	56	49	42	34	27	20	13	6	0	0
550	560	65	58	50	43	36	29	22	14	7	0	0
560	570	66	59	52	45	37	30	23	16	9	1	0
570	580	68	61	53	46	39	32	25	17	10	3	0
580	590	69	62	55	48	40	33	26	19	12	4	0
590	600	71	64	56	49	42	35	28	20	13	6	0
600	610	72	65	58	51	43	36	29	22	15	7	0
610	620	74	67	59	52	45	38	31	23	16	9	2
620	630	75	68	61	54	46	39	32	25	18	10	3
630	640	77	70	62	55	48	41	34	26	19	12	5
640	650	78	71	64	57	49	42	35	28	21	13	6
650	660	80	73	65	58	51	44	37	29	22	15	8
660	670	81	74	67	60	52	45	38	31	24	16	9
670	680	83	76	68	61	54	47	40	32	25	18	11
680	690	84	77	70	63	55	48	41	34	27	19	12
690	700	86	79	71	64	57	50	43	35	28	21	14
700	710	87	80	73	66	58	51	44	37	30	22	15
710	720	89	82	74	67	60	53	46	38	31	24	17
720	730	90	83	76	69	61	54	47	40	33	25	18
730	740	92	85	77	70	63	56	49	41	34	27	20

© 1983, 1996 Instructional Horizons. Produced and Distributed by J. Weston Walch, Publisher, Portland, Maine 04104-0658

Consumer Math Success Kit

Withholding Tables

MARRIED Persons—WEEKLY Payroll Period

(For Wages Paid in 1995)

At least	But less than	0	1	2	3	4	5	6	7	8	9	10
If the wages are—		And the number of withholding allowances claimed is—										
		The amount of income tax to be withheld is—										
$740	$750	93	86	79	72	64	57	50	43	36	28	21
750	760	95	88	80	73	66	59	52	44	37	30	23
760	770	96	89	82	75	67	60	53	46	39	31	24
770	780	98	91	83	76	69	62	55	47	40	33	26
780	790	99	92	85	78	70	63	56	49	42	34	27
790	800	101	94	86	79	72	65	58	50	43	36	29
800	810	102	95	88	81	73	66	59	52	45	37	30
810	820	104	97	89	82	75	68	61	53	46	39	32
820	830	105	98	91	84	76	69	62	55	48	40	33
830	840	108	100	92	85	78	71	64	56	49	42	35
840	850	111	101	94	87	79	72	65	58	51	43	36
850	860	113	103	95	88	81	74	67	59	52	45	38
860	870	116	104	97	90	82	75	68	61	54	46	39
870	880	119	106	98	91	84	77	70	62	55	48	41
880	890	122	108	100	93	85	78	71	64	57	49	42
890	900	125	111	101	94	87	80	73	65	58	51	44
900	910	127	114	103	96	88	81	74	67	60	52	45
910	920	130	117	104	97	90	83	76	68	61	54	47
920	930	133	119	106	99	91	84	77	70	63	55	48
930	940	136	122	109	100	93	86	79	71	64	57	50
940	950	139	125	112	102	94	87	80	73	66	58	51
950	960	141	128	114	103	96	89	82	74	67	60	53
960	970	144	131	117	105	97	90	83	76	69	61	54
970	980	147	133	120	107	99	92	85	77	70	63	56
980	990	150	136	123	109	100	93	86	79	72	64	57
990	1,000	153	139	126	112	102	95	88	80	73	66	59
1,000	1,010	155	142	128	115	103	96	89	82	75	67	60
1,010	1,020	158	145	131	118	105	98	91	83	76	69	62
1,020	1,030	161	147	134	121	107	99	92	85	78	70	63
1,030	1,040	164	150	137	123	110	101	94	86	79	72	65
1,040	1,050	167	153	140	126	113	102	95	88	81	73	66
1,050	1,060	169	156	142	129	115	104	97	89	82	75	68
1,060	1,070	172	159	145	132	118	105	98	91	84	76	69
1,070	1,080	175	161	148	135	121	108	100	92	85	78	71
1,080	1,090	178	164	151	137	124	110	101	94	87	79	72
1,090	1,100	181	167	154	140	127	113	103	95	88	81	74
1,100	1,110	183	170	156	143	129	116	104	97	90	82	75
1,110	1,120	186	173	159	146	132	119	106	98	91	84	77
1,120	1,130	189	175	162	149	135	122	108	100	93	85	78
1,130	1,140	192	178	165	151	138	124	111	101	94	87	80
1,140	1,150	195	181	168	154	141	127	114	103	96	88	81
1,150	1,160	197	184	170	157	143	130	117	104	97	90	83
1,160	1,170	200	187	173	160	146	133	119	106	99	91	84
1,170	1,180	203	189	176	163	149	136	122	109	100	93	86
1,180	1,190	206	192	179	165	152	138	125	111	102	94	87
1,190	1,200	209	195	182	168	155	141	128	114	103	96	89
1,200	1,210	211	198	184	171	157	144	131	117	105	97	90
1,210	1,220	214	201	187	174	160	147	133	120	106	99	92
1,220	1,230	217	203	190	177	163	150	136	123	109	100	93
1,230	1,240	220	206	193	179	166	152	139	125	112	102	95
1,240	1,250	223	209	196	182	169	155	142	128	115	103	96
1,250	1,260	225	212	198	185	171	158	145	131	118	105	98
1,260	1,270	228	215	201	188	174	161	147	134	120	107	99
1,270	1,280	231	217	204	191	177	164	150	137	123	110	101
1,280	1,290	234	220	207	193	180	166	153	139	126	113	102
1,290	1,300	237	223	210	196	183	169	156	142	129	115	104
1,300	1,310	239	226	212	199	185	172	159	145	132	118	105
1,310	1,320	242	229	215	202	188	175	161	148	134	121	107
1,320	1,330	245	231	218	205	191	178	164	151	137	124	110
1,330	1,340	248	234	221	207	194	180	167	153	140	127	113
1,340	1,350	251	237	224	210	197	183	170	156	143	129	116
1,350	1,360	253	240	226	213	199	186	173	159	146	132	119
1,360	1,370	256	243	229	216	202	189	175	162	148	135	121
1,370	1,380	259	245	232	219	205	192	178	165	151	138	124
1,380	1,390	262	248	235	221	208	194	181	167	154	141	127

$1,390 and over   Use Table 1(b) for a **MARRIED** person on page 32 Also see the instructions on page 30

© 1983, 1996 Instructional Horizons. Produced and Distributed
by J. Weston Walch, Publisher, Portland, Maine 04104-0658

Consumer Math Success Kit

Withholding Tables

SINGLE Persons—MONTHLY Payroll Period

(For Wages Paid in 1995)

If the wages are—		And the number of withholding allowances claimed is—										
At least	But less than	0	1	2	3	4	5	6	7	8	9	10
		The amount of income tax to be withheld is—										
$0	$220	0	0	0	0	0	0	0	0	0	0	0
220	230	1	0	0	0	0	0	0	0	0	0	0
230	240	3	0	0	0	0	0	0	0	0	0	0
240	250	4	0	0	0	0	0	0	0	0	0	0
250	260	6	0	0	0	0	0	0	0	0	0	0
260	270	7	0	0	0	0	0	0	0	0	0	0
270	280	9	0	0	0	0	0	0	0	0	0	0
280	290	10	0	0	0	0	0	0	0	0	0	0
290	300	12	0	0	0	0	0	0	0	0	0	0
300	320	14	0	0	0	0	0	0	0	0	0	0
320	340	17	0	0	0	0	0	0	0	0	0	0
340	360	20	0	0	0	0	0	0	0	0	0	0
360	380	23	0	0	0	0	0	0	0	0	0	0
380	400	26	0	0	0	0	0	0	0	0	0	0
400	420	29	0	0	0	0	0	0	0	0	0	0
420	440	32	1	0	0	0	0	0	0	0	0	0
440	460	35	4	0	0	0	0	0	0	0	0	0
460	480	38	7	0	0	0	0	0	0	0	0	0
480	500	41	10	0	0	0	0	0	0	0	0	0
500	520	44	13	0	0	0	0	0	0	0	0	0
520	540	47	16	0	0	0	0	0	0	0	0	0
540	560	50	19	0	0	0	0	0	0	0	0	0
560	580	53	22	0	0	0	0	0	0	0	0	0
580	600	56	25	0	0	0	0	0	0	0	0	0
600	640	61	29	0	0	0	0	0	0	0	0	0
640	680	67	35	4	0	0	0	0	0	0	0	0
680	720	73	41	10	0	0	0	0	0	0	0	0
720	760	79	47	16	0	0	0	0	0	0	0	0
760	800	85	53	22	0	0	0	0	0	0	0	0
800	840	91	59	28	0	0	0	0	0	0	0	0
840	880	97	65	34	3	0	0	0	0	0	0	0
880	920	103	71	40	9	0	0	0	0	0	0	0
920	960	109	77	46	15	0	0	0	0	0	0	0
960	1,000	115	83	52	21	0	0	0	0	0	0	0
1,000	1,040	121	89	58	27	0	0	0	0	0	0	0
1,040	1,080	127	95	64	33	2	0	0	0	0	0	0
1,080	1,120	133	101	70	39	8	0	0	0	0	0	0
1,120	1,160	139	107	76	45	14	0	0	0	0	0	0
1,160	1,200	145	113	82	51	20	0	0	0	0	0	0
1,200	1,240	151	119	88	57	26	0	0	0	0	0	0
1,240	1,280	157	125	94	63	32	0	0	0	0	0	0
1,280	1,320	163	131	100	69	38	6	0	0	0	0	0
1,320	1,360	169	137	106	75	44	12	0	0	0	0	0
1,360	1,400	175	143	112	81	50	18	0	0	0	0	0
1,400	1,440	181	149	118	87	56	24	0	0	0	0	0
1,440	1,480	187	155	124	93	62	30	0	0	0	0	0
1,480	1,520	193	161	130	99	68	36	5	0	0	0	0
1,520	1,560	199	167	136	105	74	42	11	0	0	0	0
1,560	1,600	205	173	142	111	80	48	17	0	0	0	0
1,600	1,640	211	179	148	117	86	54	23	0	0	0	0
1,640	1,680	217	185	154	123	92	60	29	0	0	0	0
1,680	1,720	223	191	160	129	98	66	35	4	0	0	0
1,720	1,760	229	197	166	135	104	72	41	10	0	0	0
1,760	1,800	235	203	172	141	110	78	47	16	0	0	0
1,800	1,840	241	209	178	147	116	84	53	22	0	0	0
1,840	1,880	247	215	184	153	122	90	59	28	0	0	0
1,880	1,920	253	221	190	159	128	96	65	34	3	0	0
1,920	1,960	259	227	196	165	134	102	71	40	9	0	0
1,960	2,000	265	233	202	171	140	108	77	46	15	0	0
2,000	2,040	271	239	208	177	146	114	83	52	21	0	0
2,040	2,080	277	245	214	183	152	120	89	58	27	0	0
2,080	2,120	287	251	220	189	158	126	95	64	33	1	0
2,120	2,160	299	257	226	195	164	132	101	70	39	7	0
2,160	2,200	310	263	232	201	170	138	107	76	45	13	0
2,200	2,240	321	269	238	207	176	144	113	82	51	19	0
2,240	2,280	332	275	244	213	182	150	119	88	57	25	0
2,280	2,320	343	285	250	219	188	156	125	94	63	31	0
2,320	2,360	355	296	256	225	194	162	131	100	69	37	6
2,360	2,400	366	307	262	231	200	168	137	106	75	43	12
2,400	2,440	377	319	268	237	206	174	143	112	81	49	18

© 1983, 1996 Instructional Horizons. Produced and Distributed by J. Weston Walch, Publisher, Portland, Maine 04104-0658

Consumer Math Success Kit

Withholding Tables

SINGLE Persons—MONTHLY Payroll Period
(For Wages Paid in 1995)

If the wages are—		And the number of withholding allowances claimed is—										
At least	But less than	0	1	2	3	4	5	6	7	8	9	10
		The amount of income tax to be withheld is—										
$2,440	$2,480	388	330	274	243	212	180	149	118	87	55	24
2,480	2,520	399	341	283	249	218	186	155	124	93	61	30
2,520	2,560	411	352	294	255	224	192	161	130	99	67	36
2,560	2,600	422	363	305	261	230	198	167	136	105	73	42
2,600	2,640	433	375	316	267	236	204	173	142	111	79	48
2,640	2,680	444	386	328	273	242	210	179	148	117	85	54
2,680	2,720	455	397	339	280	248	216	185	154	123	91	60
2,720	2,760	467	408	350	292	254	222	191	160	129	97	66
2,760	2,800	478	419	361	303	260	228	197	166	135	103	72
2,800	2,840	489	431	372	314	266	234	203	172	141	109	78
2,840	2,880	500	442	384	325	272	240	209	178	147	115	84
2,880	2,920	511	453	395	336	278	246	215	184	153	121	90
2,920	2,960	523	464	406	348	289	252	221	190	159	127	96
2,960	3,000	534	475	417	359	300	258	227	196	165	133	102
3,000	3,040	545	487	428	370	312	264	233	202	171	139	108
3,040	3,080	556	498	440	381	323	270	239	208	177	145	114
3,080	3,120	567	509	451	392	334	276	245	214	183	151	120
3,120	3,160	579	520	462	404	345	287	251	220	189	157	126
3,160	3,200	590	531	473	415	356	298	257	226	195	163	132
3,200	3,240	601	543	484	426	368	309	263	232	201	169	138
3,240	3,280	612	554	496	437	379	321	269	238	207	175	144
3,280	3,320	623	565	507	448	390	332	275	244	213	181	150
3,320	3,360	635	576	518	460	401	343	285	250	219	187	156
3,360	3,400	646	587	529	471	412	354	296	256	225	193	162
3,400	3,440	657	599	540	482	424	365	307	262	231	199	168
3,440	3,480	668	610	552	493	435	377	318	268	237	205	174
3,480	3,520	679	621	563	504	446	388	329	274	243	211	180
3,520	3,560	691	632	574	516	457	399	341	282	249	217	186
3,560	3,600	702	643	585	527	468	410	352	293	255	223	192
3,600	3,640	713	655	596	538	480	421	363	305	261	229	198
3,640	3,680	724	666	608	549	491	433	374	316	267	235	204
3,680	3,720	735	677	619	560	502	444	385	327	273	241	210
3,720	3,760	747	688	630	572	513	455	397	338	280	247	216
3,760	3,800	758	699	641	583	524	466	408	349	291	253	222
3,800	3,840	769	711	652	594	536	477	419	361	302	259	228
3,840	3,880	780	722	664	605	547	489	430	372	314	265	234
3,880	3,920	791	733	675	616	558	500	441	383	325	271	240
3,920	3,960	803	744	686	628	569	511	453	394	336	278	246
3,960	4,000	814	755	697	639	580	522	464	405	347	289	252
4,000	4,040	825	767	708	650	592	533	475	417	358	300	258
4,040	4,080	836	778	720	661	603	545	486	428	370	311	264
4,080	4,120	847	789	731	672	614	556	497	439	381	322	270
4,120	4,160	859	800	742	684	625	567	509	450	392	334	276
4,160	4,200	870	811	753	695	636	578	520	461	403	345	286
4,200	4,240	881	823	764	706	648	589	531	473	414	356	298
4,240	4,280	892	834	776	717	659	601	542	484	426	367	309
4,280	4,320	903	845	787	728	670	612	553	495	437	378	320
4,320	4,360	915	856	798	740	681	623	565	506	448	390	331
4,360	4,400	927	867	809	751	692	634	576	517	459	401	342
4,400	4,440	940	879	820	762	704	645	587	529	470	412	354
4,440	4,480	952	890	832	773	715	657	598	540	482	423	365
4,480	4,520	965	901	843	784	726	668	609	551	493	434	376
4,520	4,560	977	912	854	796	737	679	621	562	504	446	387
4,560	4,600	989	925	865	807	748	690	632	573	515	457	398
4,600	4,640	1 002	937	876	818	760	701	643	585	526	468	410
4,640	4,680	1 014	950	888	829	771	713	654	596	538	479	421
4,680	4,720	1 027	962	899	840	782	724	665	607	549	490	432
4,720	4,760	1 039	974	910	852	793	735	677	618	560	502	443
4,760	4,800	1 051	987	922	863	804	746	688	629	571	513	454
4,800	4,840	1 064	999	935	874	816	757	699	641	582	524	466
4,840	4,880	1 076	1,012	947	885	827	769	710	652	594	535	477
4,880	4,920	1 089	1,024	959	896	838	780	721	663	605	546	488
4,920	4,960	1 101	1,036	972	908	849	791	733	674	616	558	499
4,960	5,000	1 113	1,049	984	920	860	802	744	685	627	569	510
5,000	5,040	1 126	1,061	997	932	872	813	755	697	638	580	522

$5,040 and over   Use Table 4(a) for a **SINGLE** person on page 32 Also see the instructions on page 30

© 1983, 1996 Instructional Horizons. Produced and Distributed
by J. Weston Walch, Publisher, Portland, Maine 04104-0658   *138*   *Consumer Math Success Kit*

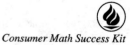

Withholding Tables

MARRIED Persons—**MONTHLY** Payroll Period

(For Wages Paid in 1995)

If the wages are—		And the number of withholding allowances claimed is—										
At least	But less than	0	1	2	3	4	5	6	7	8	9	10
		The amount of income tax to be withheld is—										
$0	$540	0	0	0	0	0	0	0	0	0	0	0
540	560	3	0	0	0	0	0	0	0	0	0	0
560	580	6	0	0	0	0	0	0	0	0	0	0
580	600	9	0	0	0	0	0	0	0	0	0	0
600	640	13	0	0	0	0	0	0	0	0	0	0
640	680	19	0	0	0	0	0	0	0	0	0	0
680	720	25	0	0	0	0	0	0	0	0	0	0
720	760	31	0	0	0	0	0	0	0	0	0	0
760	800	37	6	0	0	0	0	0	0	0	0	0
800	840	43	12	0	0	0	0	0	0	0	0	0
840	880	49	18	0	0	0	0	0	0	0	0	0
880	920	55	24	0	0	0	0	0	0	0	0	0
920	960	61	30	0	0	0	0	0	0	0	0	0
960	1,000	67	36	5	0	0	0	0	0	0	0	0
1,000	1,040	73	42	11	0	0	0	0	0	0	0	0
1,040	1,080	79	48	17	0	0	0	0	0	0	0	0
1,080	1,120	85	54	23	0	0	0	0	0	0	0	0
1,120	1,160	91	60	29	0	0	0	0	0	0	0	0
1,160	1,200	97	66	35	3	0	0	0	0	0	0	0
1,200	1,240	103	72	41	9	0	0	0	0	0	0	0
1,240	1,280	109	78	47	15	0	0	0	0	0	0	0
1,280	1,320	115	84	53	21	0	0	0	0	0	0	0
1,320	1,360	121	90	59	27	0	0	0	0	0	0	0
1,360	1,400	127	96	65	33	2	0	0	0	0	0	0
1,400	1,440	133	102	71	39	8	0	0	0	0	0	0
1,440	1,480	139	108	77	45	14	0	0	0	0	0	0
1,480	1,520	145	114	83	51	20	0	0	0	0	0	0
1,520	1,560	151	120	89	57	26	0	0	0	0	0	0
1,560	1,600	157	126	95	63	32	1	0	0	0	0	0
1,600	1,640	163	132	101	69	38	7	0	0	0	0	0
1,640	1,680	169	138	107	75	44	13	0	0	0	0	0
1,680	1,720	175	144	113	81	50	19	0	0	0	0	0
1,720	1,760	181	150	119	87	56	25	0	0	0	0	0
1,760	1,800	187	156	125	93	62	31	0	0	0	0	0
1,800	1,840	193	162	131	99	68	37	6	0	0	0	0
1,840	1,880	199	168	137	105	74	43	12	0	0	0	0
1,880	1,920	205	174	143	111	80	49	18	0	0	0	0
1,920	1,960	211	180	149	117	86	55	24	0	0	0	0
1,960	2,000	217	186	155	123	92	61	30	0	0	0	0
2,000	2,040	223	192	161	129	98	67	36	4	0	0	0
2,040	2,080	229	198	167	135	104	73	42	10	0	0	0
2,080	2,120	235	204	173	141	110	79	48	16	0	0	0
2,120	2,160	241	210	179	147	116	85	54	22	0	0	0
2,160	2,200	247	216	185	153	122	91	60	28	0	0	0
2,200	2,240	253	222	191	159	128	97	66	34	3	0	0
2,240	2,280	259	228	197	165	134	103	72	40	9	0	0
2,280	2,320	265	234	203	171	140	109	78	46	15	0	0
2,320	2,360	271	240	209	177	146	115	84	52	21	0	0
2,360	2,400	277	246	215	183	152	121	90	58	27	0	0
2,400	2,440	283	252	221	189	158	127	96	64	33	2	0
2,440	2,480	289	258	227	195	164	133	102	70	39	8	0
2,480	2,520	295	264	233	201	170	139	108	76	45	14	0
2,520	2,560	301	270	239	207	176	145	114	82	51	20	0
2,560	2,600	307	276	245	213	182	151	120	88	57	26	0
2,600	2,640	313	282	251	219	188	157	126	94	63	32	1
2,640	2,680	319	288	257	225	194	163	132	100	69	38	7
2,680	2,720	325	294	263	231	200	169	138	106	75	44	13
2,720	2,760	331	300	269	237	206	175	144	112	81	50	19
2,760	2,800	337	306	275	243	212	181	150	118	87	56	25
2,800	2,840	343	312	281	249	218	187	156	124	93	62	31
2,840	2,880	349	318	287	255	224	193	162	130	99	68	37
2,880	2,920	355	324	293	261	230	199	168	136	105	74	43
2,920	2,960	361	330	299	267	236	205	174	142	111	80	49
2,960	3,000	367	336	305	273	242	211	180	148	117	86	55
3,000	3,040	373	342	311	279	248	217	186	154	123	92	61
3,040	3,080	379	348	317	285	254	223	192	160	129	98	67
3,080	3,120	385	354	323	291	260	229	198	166	135	104	73
3,120	3,160	391	360	329	297	266	235	204	172	141	110	79
3,160	3,200	397	366	335	303	272	241	210	178	147	116	85
3,200	3,240	403	372	341	309	278	247	216	184	153	122	91

Consumer Math Success Kit

Withholding Tables

MARRIED Persons—MONTHLY Payroll Period
(For Wages Paid in 1995)

| If the wages are— | | And the number of withholding allowances claimed is— | | | | | | | | | | |
At least	But less than	0	1	2	3	4	5	6	7	8	9	10
		The amount of income tax to be withheld is—										
$3,240	$3,280	409	378	347	315	284	253	222	190	159	128	97
3,280	3,320	415	384	353	321	290	259	228	196	165	134	103
3,320	3,360	421	390	359	327	296	265	234	202	171	140	109
3,360	3,400	427	396	365	333	302	271	240	208	177	146	115
3,400	3,440	433	402	371	339	308	277	246	214	183	152	121
3,440	3,480	439	408	377	345	314	283	252	220	189	158	127
3,480	3,520	445	414	383	351	320	289	258	226	195	164	133
3,520	3,560	451	420	389	357	326	295	264	232	201	170	139
3,560	3,600	457	426	395	363	332	301	270	238	207	176	145
3,600	3,640	467	432	401	369	338	307	276	244	213	182	151
3,640	3,680	478	438	407	375	344	313	282	250	219	188	157
3,680	3,720	490	444	413	381	350	319	288	256	225	194	163
3,720	3,760	501	450	419	387	356	325	294	262	231	200	169
3,760	3,800	512	456	425	393	362	331	300	268	237	206	175
3,800	3,840	523	465	431	399	368	337	306	274	243	212	181
3,840	3,880	534	476	437	405	374	343	312	280	249	218	187
3,880	3,920	546	487	443	411	380	349	318	286	255	224	193
3,920	3,960	557	498	449	417	386	355	324	292	261	230	199
3,960	4,000	568	510	455	423	392	361	330	298	267	236	205
4,000	4,040	579	521	463	429	398	367	336	304	273	242	211
4,040	4,080	590	532	474	435	404	373	342	310	279	248	217
4,080	4,120	602	543	485	441	410	379	348	316	285	254	223
4,120	4,160	613	554	496	447	416	385	354	322	291	260	229
4,160	4,200	624	566	507	453	422	391	360	328	297	266	235
4,200	4,240	635	577	519	460	428	397	366	334	303	272	241
4,240	4,280	646	588	530	471	434	403	372	340	309	278	247
4,280	4,320	658	599	541	483	440	409	378	346	315	284	253
4,320	4,360	669	610	552	494	446	415	384	352	321	290	259
4,360	4,400	680	622	563	505	452	421	390	358	327	296	265
4,400	4,440	691	633	575	516	458	427	396	364	333	302	271
4,440	4,480	702	644	586	527	469	433	402	370	339	308	277
4,480	4,520	714	655	597	539	480	439	408	376	345	314	283
4,520	4,560	725	666	608	550	491	445	414	382	351	320	289
4,560	4,600	736	678	619	561	503	451	420	388	357	326	295
4,600	4,640	747	689	631	572	514	457	426	394	363	332	301
4,640	4,680	758	700	642	583	525	467	432	400	369	338	307
4,680	4,720	770	711	653	595	536	478	438	406	375	344	313
4,720	4,760	781	722	664	606	547	489	444	412	381	350	319
4,760	4,800	792	734	675	617	559	500	450	418	387	356	325
4,800	4,840	803	745	687	628	570	512	456	424	393	362	331
4,840	4,880	814	756	698	639	581	523	464	430	399	368	337
4,880	4,920	826	767	709	651	592	534	476	436	405	374	343
4,920	4,960	837	778	720	662	603	545	487	442	411	380	349
4,960	5,000	848	790	731	673	615	556	498	448	417	386	355
5,000	5,040	859	801	743	684	626	568	509	454	423	392	361
5,040	5,080	870	812	754	695	637	579	520	462	429	398	367
5,080	5,120	882	823	765	707	648	590	532	473	435	404	373
5,120	5,160	893	834	776	718	659	601	543	484	441	410	379
5,160	5,200	904	846	787	729	671	612	554	496	447	416	385
5,200	5,240	915	857	799	740	682	624	565	507	453	422	391
5,240	5,280	926	868	810	751	693	635	576	518	460	428	397
5,280	5,320	938	879	821	763	704	646	588	529	471	434	403
5,320	5,360	949	890	832	774	715	657	599	540	482	440	409
5,360	5,400	960	902	843	785	727	668	610	552	493	446	415
5,400	5,440	971	913	855	796	738	680	621	563	505	452	421
5,440	5,480	982	924	866	807	749	691	632	574	516	458	427
5,480	5,520	994	935	877	819	760	702	644	585	527	469	433
5,520	5,560	1 005	946	888	830	771	713	655	596	538	480	439
5,560	5,600	1 016	958	899	841	783	724	666	608	549	491	445
5,600	5,640	1 027	969	911	852	794	736	677	619	561	502	451
5,640	5,680	1 038	980	922	863	805	747	688	630	572	513	457
5,680	5,720	1 050	991	933	875	816	758	700	641	583	525	466
5,720	5,760	1 061	1 002	944	886	827	769	711	652	594	536	477
5,760	5,800	1 072	1 014	955	897	839	780	722	664	605	547	489
5,800	5,840	1 083	1 025	967	908	850	792	733	675	617	558	500

$5,840 and over   Use Table 4(b) for a **MARRIED person** on page 32 Also see the instructions on page 30

© 1983, 1996 Instructional Horizons. Produced and Distributed
by J. Weston Walch, Publisher, Portland, Maine 04104-0658

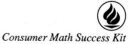

Consumer Math Success Kit

Income

Teacher Notes

Mathematical skills required:

addition, multiplication, and division of decimals
multiplication with percents

New vocabulary:

commission
deductions
draw
exemptions
gross pay
hourly rate
net pay
overtime pay
salary
wages

Related topics:

Budgets: Long-term
Budgets: Short-term
Estimating Answers
Income Tax

Teaching Suggestions:

1. Please note that the tax tables in this book may be out of date by the time you use them. The **principles** taught in this section are, of course, independent of the specific figures listed in any tax table. You may want to obtain a more recent tax table and have students refigure the solved examples and/or practice problems using the new tables.

2. See if some students would be willing to bring in their own paycheck stubs. They should cut off or mask their names on the stubs before bringing them in. Then, you can photocopy the anonymous pay stubs and use them for additional activities on this topic.

3. The emphasis in #2 might be to see the kinds of deductions that teenagers have in their paychecks and the ways in which these deductions will differ as they grow older.

4. Discuss the ways in which wages, salary, and commission differ from each other as forms of income. In what occupations is each most likely to be offered as a form of income? What are the advantages and disadvantages of each?

CHAPTER FIFTEEN

Income Tax

34. Income Tax

INTRODUCTION

April 15 is an important day for most people in the United States. That is the last day on which a person can pay her or his income tax. **Income tax** is the tax you pay on all money you have earned during the previous year. The amount of tax you must pay depends on a number of factors: wages or salary you have received; interests and dividends paid to you; your marital status; special expenses you had; and so on.

You report all this information on an income tax form. Different people use different forms. The most complicated form is called Form 1040. A simpler version of Form 1040 is Form 1040A. A still simpler form is called Form 1040EZ. Income tax forms change from year to year. The ones used in the solved examples are for 1994. You should check to see what this year's forms look like also.

© 1983, 1996 Instructional Horizons. Produced and Distributed
by J. Weston Walch, Publisher, Portland, Maine 04104-0658

34. Income Tax

● **Example:**

Bob is single and earned $9683.58 last year in wages. He also received $52.50 interest on his savings account. He had no other income. His company withheld $819.78 in federal income tax from his pay last year. What is the proper form for Bob to complete, and how should he fill it out?

Solution:

Bob is eligible to use Form 1040EZ. That is also the easiest form to use. The completed form is shown on page 147. Begin by filling out the information at the top of the form, or attach the label provided by the IRS.

Line 1:   Bob's wages of $9683.58 should be recorded here.

Line 2:   Bob's interest of $52.50 should be listed here.

Line 3: $9683.58 + $52.50 = $9736.08

Line 4:   Bob's parents do not claim him on their tax return, so mark "No" and enter $6250.00.

Line 5: $9736.08 – $6250.00 = $3486.08

Line 6: $819.78

Line 7:   Does not apply to Bob

Line 8: $819.78

Line 9: $521.00

Line 10: $819.78 – $521.00 = $298.78 (refund due to Bob)

Finally, remember to sign and date the form and list your occupation.

© 1983, 1996 Instructional Horizons. Produced and Distributed
by J. Weston Walch, Publisher, Portland, Maine 04104-0658   *146*   *Consumer Math Success Kit*

34. Income Tax

Department of the Treasury—Internal Revenue Service

Form
1040EZ
Income Tax Return for Single and
Joint Filers With No Dependents **1994** (L)

OMB No 1545 0675

Use the
IRS label
(See page 12)
Otherwise,
please print

LABEL HERE

Print your name (first, initial, last)

Robert R. Firenza
If a joint return, print spouse's name (first, initial last)

Home address (number and street) If you have a P O box see page 12   Apt no

415 Ardmore Apts., #3358
City, town or post office, state and ZIP code If you have a foreign address, see page 12

Sorrento, ND   58559
See instructions on back and in Form 1040EZ booklet.

Your social security number

| 9 | 2 | 0 | | 3 | 0 | | 4 | 5 | X | 9 |

Spouse's social security number

Presidential
Election
Campaign
(See page 12.)

Note: *Checking "Yes" will not change your tax or reduce your refund.*
Do you want $3 to go to this fund? ▶
If a joint return, does your spouse want $3 to go to this fund? ▶

Yes | No
[X] | [ ]
[ ] | [ ]

Income

Attach
Copy B of
Form(s)
W-2 here
Enclose but
do not attach,
any payment
with your
return

Note: *You*
must *check*
Yes or No

| | Dollars | Cents |

1 Total wages, salaries, and tips. This
should be shown in box 1 of your
W-2 form(s). Attach your W-2 form(s). **1**

9 | 6 8 3 | 5 8

2 Taxable interest income of $400 or less. If the total is
over $400, you cannot use Form 1040EZ. **2**

5 2 | 5 0

3 Add lines 1 and 2. This is your **adjusted gross income.**
If less than $9,000, see page 15 to find out if you can
claim the earned income credit on line 7. **3**

9 | 7 3 6 | 0 8

4 Can your parents (or someone else) claim you on their return?
[ ] **Yes.** Do worksheet   [X] **No.** If **single,** enter 6,250.00.
on back; enter   If **married,** enter 11,250.00.
amount from   For an explanation of these
line G here.   amounts, see back of form. **4**

6 | 2 5 0 | 0 0

5 Subtract line 4 from line 3. If line 4 is larger than
line 3, enter 0. This is your **taxable income.** ▶ **5**

3 | 4 8 6 | 0 8

Payments
and tax

6 Enter your Federal income tax withheld from box 2 of
your W-2 form(s). **6**

8 1 9 | 7 8

7 **Earned income credit** (see page 15). Enter type
and amount of nontaxable earned income below.
$ | $ **7**

-0-

8 Add lines 6 and 7 (don't include nontaxable earned
income). These are your **total payments.** **8**

8 1 9 | 7 8

9 **Tax.** Use the amount on **line 5** to find your tax in the
tax table on pages 28–32 of the booklet. Then, enter the
tax from the table on this line. **9**

5 2 1 | 0 0

Refund
or
amount
you
owe

10 If line 8 is larger than line 9, subtract line 9 from line 8.
This is your **refund.** **10**

2 9 8 | 7 8

11 If line 9 is larger than line 8, subtract line 8 from line 9.
This is the **amount you owe.** See page 20 for details on
how to pay and what to write on your payment. **11**

Sign
your
return

Keep a copy
of this form
for your
records

I have read this return. Under penalties of perjury, I declare that to the
best of my knowledge and belief, the return is true, correct, and accurately
lists all amounts and sources of income I received during the tax year.

Your signature

Date   Your occupation
4/14/94   waiter

Spouse's signature if joint return

Date   Spouse's occupation

34. Income Tax

1994	**Instructions for Form 1040EZ**

Use this form if

- Your filing status is single or married filing jointly
- You do not claim any dependents
- You (and your spouse if married) were under 65 on January 1, 1995, and not blind at the end of 1994
- Your taxable income (line 5) is less than $50,000
- You had **only** wages, salaries, tips, and taxable scholarship or fellowship grants, and your taxable interest income was $400 or less **But** if you earned tips, including allocated tips, that are not included in box 5 and box 7 of your W-2, you may not be able to use Form 1040EZ See page 14
- You did not receive any advance earned income credit payments

Caution: *If married and either you or your spouse had total wages of over $60,600 you may not be able to use this form See page 7*

If you are not sure about your filing status, see page 7 If you have questions about dependents, call Tele-Tax (see page 26) and listen to topic 354 If you **can't use this form,** call Tele-Tax (see page 26) and listen to topic 352

Filling in your return

Because this form is read by a machine, please print your numbers inside the boxes like this:

9 8 7 6 5 4 3 2 1 0   Do not type your numbers Do not use dollar signs.

If you received a scholarship or fellowship grant or tax-exempt interest income, such as on municipal bonds, see the booklet before filling in the form. Also, see the booklet if you received a Form 1099 INT showing income tax withheld (backup withholding)

Remember, you must report all wages, salaries, and tips even if you don't get a W-2 form from your employer You must also report all your taxable interest income, including interest from banks savings and loans, credit unions, etc , even if you don't get a Form 1099-INT

If you paid someone to prepare your return, see page 21

Worksheet for dependents who checked "Yes" on line 4

Use this worksheet to figure the amount to enter on line 4 if someone can claim you (or your spouse if married) as a dependent, even if that person chooses not to do so To find out if someone can claim you as a dependent, call Tele-Tax (see page 26) and listen to topic 354

A. Enter the amount from line 1 on the front. **A.** _____

B. Minimum standard deduction **B.** _____ 600.00

C. Enter the LARGER of line A or line B here **C.** _____

D. Maximum standard deduction If single, enter 3,800 00; if married, enter 6 350 00 **D.** _____

E. Enter the SMALLER of line C or line D here. This is your standard deduction **E.** _____

F. Exemption amount
- If single, enter 0
- If married and both you and your spouse can be claimed as dependents enter 0
- If married and only one of you can be claimed as a dependent, enter 2,450 00 **F.** _____

G. Add lines E and F Enter the total here and on line 4 on the front **G.** _____

If you checked "No" on line 4 because no one can claim you (or your spouse if married) as a dependent, enter on line 4 the amount shown below that applies to you

- Single, enter 6,250 00 **This is the total of your standard deduction (3,800 00) and personal exemption (2 450 00)**

- Married, enter 11,250 00. **This is the total of your standard deduction (6,350 00), exemption for yourself (2 450 00), and exemption for your spouse (2,450 00)**

Avoid mistakes

See page 21 of the Form 1040EZ booklet for a list of common mistakes to avoid Errors will delay your refund

Mailing your return

Mail your return by **April 17, 1995** Use the envelope that came with your booklet If you don't have that envelope see page 33 for the address to use

Consumer Math Success Kit

34. Income Tax

Section 5—1994 Tax Table

For persons with taxable income
of less than $50,000

Example Mr Brown is single. His taxable income on line 5 of Form 1040EZ is $23,250 First, he finds the $23,250-23,300 income line Next, he finds the "Single" column and reads down the column The amount shown where the income line and filing status column meet → is $3,560 This is the tax amount he must enter on line 9 of Form 1040EZ.

At least	But less than	Single	Married filing jointly
23,200	23,250	3,546	3 484
23,250	23,300	(3,560)	3 491
23,300	23,350	3 574	3,499
23,350	23,400	3,588	3,506

$0 – $1,500

At least	But less than	Single	Married filing jointly
$0	$5	$0	$0
5	15	2	2
15	25	3	3
25	50	6	6
50	75	9	9
75	100	13	13
100	125	17	17
125	150	21	21
150	175	24	24
175	200	28	28
200	225	32	32
225	250	36	36
250	275	39	39
275	300	43	43
300	325	47	47
325	350	51	51
350	375	54	54
375	400	58	58
400	425	62	62
425	450	66	66
450	475	69	69
475	500	73	73
500	525	77	77
525	550	81	81
550	575	84	84
575	600	88	88
600	625	92	92
625	650	96	96
650	675	99	99
675	700	103	103
700	725	107	107
725	750	111	111
750	775	114	114
775	800	118	118
800	825	122	122
825	850	126	126
850	875	129	129
875	900	133	133
900	925	137	137
925	950	141	141
950	975	144	144
975	1,000	148	148

1,000

At least	But less than	Single	Married filing jointly
1,000	1,025	152	152
1,025	1,050	156	156
1,050	1,075	159	159
1,075	1,100	163	163
1,100	1,125	167	167
1,125	1,150	171	171
1,150	1,175	174	174
1,175	1,200	178	178
1,200	1,225	182	182
1,225	1,250	186	186
1,250	1,275	189	189
1,275	1,300	193	193
1,300	1,325	197	197
1,325	1,350	201	201
1,350	1,375	204	204
1,375	1,400	208	208
1,400	1,425	212	212
1,425	1,450	216	216
1,450	1,475	219	219
1,475	1,500	223	223

1,500 – 2,000

At least	But less than	Single	Married filing jointly
1,500	1,525	227	227
1,525	1,550	231	231
1,550	1,575	234	234
1,575	1,600	238	238
1,600	1,625	242	242
1,625	1,650	246	246
1,650	1,675	249	249
1,675	1,700	253	253
1,700	1,725	257	257
1,725	1,750	261	261
1,750	1,775	264	264
1,775	1,800	268	268
1,800	1,825	272	272
1,825	1,850	276	276
1,850	1,875	279	279
1,875	1,900	283	283
1,900	1,925	287	287
1,925	1,950	291	291
1,950	1,975	294	294
1,975	2,000	298	298

2,000

At least	But less than	Single	Married filing jointly
2,000	2,025	302	302
2,025	2,050	306	306
2,050	2,075	309	309
2,075	2,100	313	313
2,100	2,125	317	317
2,125	2,150	321	321
2,150	2,175	324	324
2,175	2,200	328	328
2,200	2,225	332	332
2,225	2,250	336	336
2,250	2,275	339	339
2,275	2,300	343	343
2,300	2,325	347	347
2,325	2,350	351	351
2,350	2,375	354	354
2,375	2,400	358	358
2,400	2,425	362	362
2,425	2,450	366	366
2,450	2,475	369	369
2,475	2,500	373	373
2,500	2,525	377	377
2,525	2,550	381	381
2,550	2,575	384	384
2,575	2,600	388	388
2,600	2,625	392	392
2,625	2,650	396	396
2,650	2,675	399	399
2,675	2,700	403	403
2,700	2,725	407	407
2,725	2,750	411	411
2,750	2,775	414	414
2,775	2,800	418	418
2,800	2,825	422	422
2,825	2,850	426	426
2,850	2,875	429	429
2,875	2,900	433	433
2,900	2,925	437	437
2,925	2,950	441	441
2,950	2,975	444	444
2,975	3,000	448	448

3,000

At least	But less than	Single	Married filing jointly
3,000	3,050	454	454
3,050	3,100	461	461
3,100	3,150	469	469
3,150	3,200	476	476
3,200	3,250	484	484
3,250	3,300	491	491
3,300	3,350	499	499
3,350	3,400	506	506
3,400	3,450	514	514
3,450	3,500	521	521
3,500	3,550	529	529
3,550	3,600	536	536
3,600	3,650	544	544
3,650	3,700	551	551
3,700	3,750	559	559
3,750	3,800	566	566
3,800	3,850	574	574
3,850	3,900	581	581
3,900	3,950	589	589
3,950	4,000	596	596

4,000

At least	But less than	Single	Married filing jointly
4,000	4,050	604	604
4,050	4,100	611	611
4,100	4,150	619	619
4,150	4,200	626	626
4,200	4,250	634	634
4,250	4,300	641	641
4,300	4,350	649	649
4,350	4,400	656	656
4,400	4,450	664	664
4,450	4,500	671	671
4,500	4,550	679	679
4,550	4,600	686	686
4,600	4,650	694	694
4,650	4,700	701	701
4,700	4,750	709	709
4,750	4,800	716	716
4,800	4,850	724	724
4,850	4,900	731	731
4,900	4,950	739	739
4,950	5,000	746	746

5,000

At least	But less than	Single	Married filing jointly
5,000	5,050	754	754
5,050	5,100	761	761
5,100	5,150	769	769
5,150	5,200	776	776
5,200	5,250	784	784
5,250	5,300	791	791
5,300	5,350	799	799
5,350	5,400	806	806
5,400	5,450	814	814
5,450	5,500	821	821
5,500	5,550	829	829
5,550	5,600	836	836
5,600	5,650	844	844
5,650	5,700	851	851
5,700	5,750	859	859
5,750	5,800	866	866
5,800	5,850	874	874
5,850	5,900	881	881
5,900	5,950	889	889
5,950	6,000	896	896

6,000

At least	But less than	Single	Married filing jointly
6,000	6,050	904	904
6,050	6,100	911	911
6,100	6,150	919	919
6,150	6,200	926	926
6,200	6,250	934	934
6,250	6,300	941	941
6,300	6,350	949	949
6,350	6,400	956	956
6,400	6,450	964	964
6,450	6,500	971	971
6,500	6,550	979	979
6,550	6,600	986	986
6,600	6,650	994	994
6,650	6,700	1,001	1 001
6,700	6,750	1,009	1 009
6,750	6,800	1 016	1 016
6,800	6,850	1 024	1,024
6,850	6,900	1,031	1 031
6,900	6,950	1 039	1 039
6,950	7,000	1,046	1 046

7,000

At least	But less than	Single	Married filing jointly
7,000	7,050	1 054	1 054
7,050	7,100	1,061	1 061
7,100	7,150	1,069	1 069
7,150	7,200	1,076	1 076
7,200	7,250	1 084	1 084
7,250	7,300	1,091	1 091
7,300	7,350	1,099	1 099
7,350	7,400	1 106	1 106
7,400	7,450	1,114	1 114
7,450	7,500	1 121	1,121
7,500	7,550	1 129	1 129
7,550	7,600	1,136	1 136
7,600	7,650	1 144	1 144
7,650	7,700	1 151	1 151
7,700	7,750	1 159	1 159
7,750	7,800	1 166	1 166
7,800	7,850	1 174	1 174
7,850	7,900	1,181	1 181
7,900	7,950	1,189	1 189
7,950	8,000	1 196	1 196

8,000

At least	But less than	Single	Married filing jointly
8,000	8,050	1,204	1 204
8,050	8,100	1,211	1,211
8,100	8,150	1,219	1 219
8,150	8,200	1,226	1 226
8,200	8,250	1 234	1 234
8,250	8,300	1,241	1,241
8,300	8,350	1 249	1,249
8,350	8,400	1,256	1,256
8,400	8,450	1 264	1,264
8,450	8,500	1,271	1 271
8,500	8,550	1,279	1 279
8,550	8,600	1,286	1,286
8,600	8,650	1 294	1,294
8,650	8,700	1 301	1 301
8,700	8,750	1 309	1 309
8,750	8,800	1 316	1 316
8,800	8,850	1 324	1 324
8,850	8,900	1 331	1 331
8,900	8,950	1,339	1,339
8,950	9,000	1,346	1,346

Continued on next page

34. Income Tax

1994 1040EZ Tax Table—*Continued*

If Form 1040EZ, line 5, is—		And you are—		If Form 1040EZ, line 5, is—		And you are—		If Form 1040EZ, line 5, is—		And you are—		If Form 1040EZ, line 5, is—		And you are—	
At least	But less than	Single	Married filing jointly	At least	But less than	Single	Married filing jointly	At least	But less than	Single	Married filing jointly	At least	But less than	Single	Married filing jointly
		Your tax is—				Your tax is—				Your tax is—				Your tax is—	
9,000				**12,000**				**15,000**				**18,000**			
9,000	9,050	1 354	1 354	12,000	12,050	1 804	1,804	15,000	15,050	2 254	2 254	18,000	18,050	2 704	2 704
9,050	9,100	1 361	1 361	12,050	12,100	1 811	1 811	15,050	15,100	2 261	2 261	18,050	18,100	2 711	2 711
9,100	9,150	1 369	1 369	12,100	12,150	1 819	1 819	15,100	15,150	2 269	2 269	18,100	18,150	2 719	2 719
9,150	9,200	1 376	1 376	12,150	12,200	1 826	1 826	15,150	15,200	2 276	2 276	18,150	18,200	2 726	2 726
9,200	9,250	1 384	1 384	12,200	12,250	1 834	1,834	15,200	15,250	2 284	2 284	18,200	18,250	2 734	2 734
9,250	9,300	1 391	1 391	12,250	12,300	1 841	1 841	15,250	15,300	2 291	2 291	18,250	18,300	2 741	2 741
9,300	9,350	1 399	1 399	12,300	12,350	1 849	1 849	15,300	15,350	2 299	2 299	18,300	18,350	2 749	2 749
9,350	9,400	1 406	1 406	12,350	12,400	1 856	1 856	15,350	15,400	2 306	2 306	18,350	18,400	2 756	2 756
9,400	9,450	1 414	1 414	12,400	12,450	1 864	1,864	15,400	15,450	2 314	2,314	18,400	18,450	2 764	2 764
9,450	9,500	1 421	1 421	12,450	12,500	1 871	1 871	15,450	15,500	2 321	2 321	18,450	18,500	2 771	2 771
9,500	9,550	1 429	1,429	12,500	12,550	1 879	1 879	15,500	15,550	2,329	2 329	18,500	18,550	2 779	2 779
9,550	9,600	1 436	1 436	12,550	12,600	1,886	1,886	15,550	15,600	2,336	2 336	18,550	18,600	2 786	2 786
9,600	9,650	1 444	1 444	12,600	12,650	1 894	1 894	15,600	15,650	2 344	2 344	18,600	18,650	2 794	2 794
9,650	9,700	1 451	1 451	12,650	12,700	1 901	1,901	15,650	15,700	2 351	2 351	18,650	18,700	2 801	2 801
9,700	9,750	1 459	1 459	12,700	12,750	1 909	1 909	15,700	15,750	2 359	2 359	18,700	18,750	2 809	2 809
9,750	9,800	1 466	1 466	12,750	12,800	1,916	1,916	15,750	15,800	2 366	2 366	18,750	18,800	2 816	2 816
9,800	9,850	1,474	1 474	12,800	12,850	1 924	1 924	15,800	15,850	2 374	2 374	18,800	18,850	2 824	2 824
9,850	9,900	1,481	1 481	12,850	12,900	1 931	1 931	15,850	15,900	2 381	2 381	18,850	18,900	2 831	2 831
9,900	9,950	1 489	1 489	12,900	12,950	1 939	1 939	15,900	15,950	2 389	2 389	18,900	18,950	2 839	2 839
9,950	10,000	1 496	1 496	12,950	13,000	1 946	1 946	15,950	16,000	2 396	2 396	18,950	19,000	2 846	2 846
10,000				**13,000**				**16,000**				**19,000**			
10,000	10,050	1 504	1 504	13,000	13,050	1 954	1 954	16,000	16,050	2 404	2 404	19,000	19,050	2 854	2 854
10,050	10,100	1 511	1 511	13,050	13,100	1 961	1,961	16,050	16,100	2 411	2 411	19,050	19,100	2 861	2 861
10,100	10,150	1,519	1 519	13,100	13,150	1 969	1,969	16,100	16,150	2 419	2 419	19,100	19,150	2 869	2 869
10,150	10,200	1 526	1 526	13,150	13,200	1,976	1 976	16,150	16,200	2 426	2 426	19,150	19,200	2 876	2 876
10,200	10,250	1 534	1 534	13,200	13,250	1 984	1,984	16,200	16,250	2,434	2 434	19,200	19,250	2 884	2 884
10,250	10,300	1 541	1 541	13,250	13,300	1,991	1 991	16,250	16,300	2 441	2 441	19,250	19,300	2 891	2 891
10,300	10,350	1 549	1 549	13,300	13,350	1 999	1 999	16,300	16,350	2 449	2 449	19,300	19,350	2 899	2 899
10,350	10,400	1 556	1 556	13,350	13,400	2,006	2,006	16,350	16,400	2 456	2,456	19,350	19,400	2 906	2 906
10,400	10,450	1 564	1 564	13,400	13,450	2 014	2 014	16,400	16,450	2 464	2 464	19,400	19,450	2 914	2 914
10,450	10,500	1,571	1 571	13,450	13,500	2,021	2 021	16,450	16,500	2 471	2,471	19,450	19,500	2 921	2 921
10,500	10,550	1 579	1 579	13,500	13,550	2,029	2 029	16,500	16,550	2 479	2 479	19,500	19,550	2 929	2 929
10,550	10,600	1,586	1 586	13,550	13,600	2 036	2 036	16,550	16,600	2 486	2 486	19,550	19,600	2 936	2 936
10,600	10,650	1,594	1,594	13,600	13,650	2 044	2 044	16,600	16,650	2,494	2 494	19,600	19,650	2 944	2 944
10,650	10,700	1 601	1 601	13,650	13,700	2 051	2 051	16,650	16,700	2 501	2 501	19,650	19,700	2 951	2 951
10,700	10,750	1 609	1 609	13,700	13,750	2 059	2 059	16,700	16,750	2,509	2 509	19,700	19,750	2 959	2 959
10,750	10,800	1,616	1 616	13,750	13,800	2 066	2 066	16,750	16,800	2,516	2 516	19,750	19,800	2 966	2 966
10,800	10,850	1 624	1 624	13,800	13,850	2 074	2 074	16,800	16,850	2 524	2 524	19,800	19,850	2 974	2 974
10,850	10,900	1 631	1 631	13,850	13,900	2 081	2 081	16,850	16,900	2 531	2 531	19,850	19,900	2 981	2 981
10,900	10,950	1,639	1 639	13,900	13,950	2 089	2,089	16,900	16,950	2 539	2 539	19,900	19,950	2 989	2 989
10,950	11,000	1 646	1 646	13,950	14,000	2 096	2 096	16,950	17,000	2,546	2 546	19,950	20,000	2 996	2 996
11,000				**14,000**				**17,000**				**20,000**			
11,000	11,050	1 654	1 654	14,000	14,050	2 104	2 104	17,000	17,050	2 554	2 554	20,000	20,050	3 004	3 004
11,050	11,100	1 661	1 661	14,050	14,100	2 111	2 111	17,050	17,100	2 561	2 561	20,050	20,100	3 011	3 011
11,100	11,150	1 669	1 669	14,100	14,150	2 119	2 119	17,100	17,150	2 569	2 569	20,100	20,150	3 019	3 019
11,150	11,200	1 676	1 676	14,150	14,200	2 126	2,126	17,150	17,200	2 576	2 576	20,150	20,200	3 026	3 026
11,200	11,250	1 684	1 684	14,200	14,250	2 134	2 134	17,200	17,250	2,584	2 584	20,200	20,250	3 034	3 034
11,250	11,300	1,691	1,691	14,250	14,300	2 141	2 141	17,250	17,300	2 591	2 591	20,250	20,300	3 041	3 041
11,300	11,350	1,699	1 699	14,300	14,350	2 149	2 149	17,300	17,350	2 599	2 599	20,300	20,350	3 049	3 049
11,350	11,400	1 706	1 706	14,350	14,400	2 156	2,156	17,350	17,400	2 606	2 606	20,350	20,400	3 056	3 056
11,400	11,450	1 714	1 714	14,400	14,450	2 164	2,164	17,400	17,450	2 614	2 614	20,400	20,450	3 064	3 064
11,450	11,500	1 721	1,721	14,450	14,500	2 171	2 171	17,450	17,500	2 621	2 621	20,450	20,500	3 071	3 071
11,500	11,550	1 729	1 729	14,500	14,550	2 179	2 179	17,500	17,550	2 629	2,629	20,500	20,550	3 079	3 079
11,550	11,600	1 736	1 736	14,550	14,600	2 186	2 186	17,550	17,600	2 636	2,636	20,550	20,600	3 086	3 086
11,600	11,650	1 744	1 744	14,600	14,650	2 194	2 194	17,600	17,650	2 644	2 644	20,600	20,650	3 094	3 094
11,650	11,700	1 751	1 751	14,650	14,700	2 201	2 201	17,650	17,700	2 651	2 651	20,650	20,700	3 101	3 101
11,700	11,750	1 759	1,759	14,700	14,750	2 209	2 209	17,700	17,750	2 659	2 659	20,700	20,750	3 109	3 109
11,750	11,800	1,766	1 766	14,750	14,800	2 216	2,216	17,750	17,800	2 666	2 666	20,750	20,800	3 116	3 116
11,800	11,850	1,774	1 774	14,800	14,850	2 224	2 224	17,800	17,850	2 674	2 674	20,800	20,850	3 124	3 124
11,850	11,900	1 781	1 781	14,850	14,900	2 231	2 231	17,850	17,900	2 681	2 681	20,850	20,900	3 131	3 131
11,900	11,950	1 789	1 789	14,900	14,950	2 239	2 239	17,900	17,950	2 689	2 689	20,900	20,950	3 139	3 139
11,950	12,000	1 796	1 796	14,950	15,000	2 246	2 246	17,950	18,000	2 696	2 696	20,950	21,000	3 146	3 146

Continued on next page

© 1983, 1996 Instructional Horizons. Produced and Distributed by J. Weston Walch, Publisher, Portland, Maine 04104-0658

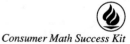

34. Income Tax

1994 1040EZ Tax Table—*Continued*

21,000

If Form 1040EZ, line 5, is— At least	But less than	Single	Married filing jointly
21,000	21,050	3 154	3 154
21,050	21,100	3 161	3 161
21,100	21,150	3 169	3 169
21,150	21,200	3 176	3 176
21,200	21,250	3 184	3 184
21,250	21,300	3,191	3 191
21,300	21,350	3 199	3 199
21,350	21,400	3 206	3 206
21,400	21,450	3 214	3 214
21,450	21,500	3 221	3 221
21,500	21,550	3 229	3 229
21,550	21,600	3 236	3 236
21,600	21,650	3,244	3 244
21,650	21,700	3 251	3 251
21,700	21,750	3 259	3 259
21,750	21,800	3 266	3 266
21,800	21,850	3 274	3 274
21,850	21,900	3 281	3 281
21,900	21,950	3 289	3 289
21,950	22,000	3 296	3 296

22,000

At least	But less than	Single	Married filing jointly
22,000	22,050	3 304	3 304
22,050	22,100	3,311	3 311
22,100	22,150	3 319	3 319
22,150	22,200	3,326	3 326
22,200	22,250	3 334	3 334
22,250	22,300	3 341	3 341
22,300	22,350	3 349	3 349
22,350	22,400	3 356	3 356
22,400	22,450	3 364	3 364
22,450	22,500	3 371	3 371
22,500	22,550	3 379	3 379
22,550	22,600	3 386	3 386
22,600	22,650	3 394	3 394
22,650	22,700	3 401	3 401
22,700	22,750	3 409	3 409
22,750	22,800	3 420	3 416
22,800	22,850	3 434	3 424
22,850	22,900	3 448	3 431
22,900	22,950	3 462	3,439
22,950	23,000	3 476	3,446

23,000

At least	But less than	Single	Married filing jointly
23,000	23,050	3 490	3 454
23,050	23,100	3 504	3 461
23,100	23,150	3 518	3 469
23,150	23,200	3 532	3 476
23,200	23,250	3 546	3 484
23,250	23,300	3 560	3 491
23,300	23,350	3 574	3 499
23,350	23,400	3 588	3 506
23,400	23,450	3 602	3 514
23,450	23,500	3 616	3 521
23,500	23,550	3 630	3 529
23,550	23,600	3 644	3 536
23,600	23,650	3 658	3 544
23,650	23,700	3 672	3,551
23,700	23,750	3 686	3 559
23,750	23,800	3 700	3 566
23,800	23,850	3 714	3 574
23,850	23,900	3 728	3 581
23,900	23,950	3 742	3 589
23,950	24,000	3,756	3 596

24,000

At least	But less than	Single	Married filing jointly
24,000	24,050	3 770	3 604
24,050	24,100	3 784	3 611
24,100	24,150	3 798	3 619
24,150	24,200	3 812	3 626
24,200	24,250	3 826	3 634
24,250	24,300	3 840	3 641
24,300	24,350	3 854	3 649
24,350	24,400	3 868	3 656
24,400	24,450	3 882	3 664
24,450	24,500	3 896	3 671
24,500	24,550	3 910	3 679
24,550	24,600	3,924	3 686
24,600	24,650	3 938	3 694
24,650	24,700	3 952	3 701
24,700	24,750	3 966	3 709
24,750	24,800	3 980	3 716
24,800	24,850	3 994	3 724
24,850	24,900	4 008	3 731
24,900	24,950	4 022	3 739
24,950	25,000	4 036	3 746

25,000

At least	But less than	Single	Married filing jointly
25,000	25,050	4 050	3 754
25,050	25,100	4 064	3 761
25,100	25,150	4 078	3 769
25,150	25,200	4 092	3 776
25,200	25,250	4 106	3 784
25,250	25,300	4,120	3 791
25,300	25,350	4 134	3 799
25,350	25,400	4,148	3 806
25,400	25,450	4 162	3 814
25,450	25,500	4,176	3 821
25,500	25,550	4 190	3 829
25,550	25,600	4 204	3 836
25,600	25,650	4 218	3 844
25,650	25,700	4 232	3 851
25,700	25,750	4 246	3 859
25,750	25,800	4,260	3 866
25,800	25,850	4 274	3 874
25,850	25,900	4 288	3 881
25,900	25,950	4,302	3 889
25,950	26,000	4 316	3 896

26,000

At least	But less than	Single	Married filing jointly
26,000	26,050	4,330	3 904
26,050	26,100	4 344	3 911
26,100	26,150	4 358	3 919
26,150	26,200	4 372	3 926
26,200	26,250	4 386	3 934
26,250	26,300	4 400	3 941
26,300	26,350	4 414	3 949
26,350	26,400	4 428	3 956
26,400	26,450	4,442	3 964
26,450	26,500	4 456	3 971
26,500	26,550	4 470	3 979
26,550	26,600	4 484	3 986
26,600	26,650	4,498	3 994
26,650	26,700	4 512	4 001
26,700	26,750	4 526	4 009
26,750	26,800	4 540	4 016
26,800	26,850	4 554	4 024
26,850	26,900	4 568	4 031
26,900	26,950	4 582	4 039
26,950	27,000	4 596	4 046

27,000

At least	But less than	Single	Married filing jointly
27,000	27,050	4 610	4 054
27,050	27,100	4 624	4 061
27,100	27,150	4 638	4 069
27,150	27,200	4 652	4 076
27,200	27,250	4 666	4 084
27,250	27,300	4 680	4 091
27,300	27,350	4 694	4 099
27,350	27,400	4 708	4 106
27,400	27,450	4 722	4 114
27,450	27,500	4 736	4 121
27,500	27,550	4 750	4 129
27,550	27,600	4 764	4 136
27,600	27,650	4 778	4 144
27,650	27,700	4 792	4 151
27,700	27,750	4 806	4 159
27,750	27,800	4 820	4 166
27,800	27,850	4 834	4 174
27,850	27,900	4 848	4 181
27,900	27,950	4 862	4 189
27,950	28,000	4 876	4 196

28,000

At least	But less than	Single	Married filing jointly
28,000	28,050	4 890	4 204
28,050	28,100	4 904	4 211
28,100	28,150	4 918	4 219
28,150	28,200	4 932	4 226
28,200	28,250	4 946	4 234
28,250	28,300	4 960	4 241
28,300	28,350	4 974	4 249
28,350	28,400	4,988	4 256
28,400	28,450	5 002	4 264
28,450	28,500	5 016	4 271
28,500	28,550	5 030	4 279
28,550	28,600	5 044	4 286
28,600	28,650	5 058	4 294
28,650	28,700	5 072	4 301
28,700	28,750	5 086	4 309
28,750	28,800	5,100	4 316
28,800	28,850	5 114	4 324
28,850	28,900	5 128	4 331
28,900	28,950	5 142	4 339
28,950	29,000	5 156	4 346

29,000

At least	But less than	Single	Married filing jointly
29,000	29,050	5 170	4 354
29,050	29,100	5 184	4 361
29,100	29,150	5 198	4 369
29,150	29,200	5 212	4 376
29,200	29,250	5,226	4 384
29,250	29,300	5,240	4 391
29,300	29,350	5 254	4 399
29,350	29,400	5 268	4 406
29,400	29,450	5 282	4 414
29,450	29,500	5 296	4 421
29,500	29,550	5 310	4 429
29,550	29,600	5 324	4 436
29,600	29,650	5 338	4 444
29,650	29,700	5,352	4,451
29,700	29,750	5 366	4 459
29,750	29,800	5 380	4 466
29,800	29,850	5 394	4 474
29,850	29,900	5 408	4 481
29,900	29,950	5 422	4 489
29,950	30,000	5 436	4 496

30,000

At least	But less than	Single	Married filing jointly
30,000	30,050	5 450	4 504
30,050	30,100	5 464	4 511
30,100	30,150	5 478	4 519
30,150	30,200	5 492	4 526
30,200	30,250	5 506	4 534
30,250	30,300	5 520	4 541
30,300	30,350	5 534	4 549
30,350	30,400	5,548	4 556
30,400	30,450	5 562	4 564
30,450	30,500	5 576	4 571
30,500	30,550	5 590	4 579
30,550	30,600	5 604	4 586
30,600	30,650	5 618	4 594
30,650	30,700	5 632	4 601
30,700	30,750	5 646	4 609
30,750	30,800	5 660	4 616
30,800	30,850	5 674	4 624
30,850	30,900	5 688	4 631
30,900	30,950	5 702	4 639
30,950	31,000	5 716	4 646

31,000

At least	But less than	Single	Married filing jointly
31,000	31,050	5 730	4 654
31,050	31,100	5 744	4 661
31,100	31,150	5 758	4 669
31,150	31,200	5,772	4 676
31,200	31,250	5 786	4,684
31,250	31,300	5 800	4 691
31,300	31,350	5 814	4 699
31,350	31,400	5,828	4 706
31,400	31,450	5 842	4 714
31,450	31,500	5 856	4 721
31,500	31,550	5 870	4,729
31,550	31,600	5,884	4 736
31,600	31,650	5 898	4 744
31,650	31,700	5 912	4 751
31,700	31,750	5 926	4,759
31,750	31,800	5 940	4,766
31,800	31,850	5 954	4,774
31,850	31,900	5 968	4,781
31,900	31,950	5 982	4,789
31,950	32,000	5 996	4 796

32,000

At least	But less than	Single	Married filing jointly
32,000	32,050	6 010	4 804
32,050	32,100	6 024	4,811
32,100	32,150	6 038	4 819
32,150	32,200	6 052	4 826
32,200	32,250	6 066	4 834
32,250	32,300	6 080	4 841
32,300	32,350	6 094	4 849
32,350	32,400	6 108	4 856
32,400	32,450	6,122	4,864
32,450	32,500	6,136	4,871
32,500	32,550	6 150	4 879
32,550	32,600	6 164	4 886
32,600	32,650	6 178	4,894
32,650	32,700	6 192	4 901
32,700	32,750	6,206	4,909
32,750	32,800	6 220	4 916
32,800	32,850	6 234	4,924
32,850	32,900	6 248	4 931
32,900	32,950	6 262	4,939
32,950	33,000	6 276	4,946

Continued on next page

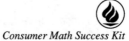

Consumer Math Success Kit

34. Income Tax

1994 1040EZ Tax Table—*Continued*

Each section: columns are "If Form 1040EZ, line 5, is—" (At least / But less than) and "And you are—" (Single / Married filing jointly). "Your tax is—".

33,000

At least	But less than	Single	Married filing jointly
33,000	33,050	6 290	4,954
33,050	33,100	6 304	4,961
33,100	33,150	6 318	4,969
33,150	33,200	6 332	4,976
33,200	33,250	6 346	4,984
33,250	33,300	6 360	4,991
33,300	33,350	6 374	4,999
33,350	33,400	6 388	5,006
33,400	33,450	6 402	5,014
33,450	33,500	6 416	5,021
33,500	33,550	6 430	5,029
33,550	33,600	6 444	5,036
33,600	33,650	6 458	5,044
33,650	33,700	6 472	5,051
33,700	33,750	6 486	5,059
33,750	33,800	6 500	5,066
33,800	33,850	6,514	5,074
33,850	33,900	6 528	5,081
33,900	33,950	6 542	5,089
33,950	34,000	6,556	5,096

34,000

At least	But less than	Single	Married filing jointly
34,000	34,050	6 570	5,104
34,050	34,100	6 584	5,111
34,100	34,150	6 598	5,119
34,150	34,200	6 612	5,126
34,200	34,250	6 626	5,134
34,250	34,300	6 640	5,141
34,300	34,350	6 654	5,149
34,350	34,400	6 668	5,156
34,400	34,450	6 682	5,164
34,450	34,500	6 696	5,171
34,500	34,550	6 710	5,179
34,550	34,600	6 724	5,186
34,600	34,650	6 738	5,194
34,650	34,700	6 752	5,201
34,700	34,750	6 766	5,209
34,750	34,800	6,780	5,216
34,800	34,850	6 794	5,224
34,850	34,900	6 808	5,231
34,900	34,950	6 822	5,239
34,950	35,000	6 836	5,246

35,000

At least	But less than	Single	Married filing jointly
35,000	35,050	6 850	5,254
35,050	35,100	6 864	5,261
35,100	35,150	6 878	5,269
35,150	35,200	6 892	5,276
35,200	35,250	6 906	5,284
35,250	35,300	6 920	5,291
35,300	35,350	6 934	5,299
35,350	35,400	6 948	5,306
35,400	35,450	6 962	5,314
35,450	35,500	6 976	5,321
35,500	35,550	6 990	5,329
35,550	35,600	7 004	5,336
35,600	35,650	7 018	5,344
35,650	35,700	7 032	5,351
35,700	35,750	7 046	5,359
35,750	35,800	7 060	5,366
35,800	35,850	7 074	5,374
35,850	35,900	7 088	5,381
35,900	35,950	7 102	5,389
35,950	36,000	7 116	5,396

36,000

At least	But less than	Single	Married filing jointly
36,000	36,050	7 130	5,404
36,050	36,100	7 144	5,411
36,100	36,150	7 158	5,419
36,150	36,200	7 172	5,426
36,200	36,250	7 186	5,434
36,250	36,300	7 200	5,441
36,300	36,350	7 214	5,449
36,350	36,400	7 228	5,456
36,400	36,450	7 242	5,464
36,450	36,500	7 256	5,471
36,500	36,550	7 270	5,479
36,550	36,600	7 284	5,486
36,600	36,650	7 298	5,494
36,650	36,700	7 312	5,501
36,700	36,750	7 326	5,509
36,750	36,800	7 340	5,516
36,800	36,850	7 354	5,524
36,850	36,900	7 368	5,531
36,900	36,950	7 382	5,539
36,950	37,000	7 396	5,546

37,000

At least	But less than	Single	Married filing jointly
37,000	37,050	7,410	5,554
37,050	37,100	7,424	5,561
37,100	37,150	7,438	5,569
37,150	37,200	7,452	5,576
37,200	37,250	7,466	5,584
37,250	37,300	7,480	5,591
37,300	37,350	7,494	5,599
37,350	37,400	7,508	5,606
37,400	37,450	7,522	5,614
37,450	37,500	7,536	5,621
37,500	37,550	7,550	5,629
37,550	37,600	7,564	5,636
37,600	37,650	7,578	5,644
37,650	37,700	7,592	5,651
37,700	37,750	7,606	5,659
37,750	37,800	7,620	5,666
37,800	37,850	7,634	5,674
37,850	37,900	7,648	5,681
37,900	37,950	7,662	5,689
37,950	38,000	7,676	5,696

38,000

At least	But less than	Single	Married filing jointly
38,000	38,050	7,690	5,707
38,050	38,100	7,704	5,721
38,100	38,150	7,718	5,735
38,150	38,200	7,732	5,749
38,200	38,250	7,746	5,763
38,250	38,300	7,760	5,777
38,300	38,350	7,774	5,791
38,350	38,400	7,788	5,805
38,400	38,450	7,802	5,819
38,450	38,500	7,816	5,833
38,500	38,550	7,830	5,847
38,550	38,600	7,844	5,861
38,600	38,650	7,858	5,875
38,650	38,700	7,872	5,889
38,700	38,750	7,886	5,903
38,750	38,800	7,900	5,917
38,800	38,850	7,914	5,931
38,850	38,900	7,928	5,945
38,900	38,950	7,942	5,959
38,950	39,000	7,956	5,973

39,000

At least	But less than	Single	Married filing jointly
39,000	39,050	7 970	5,987
39,050	39,100	7 984	6,001
39,100	39,150	7 998	6,015
39,150	39,200	8 012	6,029
39,200	39,250	8 026	6,043
39,250	39,300	8 040	6,057
39,300	39,350	8,054	6,071
39,350	39,400	8 068	6,085
39,400	39,450	8 082	6,099
39,450	39,500	8 096	6,113
39,500	39,550	8 110	6,127
39,550	39,600	8 124	6,141
39,600	39,650	8 138	6,155
39,650	39,700	8 152	6,169
39,700	39,750	8 166	6,183
39,750	39,800	8 180	6,197
39,800	39,850	8 194	6,211
39,850	39,900	8 208	6,225
39,900	39,950	8 222	6,239
39,950	40,000	8,236	6,253

40,000

At least	But less than	Single	Married filing jointly
40,000	40,050	8 250	6,267
40,050	40,100	8 264	6,281
40,100	40,150	8 278	6,295
40,150	40,200	8 292	6,309
40,200	40,250	8 306	6,323
40,250	40,300	8 320	6,337
40,300	40,350	8 334	6,351
40,350	40,400	8 348	6,365
40,400	40,450	8 362	6,379
40,450	40,500	8 376	6,393
40,500	40,550	8 390	6,407
40,550	40,600	8 404	6,421
40,600	40,650	8,418	6,435
40,650	40,700	8 432	6,449
40,700	40,750	8,446	6,463
40,750	40,800	8 460	6,477
40,800	40,850	8 474	6,491
40,850	40,900	8 488	6,505
40,900	40,950	8 502	6,519
40,950	41,000	8 516	6,533

41,000

At least	But less than	Single	Married filing jointly
41,000	41,050	8 530	6,547
41,050	41,100	8 544	6,561
41,100	41,150	8,558	6,575
41,150	41,200	8,572	6,589
41,200	41,250	8 586	6,603
41,250	41,300	8 600	6,617
41,300	41,350	8 614	6,631
41,350	41,400	8,628	6,645
41,400	41,450	8 642	6,659
41,450	41,500	8 656	6,673
41,500	41,550	8 670	6,687
41,550	41,600	8 684	6,701
41,600	41,650	8,698	6,715
41,650	41,700	8,712	6,729
41,700	41,750	8,726	6,743
41,750	41,800	8 740	6,757
41,800	41,850	8 754	6,771
41,850	41,900	8 768	6,785
41,900	41,950	8 782	6,799
41,950	42,000	8,796	6,813

42,000

At least	But less than	Single	Married filing jointly
42,000	42,050	8 810	6 827
42,050	42,100	8 824	6 841
42,100	42,150	8 838	6 855
42,150	42,200	8 852	6 869
42,200	42,250	8 866	6 883
42,250	42,300	8 880	6 897
42,300	42,350	8 894	6,911
42,350	42,400	8 908	6 925
42,400	42,450	8,922	6 939
42,450	42,500	8 936	6 953
42,500	42,550	8 950	6 967
42,550	42,600	8,964	6 981
42,600	42,650	8 978	6 995
42,650	42,700	8 992	7,009
42,700	42,750	9 006	7 023
42,750	42,800	9 020	7 037
42,800	42,850	9 034	7 051
42,850	42,900	9 048	7 065
42,900	42,950	9 062	7,079
42,950	43,000	9 076	7,093

43,000

At least	But less than	Single	Married filing jointly
43,000	43,050	9 090	7,107
43,050	43,100	9 104	7,121
43,100	43,150	9 118	7,135
43,150	43,200	9,132	7 149
43,200	43,250	9 146	7 163
43,250	43,300	9 160	7 177
43,300	43,350	9 174	7 191
43,350	43,400	9 188	7 205
43,400	43,450	9 202	7 219
43,450	43,500	9 216	7 233
43,500	43,550	9 230	7,247
43,550	43,600	9 244	7 261
43,600	43,650	9 258	7 275
43,650	43,700	9 272	7 289
43,700	43,750	9 286	7 303
43,750	43,800	9 300	7 317
43,800	43,850	9 314	7 331
43,850	43,900	9 328	7 345
43,900	43,950	9 342	7 359
43,950	44,000	9 356	7 373

44,000

At least	But less than	Single	Married filing jointly
44,000	44,050	9 370	7,387
44,050	44,100	9 384	7 401
44,100	44,150	9 398	7,415
44,150	44,200	9 412	7 429
44,200	44,250	9 426	7,443
44,250	44,300	9 440	7,457
44,300	44,350	9 454	7 471
44,350	44,400	9 468	7,485
44,400	44,450	9,482	7 499
44,450	44,500	9 496	7 513
44,500	44,550	9 510	7,527
44,550	44,600	9 524	7,541
44,600	44,650	9 538	7,555
44,650	44,700	9 552	7 569
44,700	44,750	9 566	7,583
44,750	44,800	9 580	7 597
44,800	44,850	9 594	7 611
44,850	44,900	9 608	7 625
44,900	44,950	9 622	7 639
44,950	45,000	9 636	7,653

Continued on next page

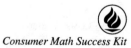

34. Income Tax

1994 1040EZ Tax Table—*Continued*

If Form 1040EZ, line 5, is—		And you are—		If Form 1040EZ, line 5, is—		And you are—	
At least	But less than	Single	Married filing jointly	At least	But less than	Single	Married filing jointly
		Your tax is—				Your tax is—	
45,000				**48,000**			
45,000	45,050	9 650	7 667	48,000	48,050	10 490	8 507
45,050	45,100	9 664	7 681	48,050	48,100	10 504	8 521
45,100	45,150	9,678	7 695	48,100	48,150	10 518	8 535
45,150	45,200	9 692	7 709	48,150	48,200	10 532	8 549
45,200	45,250	9 706	7 723	48,200	48,250	10 546	8 563
45,250	45,300	9 720	7 737	48,250	48,300	10 560	8 577
45,300	45,350	9 734	7,751	48,300	48,350	10,574	8 591
45,350	45,400	9 748	7 765	48,350	48,400	10 588	8 605
45,400	45,450	9 762	7 779	48,400	48,450	10,602	8 619
45,450	45,500	9 776	7 793	48,450	48,500	10,616	8 633
45,500	45,550	9 790	7 807	48,500	48,550	10,630	8 647
45,550	45,600	9 804	7,821	48,550	48,600	10,644	8 661
45,600	45,650	9 818	7 835	48,600	48,650	10 658	8 675
45,650	45,700	9,832	7 849	48,650	48,700	10,672	8 689
45,700	45,750	9,846	7 863	48,700	48,750	10 686	8,703
45,750	45,800	9 860	7,877	48,750	48,800	10 700	8 717
45,800	45,850	9 874	7 891	48,800	48,850	10 714	8 731
45,850	45,900	9 888	7 905	48,850	48,900	10 728	8 745
45,900	45,950	9 902	7 919	48,900	48,950	10 742	8 759
45,950	46,000	9 916	7 933	48,950	49,000	10 756	8 773
46,000				**49,000**			
46,000	46,050	9 930	7 947	49,000	49,050	10 770	8 787
46,050	46,100	9 944	7 961	49,050	49,100	10,784	8 801
46,100	46,150	9 958	7 975	49,100	49,150	10 798	8 815
46,150	46,200	9 972	7 989	49,150	49,200	10 812	8 829
46,200	46,250	9 986	8 003	49,200	49,250	10 826	8 843
46,250	46,300	10 000	8 017	49,250	49,300	10,840	8 857
46,300	46,350	10 014	8 031	49,300	49,350	10 854	8 871
46,350	46,400	10 028	8,045	49,350	49,400	10 868	8 885
46,400	46,450	10 042	8 059	49,400	49,450	10 882	8 899
46,450	46,500	10 056	8 073	49,450	49,500	10 896	8 913
46,500	46,550	10 070	8 087	49,500	49,550	10,910	8 927
46,550	46,600	10 084	8 101	49,550	49,600	10 924	8 941
46,600	46,650	10 098	8 115	49,600	49,650	10,938	8,955
46,650	46,700	10 112	8,129	49,650	49,700	10 952	8 969
46,700	46,750	10 126	8 143	49,700	49,750	10 966	8 983
46,750	46,800	10 140	8 157	49,750	49,800	10 980	8 997
46,800	46,850	10 154	8 171	49,800	49,850	10,994	9 011
46,850	46,900	10 168	8 185	49,850	49,900	11 008	9 025
46,900	46,950	10 182	8,199	49,900	49,950	11 022	9 039
46,950	47,000	10 196	8 213	49,950	50,000	11 036	9 053
47,000							
47,000	47,050	10 210	8 227				
47,050	47,100	10 224	8 241				
47,100	47,150	10 238	8 255				
47,150	47,200	10 252	8 269				
47,200	47,250	10 266	8,283				
47,250	47,300	10 280	8 297				
47,300	47,350	10 294	8 311				
47,350	47,400	10 308	8 325				
47,400	47,450	10 322	8 339				
47,450	47,500	10 336	8,353				
47,500	47,550	10 350	8 367				
47,550	47,600	10 364	8 381				
47,600	47,650	10 378	8 395				
47,650	47,700	10 392	8 409				
47,700	47,750	10 406	8 423				
47,750	47,800	10 420	8 437				
47,800	47,850	10 434	8 451				
47,850	47,900	10 448	8 465				
47,900	47,950	10 462	8 479				
47,950	48,000	10 476	8 493				

$50,000 or over— use Form 1040

© 1983, 1996 Instructional Horizons. Produced and Distributed by J. Weston Walch, Publisher, Portland, Maine 04104-0658

34. Income Tax

- **Extra Solved Example 1:**

Beatrice is married but separated from her husband. She has no children or other dependents. Last year she earned $21,445.58 as a hairdresser. She also received $62.50 in interest from a savings account and $85.50 in dividends from stocks. She had no other income, but she contributed $500 to her IRA plan. Her employer deducted $2682.00.

Solution:

Begin by completing the information requested at the top of the form: name and address (or attach the IRS mailing label), Social Security number, a choice about contributing to the Presidential Campaign Fund, marital status, and number of exemptions. Notice that Beatrice is married, but is filing a separate return (Line 3) and claiming only herself as an exemption (Line 6a). Thus, she should enter the number 1 on Line 6e.

Line 7:   Beatrice's wages of $21,445.58 go here.

Line 8a: Her savings account interest of $62.50 goes here.

Line 9:   The dividends from her stocks of $85.50 go here.

Lines 10, 11, 12, and 13:   Beatrice has nothing to enter on these lines.

Line 14: $21,445.58 + $62.50 + $85.50 = $21,593.58

Line 15a: Beatrice's IRA deduction of $500.00 goes here and on Line 15c.

Line 16: $21,593.58 – $500.00 = $21,093.58

Line 17:   [The same as Line 16]: $21,093.58

Line 18:   Nothing of these categories applies to Beatrice.

Line 19:   Beatrice qualifies for a $3175 deduction here.

Line 20: $21,093.58 – $3175.00 = $17,918.58

Line 21:   Beatrice has one exemption, so she enters $2450 here.

Line 22: $17,918.58 – $2450.00 = $15,468.58

Line 23:   From the tax tables, Beatrice owes $2321 in taxes.

Line 24:   Nothing to be entered here

Line 25: $2321

Line 26:   Nothing to be entered here

Line 27: $2321

Line 28a: $2682 [Nothing on Lines 28b or 28c]

Line 28d: $2682

Line 29: $361.00

Line 30: $361.00

Beatrice has overpaid her taxes by $361 and will be refunded that amount by the IRS.

At the end of the page, Beatrice must sign and date her return and state her occupation.

34. Income Tax

Form **1040A**	Department of the Treasury—Internal Revenue Service **U.S. Individual Income Tax Return** (T) 1994		IRS Use Only—Do not write or staple in this space.

Label
(See page 16)

Use the IRS label Otherwise please print or type

L A B E L H E R E

Your first name and initial: Beatrice C. Last name: Vandalia

If a joint return, spouse's first name and initial Last name

Home address (number and street). If you have a P O box, see page 17: 309A Applevine Way   Apt no

City town or post office state and ZIP code. If you have a foreign address, see page 17: Dartsworth AZ 88204

OMB No 1545-0085

Your social security number: 368 :35 :45Y8

Spouse's social security number: 415 :55 :55W5

For Privacy Act and Paperwork Reduction Act Notice, see page 4.

Presidential Election Campaign Fund (See page 17)
Do you want $3 to go to this fund? . . Yes [X] No [ ]
If a joint return, does your spouse want $3 to go to this fund? . .

Note: Checking "Yes" will not change your tax or reduce your refund.

Check the box for your filing status
(See page 17)
Check only one box

1 [ ] Single
2 [ ] Married filing joint return (even if only one had income)
3 [X] Married filing separate return Enter spouse's social security number above and full name here. ▶ Andrew R. Vandalia 415-55-55W5
4 [ ] Head of household (with qualifying person) (See page 18) If the qualifying person is a child but not your dependent, enter this child's name here ▶
5 [ ] Qualifying widow(er) with dependent child (year spouse died ▶ 19   ). (See page 19.)

Figure your exemptions
(See page 20)

If more than seven dependents, see page 23

6a [X] Yourself. If your parent (or someone else) can claim you as a dependent on his or her tax return, do not check box 6a. But be sure to check the box on line 18b on page 2

b [ ] Spouse

c Dependents:

(1) Name (first, initial, and last name)	(2) Check if under age 1	(3) If age 1 or older, dependent's social security number	(4) Dependent's relationship to you	(5) No of months lived in your home in 1994
		:		
		:		
		:		
		:		
		:		

No. of boxes checked on 6a and 6b: 1

No. of your children on 6c who:
• lived with you
• didn't live with you due to divorce or separation (see page 23)

Dependents on 6c not entered above

d If your child didn't live with you but is claimed as your dependent under a pre-1985 agreement, check here . . . ▶ [ ]

e Total number of exemptions claimed.

Add numbers entered on lines above: 1

Figure your total income

Attach Copy B of your Forms W-2 and 1099-R here

If you didn't get a W-2 see page 25

Enclose, but do not attach, any payment with your return

7	Wages, salaries, tips, etc. This should be shown in box 1 of your W-2 form(s). Attach Form(s) W-2.	7	21,445	58
8a	**Taxable** interest income (see page 25). If over $400, attach Schedule 1.	8a	62	50
b	Tax-exempt interest. DO NOT include on line 8a. 8b			
9	Dividends. If over $400, attach Schedule 1.	9	85	50
10a	Total IRA distributions. 10a	10b Taxable amount (see page 26). 10b	-0-	
11a	Total pensions and annuities. 11a	11b Taxable amount (see page 27). 11b	-0-	
12	Unemployment compensation (see page 30).	12	-0-	
13a	Social security benefits. 13a	13b Taxable amount (see page 31). 13b	-0-	
14	Add lines 7 through 13b (far right column). This is your **total income**. ▶	14	21,593	58

Figure your adjusted gross income

15a	Your IRA deduction (see page 34). 15a 500 00			
b	Spouse's IRA deduction (see page 34). 15b			
c	Add lines 15a and 15b. These are your **total adjustments**.	15c	500	00
16	Subtract line 15c from line 14. This is your **adjusted gross income**. If less than $25,296 and a child lived with you (less than $9,000 if a child didn't live with you), see "Earned income credit" on page 44. ▶	16	21,093	58

Cat No 11327A   1994 Form 1040A page 1

Consumer Math Success Kit

34. Income Tax

1994 Form 1040A page 2

Figure your standard deduction, exemption amount, and taxable income	**17** Enter the amount from line 16.	**17**	21,093 │ 58

18a Check if: ☐ You were 65 or older   ☐ Blind   **Enter number of boxes checked ▶**   **18a** | 0

      ☐ Spouse was 65 or older   ☐ Blind

  b If your parent (or someone else) can claim you as a dependent, check here . . . . ▶ **18b** ☐

  c If you are married filing separately and your spouse files Form 1040 and itemizes deductions, see page 38 and check here. ▶ **18c** ☐

19 Enter the **standard deduction** shown below for your filing status **But if you checked any box on line 18a or b,** go to page 38 to find your standard deduction. **If you checked box 18c,** enter -0-.

    • Single—$3,800   • Married filing jointly or Qualifying widow(er)—$6,350

    • Head of household—$5,600   • Married filing separately—$3,175   **19** | 3,175 │ 00

20 Subtract line 19 from line 17. If line 19 is more than line 17, enter -0-.	**20**	17,918 │ 58
21 Multiply $2,450 by the total number of exemptions claimed on line 6e.	**21**	2,450 │ 00
22 Subtract line 21 from line 20. If line 21 is more than line 20, enter -0-. This is your **taxable income.** ▶	**22**	15,468 │ 58

Figure your tax, credits, and payments If you want the IRS to figure your tax, see the instructions for line 22 on page 39	**23** Find the tax on the amount on line 22. Check if from: ☒ Tax Table (pages 62–67) or ☐ Form 8615 (see page 40).	**23**	2,321 │ 00

24a Credit for child and dependent care expenses. Attach Schedule 2.   **24a**

  b Credit for the elderly or the disabled. Attach Schedule 3.   **24b**

c Add lines 24a and 24b. These are your **total credits.**	**24c**	-0-	
25 Subtract line 24c from line 23. If line 24c is more than line 23, enter -0-.	**25**	2,321 │ 00
26 Advance earned income credit payments from Form W-2.	**26**	-0-	
27 Add lines 25 and 26. This is your **total tax.** ▶	**27**	2,321 │ 00

28a Total Federal income tax withheld. If any tax is from Form(s) 1099, check here. ▶ ☐   **28a** | 2,682 │ 00

  b 1994 estimated tax payments and amount applied from 1993 return.   **28b**

  c **Earned income credit.** If required, attach Schedule EIC (see page 44).   **28c**

     Nontaxable earned income: amount ▶   and type ▶

d Add lines 28a, 28b, and 28c (don't include nontaxable earned income). These are your **total payments.** ▶	**28d**	2,682 │ 00

Figure your refund or amount you owe	**29** If line 28d is more than line 27, subtract line 27 from line 28d. This is the amount you **overpaid.**	**29**	361 │ 00
	30 Amount of line 29 you want **refunded to you.**	**30**	361 │ 00

31 Amount of line 29 you want **applied to your 1995 estimated tax.**   **31**

32 If line 27 is more than line 28d, subtract line 28d from line 27 This is the **amount you owe.** For details on how to pay, including what to write on your payment, see page 52.   **32**

33 Estimated tax penalty (see page 52). Also, include on line 32.   **33**

Sign your return Keep a copy of this return for your records.	Under penalties of perjury, I declare that I have examined this return and accompanying schedules and statements, and to the best of my knowledge and belief, they are true, correct, and accurately list all amounts and sources of income I received during the tax year Declaration of preparer (other than the taxpayer) is based on all information of which the preparer has any knowledge

Your signature   *[signature]*   Date   04/18/95   Your occupation

Spouse's signature If joint return, BOTH must sign   Date   Spouse's occupation

Paid preparer's use only	Preparer's signature ▶ Date Check if self-employed ☐ Preparer's social security no
	Firm's name (or yours if self-employed) and address ▶ E.I. No. ZIP code

✿ Printed on recycled paper   1994 Form 1040A page 2

34. Income Tax

Section 5—1994 Tax Table

For persons with taxable incomes of less than $50,000

Example Mr and Mrs Green are filing a joint return Their taxable income on line 22 of Form 1040A is $23,250 First, they find the $23,250–23,300 income line Next, they find the column for married filing jointly and read down the column The amount shown where the income line and filing status column meet is $3,491 This is the tax amount they must enter on line 23 of Form 1040A

At least	But less than	Single	Married filing jointly	Married filing separately	Head of a household
			Your tax is—		
23,200	23,250	3,546	3,484	4,033	3,484
23,250	23,300	3,560	(3,491)	4,047	3,491
23,300	23,350	3 574	3 499	4 061	3 499
23,350	23,400	3,588	3,506	4,075	3,506

At least	But less than	Single	Married filing jointly	Married filing separately	Head of a house-hold
			Your tax is—		
0	5	0	0	0	0
5	15	2	2	2	2
15	25	3	3	3	3
25	50	6	6	6	6
50	75	9	9	9	9
75	100	13	13	13	13
100	125	17	17	17	17
125	150	21	21	21	21
150	175	24	24	24	24
175	200	28	28	28	28
200	225	32	32	32	32
225	250	36	36	36	36
250	275	39	39	39	39
275	300	43	43	43	43
300	325	47	47	47	47
325	350	51	51	51	51
350	375	54	54	54	54
375	400	58	58	58	58
400	425	62	62	62	62
425	450	66	66	66	66
450	475	69	69	69	69
475	500	73	73	73	73
500	525	77	77	77	77
525	550	81	81	81	81
550	575	84	84	84	84
575	600	88	88	88	88
600	625	92	92	92	92
625	650	96	96	96	96
650	675	99	99	99	99
675	700	103	103	103	103
700	725	107	107	107	107
725	750	111	111	111	111
750	775	114	114	114	114
775	800	118	118	118	118
800	825	122	122	122	122
825	850	126	126	126	126
850	875	129	129	129	129
875	900	133	133	133	133
900	925	137	137	137	137
925	950	141	141	141	141
950	975	144	144	144	144
975	1,000	148	148	148	148

1,000

At least	But less than	Single	Married filing jointly	Married filing separately	Head of a house-hold
1,000	1,025	152	152	152	152
1,025	1,050	156	156	156	156
1,050	1,075	159	159	159	159
1,075	1,100	163	163	163	163
1,100	1,125	167	167	167	167
1,125	1,150	171	171	171	171
1,150	1,175	174	174	174	174
1,175	1,200	178	178	178	178
1,200	1,225	182	182	182	182
1,225	1,250	186	186	186	186
1,250	1,275	189	189	189	189
1,275	1,300	193	193	193	193

At least	But less than	Single	Married filing jointly	Married filing separately	Head of a house-hold
			Your tax is—		
1,300	1,325	197	197	197	197
1,325	1,350	201	201	201	201
1,350	1,375	204	204	204	204
1,375	1,400	208	208	208	208
1,400	1,425	212	212	212	212
1,425	1,450	216	216	216	216
1,450	1,475	219	219	219	219
1,475	1,500	223	223	223	223
1,500	1,525	227	227	227	227
1,525	1,550	231	231	231	231
1,550	1,575	234	234	234	234
1,575	1,600	238	238	238	238
1,600	1,625	242	242	242	242
1,625	1,650	246	246	246	246
1,650	1,675	249	249	249	249
1,675	1,700	253	253	253	253
1,700	1,725	257	257	257	257
1,725	1,750	261	261	261	261
1,750	1,775	264	264	264	264
1,775	1,800	268	268	268	268
1,800	1,825	272	272	272	272
1,825	1,850	276	276	276	276
1,850	1,875	279	279	279	279
1,875	1,900	283	283	283	283
1,900	1,925	287	287	287	287
1,925	1,950	291	291	291	291
1,950	1,975	294	294	294	294
1,975	2,000	298	298	298	298

2,000

At least	But less than	Single	Married filing jointly	Married filing separately	Head of a house-hold
2,000	2,025	302	302	302	302
2,025	2,050	306	306	306	306
2,050	2,075	309	309	309	309
2,075	2,100	313	313	313	313
2,100	2,125	317	317	317	317
2,125	2,150	321	321	321	321
2,150	2,175	324	324	324	324
2,175	2,200	328	328	328	328
2,200	2,225	332	332	332	332
2,225	2,250	336	336	336	336
2,250	2,275	339	339	339	339
2,275	2,300	343	343	343	343
2,300	2,325	347	347	347	347
2,325	2,350	351	351	351	351
2,350	2,375	354	354	354	354
2,375	2,400	358	358	358	358
2,400	2,425	362	362	362	362
2,425	2,450	366	366	366	366
2,450	2,475	369	369	369	369
2,475	2,500	373	373	373	373
2,500	2,525	377	377	377	377
2,525	2,550	381	381	381	381
2,550	2,575	384	384	384	384
2,575	2,600	388	388	388	388
2,600	2,625	392	392	392	392
2,625	2,650	396	396	396	396
2,650	2,675	399	399	399	399
2,675	2,700	403	403	403	403

At least	But less than	Single	Married filing jointly	Married filing separately	Head of a house-hold
			Your tax is—		
2,700	2,725	407	407	407	407
2,725	2,750	411	411	411	411
2,750	2,775	414	414	414	414
2,775	2,800	418	418	418	418
2,800	2,825	422	422	422	422
2,825	2,850	426	426	426	426
2,850	2,875	429	429	429	429
2,875	2,900	433	433	433	433
2,900	2,925	437	437	437	437
2,925	2,950	441	441	441	441
2,950	2,975	444	444	444	444
2,975	3,000	448	448	448	448

3,000

At least	But less than	Single	Married filing jointly	Married filing separately	Head of a house-hold
3,000	3,050	454	454	454	454
3,050	3,100	461	461	461	461
3,100	3,150	469	469	469	469
3,150	3,200	476	476	476	476
3,200	3,250	484	484	484	484
3,250	3,300	491	491	491	491
3,300	3,350	499	499	499	499
3,350	3,400	506	506	506	506
3,400	3,450	514	514	514	514
3,450	3,500	521	521	521	521
3,500	3,550	529	529	529	529
3,550	3,600	536	536	536	536
3,600	3,650	544	544	544	544
3,650	3,700	551	551	551	551
3,700	3,750	559	559	559	559
3,750	3,800	566	566	566	566
3,800	3,850	574	574	574	574
3,850	3,900	581	581	581	581
3,900	3,950	589	589	589	589
3,950	4,000	596	596	596	596

4,000

At least	But less than	Single	Married filing jointly	Married filing separately	Head of a house-hold
4,000	4,050	604	604	604	604
4,050	4,100	611	611	611	611
4,100	4,150	619	619	619	619
4,150	4,200	626	626	626	626
4,200	4,250	634	634	634	634
4,250	4,300	641	641	641	641
4,300	4,350	649	649	649	649
4,350	4,400	656	656	656	656
4,400	4,450	664	664	664	664
4,450	4,500	671	671	671	671
4,500	4,550	679	679	679	679
4,550	4,600	686	686	686	686
4,600	4,650	694	694	694	694
4,650	4,700	701	701	701	701
4,700	4,750	709	709	709	709
4,750	4,800	716	716	716	716
4,800	4,850	724	724	724	724
4,850	4,900	731	731	731	731
4,900	4,950	739	739	739	739
4,950	5,000	746	746	746	746

Continued on next page

This column must also be used by a qualifying widow(er)

© 1983, 1996 Instructional Horizons. Produced and Distributed by J. Weston Walch, Publisher, Portland, Maine 04104-0658   157   Consumer Math Success Kit

34. Income Tax

1994 Tax Table—*Continued*

If Form 1040A, line 22, is—		And you are—				If Form 1040A, line 22, is—		And you are—				If Form 1040A, line 22, is—		And you are—			
At least	But less than	Single	Married filing jointly	Married filing separately	Head of a household	At least	But less than	Single	Married filing jointly	Married filing separately	Head of a household	At least	But less than	Single	Married filing jointly	Married filing separately	Head of a household
		Your tax is—						Your tax is—						Your tax is—			
5,000						**8,000**						**11,000**					
5,000	5,050	754	754	754	754	8,000	8,050	1 204	1 204	1 204	1,204	11,000	11,050	1 654	1 654	1 654	1 654
5,050	5,100	761	761	761	761	8,050	8,100	1 211	1 211	1 211	1,211	11,050	11,100	1 661	1 661	1 661	1 661
5,100	5,150	769	769	769	769	8,100	8,150	1 219	1 219	1 219	1 219	11,100	11,150	1 669	1 669	1 669	1 669
5,150	5,200	776	776	776	776	8,150	8,200	1 226	1 226	1 226	1 226	11,150	11,200	1 676	1 676	1 676	1 676
5,200	5,250	784	784	784	784	8,200	8,250	1 234	1 234	1 234	1 234	11,200	11,250	1 684	1 684	1 684	1 684
5,250	5,300	791	791	791	791	8,250	8,300	1 241	1 241	1 241	1 241	11,250	11,300	1 691	1 691	1 691	1 691
5,300	5,350	799	799	799	799	8,300	8,350	1 249	1 249	1 249	1 249	11,300	11,350	1 699	1 699	1 699	1 699
5,350	5,400	806	806	806	806	8,350	8,400	1 256	1 256	1 256	1 256	11,350	11,400	1 706	1 706	1 706	1 706
5,400	5,450	814	814	814	814	8,400	8,450	1 264	1 264	1 264	1 264	11,400	11,450	1 714	1 714	1 714	1 714
5,450	5,500	821	821	821	821	8,450	8,500	1 271	1 271	1 271	1 271	11,450	11,500	1 721	1 721	1 721	1 721
5,500	5,550	829	829	829	829	8,500	8,550	1 279	1 279	1 279	1 279	11,500	11,550	1 729	1 729	1 729	1 729
5,550	5,600	836	836	836	836	8,550	8,600	1 286	1 286	1,286	1 286	11,550	11,600	1 736	1 736	1 736	1 736
5,600	5,650	844	844	844	844	8,600	8,650	1 294	1 294	1 294	1 294	11,600	11,650	1 744	1 744	1 744	1 744
5,650	5,700	851	851	851	851	8,650	8,700	1 301	1 301	1 301	1 301	11,650	11,700	1 751	1 751	1 751	1 751
5,700	5,750	859	859	859	859	8,700	8,750	1 309	1 309	1 309	1 309	11,700	11,750	1 759	1 759	1 759	1 759
5,750	5,800	866	866	866	866	8,750	8,800	1,316	1 316	1,316	1 316	11,750	11,800	1 766	1 766	1 766	1 766
5,800	5,850	874	874	874	874	8,800	8,850	1 324	1 324	1 324	1,324	11,800	11,850	1 774	1 774	1 774	1 774
5,850	5,900	881	881	881	881	8,850	8,900	1 331	1 331	1,331	1,331	11,850	11,900	1 781	1 781	1 781	1 781
5,900	5,950	889	889	889	889	8,900	8,950	1,339	1 339	1,339	1 339	11,900	11,950	1 789	1 789	1 789	1 789
5,950	6,000	896	896	896	896	8,950	9,000	1 346	1 346	1,346	1,346	11,950	12,000	1 796	1 796	1 796	1 796
6,000						**9,000**						**12,000**					
6,000	6,050	904	904	904	904	9,000	9,050	1 354	1 354	1 354	1 354	12,000	12,050	1 804	1 804	1 804	1 804
6,050	6,100	911	911	911	911	9,050	9,100	1 361	1 361	1 361	1 361	12,050	12,100	1 811	1 811	1 811	1 811
6,100	6,150	919	919	919	919	9,100	9,150	1 369	1 369	1 369	1 369	12,100	12,150	1 819	1 819	1 819	1 819
6,150	6,200	926	926	926	926	9,150	9,200	1 376	1 376	1,376	1 376	12,150	12,200	1 826	1 826	1 826	1 826
6,200	6,250	934	934	934	934	9,200	9,250	1 384	1 384	1 384	1 384	12,200	12,250	1 834	1 834	1 834	1 834
6,250	6,300	941	941	941	941	9,250	9,300	1 391	1 391	1 391	1,391	12,250	12,300	1 841	1 841	1 841	1 841
6,300	6,350	949	949	949	949	9,300	9,350	1 399	1 399	1 399	1 399	12,300	12,350	1 849	1 849	1 849	1 849
6,350	6,400	956	956	956	956	9,350	9,400	1 406	1 406	1 406	1 406	12,350	12,400	1 856	1 856	1 856	1 856
6,400	6,450	964	964	964	964	9,400	9,450	1 414	1 414	1 414	1,414	12,400	12,450	1 864	1 864	1 864	1 864
6,450	6,500	971	971	971	971	9,450	9,500	1 421	1 421	1,421	1 421	12,450	12,500	1 871	1 871	1 871	1 871
6,500	6,550	979	979	979	979	9,500	9,550	1 429	1 429	1 429	1,429	12,500	12,550	1 879	1 879	1 879	1 879
6,550	6,600	986	986	986	986	9,550	9,600	1 436	1 436	1,436	1,436	12,550	12,600	1 886	1 886	1 886	1 886
6,600	6,650	994	994	994	994	9,600	9,650	1 444	1 444	1,444	1 444	12,600	12,650	1 894	1 894	1 894	1,894
6,650	6,700	1 001	1 001	1,001	1,001	9,650	9,700	1,451	1 451	1 451	1 451	12,650	12,700	1 901	1 901	1 901	1 901
6,700	6,750	1,009	1,009	1 009	1,009	9,700	9,750	1,459	1 459	1 459	1 459	12,700	12,750	1 909	1 909	1 909	1 909
6,750	6,800	1,016	1,016	1,016	1,016	9,750	9,800	1 466	1 466	1,466	1 466	12,750	12,800	1 916	1 916	1 916	1 916
6,800	6,850	1,024	1 024	1 024	1 024	9,800	9,850	1 474	1 474	1 474	1,474	12,800	12,850	1 924	1 924	1 924	1 924
6,850	6,900	1 031	1,031	1,031	1 031	9,850	9,900	1 481	1 481	1 481	1 481	12,850	12,900	1 931	1 931	1 931	1 931
6,900	6,950	1 039	1,039	1,039	1,039	9,900	9,950	1 489	1 489	1 489	1 489	12,900	12,950	1 939	1 939	1 939	1 939
6,950	7,000	1,046	1 046	1,046	1,046	9,950	10,000	1 496	1 496	1 496	1,496	12,950	13,000	1 946	1 946	1 946	1 946
7,000						**10,000**						**13,000**					
7,000	7,050	1 054	1 054	1,054	1,054	10,000	10,050	1,504	1 504	1 504	1 504	13,000	13,050	1 954	1 954	1 954	1 954
7,050	7,100	1 061	1 061	1,061	1,061	10,050	10,100	1 511	1 511	1 511	1,511	13,050	13,100	1 961	1 961	1 961	1 961
7,100	7,150	1 069	1 069	1,069	1,069	10,100	10,150	1 519	1 519	1 519	1 519	13,100	13,150	1 969	1 969	1 969	1 969
7,150	7,200	1,076	1,076	1,076	1,076	10,150	10,200	1 526	1 526	1,526	1 526	13,150	13,200	1 976	1 976	1 976	1,976
7,200	7,250	1 084	1 084	1 084	1,084	10,200	10,250	1 534	1 534	1,534	1 534	13,200	13,250	1 984	1 984	1 984	1 984
7,250	7,300	1 091	1 091	1 091	1 091	10,250	10,300	1 541	1 541	1 541	1 541	13,250	13,300	1 991	1 991	1 991	1 991
7,300	7,350	1,099	1 099	1,099	1,099	10,300	10,350	1 549	1 549	1 549	1 549	13,300	13,350	1 999	1 999	1 999	1 999
7,350	7,400	1 106	1 106	1,106	1,106	10,350	10,400	1 556	1 556	1 556	1 556	13,350	13,400	2 006	2 006	2 006	2 006
7,400	7,450	1 114	1 114	1 114	1,114	10,400	10,450	1 564	1 564	1 564	1,564	13,400	13,450	2 014	2 014	2 014	2 014
7,450	7,500	1 121	1 121	1,121	1,121	10,450	10,500	1 571	1 571	1 571	1 571	13,450	13,500	2 021	2 021	2 021	2 021
7,500	7,550	1 129	1 129	1 129	1,129	10,500	10,550	1 579	1 579	1 579	1 579	13,500	13,550	2 029	2 029	2 029	2 029
7,550	7,600	1,136	1 136	1,136	1,136	10,550	10,600	1,586	1 586	1 586	1 586	13,550	13,600	2 036	2 036	2 036	2 036
7,600	7,650	1 144	1 144	1 144	1,144	10,600	10,650	1 594	1 594	1 594	1 594	13,600	13,650	2 044	2 044	2 044	2 044
7,650	7,700	1 151	1 151	1 151	1,151	10,650	10,700	1 601	1 601	1 601	1 601	13,650	13,700	2 051	2 051	2 051	2 051
7,700	7,750	1,159	1 159	1,159	1,159	10,700	10,750	1 609	1 609	1,609	1 609	13,700	13,750	2 059	2 059	2 059	2 059
7,750	7,800	1 166	1 166	1 166	1 166	10,750	10,800	1 616	1 616	1,616	1 616	13,750	13,800	2 066	2 066	2 066	2 066
7,800	7,850	1 174	1 174	1,174	1,174	10,800	10,850	1 624	1 624	1,624	1 624	13,800	13,850	2 074	2 074	2 074	2 074
7,850	7,900	1 181	1 181	1 181	1 181	10,850	10,900	1 631	1 631	1 631	1 631	13,850	13,900	2 081	2 081	2 081	2 081
7,900	7,950	1 189	1 189	1 189	1 189	10,900	10,950	1 639	1 639	1 639	1 639	13,900	13,950	2 089	2 089	2 089	2 089
7,950	8,000	1 196	1 196	1 196	1 196	10,950	11,000	1 646	1 646	1 646	1 646	13,950	14,000	2 096	2 096	2 096	2 096

This column must also be used by a qualifying widow(er)   Continued on next page

© 1983, 1996 Instructional Horizons. Produced and Distributed by J. Weston Walch, Publisher, Portland, Maine 04104-0658

34. Income Tax

1994 Tax Table—Continued

If Form 1040A, line 22, is—		And you are—			
At least	But less than	Single	Married filing jointly	Married filing separately	Head of a household
				Your tax is—	
14,000					
14,000	14,050	2 104	2 104	2 104	2 104
14,050	14,100	2 111	2 111	2 111	2 111
14,100	14,150	2 119	2 119	2 119	2 119
14,150	14,200	2 126	2 126	2 126	2 126
14,200	14,250	2 134	2 134	2 134	2 134
14,250	14,300	2 141	2 141	2 141	2 141
14,300	14,350	2 149	2 149	2 149	2,149
14,350	14,400	2 156	2 156	2 156	2 156
14,400	14,450	2 164	2 164	2 164	2 164
14,450	14,500	2 171	2,171	2,171	2 171
14,500	14,550	2 179	2 179	2 179	2,179
14,550	14,600	2 186	2 186	2 186	2 186
14,600	14,650	2 194	2 194	2 194	2 194
14,650	14,700	2 201	2 201	2 201	2 201
14,700	14,750	2 209	2,209	2 209	2 209
14,750	14,800	2,216	2 216	2 216	2 216
14,800	14,850	2 224	2 224	2 224	2 224
14,850	14,900	2 231	2 231	2 231	2,231
14,900	14,950	2,239	2 239	2 239	2,239
14,950	15,000	2 246	2 246	2 246	2 246
15,000					
15,000	15,050	2 254	2 254	2 254	2 254
15,050	15,100	2 261	2,261	2 261	2 261
15,100	15,150	2 269	2 269	2 269	2 269
15,150	15,200	2,276	2 276	2 276	2 276
15,200	15,250	2 284	2 284	2 284	2 284
15,250	15,300	2 291	2 291	2 291	2,291
15,300	15,350	2 299	2 299	2,299	2 299
15,350	15,400	2 306	2 306	2 306	2 306
15,400	15,450	2 314	2 314	2 314	2 314
15,450	15,500	2 321	2 321	2 321	2 321
15,500	15,550	2 329	2 329	2 329	2 329
15,550	15,600	2 336	2 336	2 336	2 336
15,600	15,650	2 344	2 344	2 344	2 344
15,650	15,700	2 351	2 351	2 351	2 351
15,700	15,750	2 359	2 359	2 359	2 359
15,750	15,800	2 366	2 366	2 366	2 366
15,800	15,850	2 374	2 374	2 374	2 374
15,850	15,900	2 381	2 381	2 381	2 381
15,900	15,950	2 389	2 389	2 389	2 389
15,950	16,000	2 396	2 396	2 396	2 396
16,000					
16,000	16,050	2 404	2 404	2 404	2 404
16,050	16,100	2 411	2 411	2 411	2 411
16,100	16,150	2 419	2 419	2 419	2 419
16,150	16,200	2 426	2 426	2 426	2 426
16,200	16,250	2 434	2 434	2 434	2 434
16,250	16,300	2 441	2 441	2 441	2 441
16,300	16,350	2 449	2 449	2 449	2 449
16,350	16,400	2 456	2 456	2 456	2 456
16,400	16,450	2 464	2 464	2 464	2 464
16,450	16,500	2 471	2 471	2 471	2 471
16,500	16,550	2 479	2 479	2 479	2 479
16,550	16,600	2 486	2 486	2 486	2 486
16,600	16,650	2 494	2 494	2 494	2 494
16,650	16,700	2 501	2 501	2 501	2 501
16,700	16,750	2 509	2 509	2,509	2 509
16,750	16,800	2 516	2 516	2 516	2 516
16,800	16,850	2 524	2 524	2 524	2 524
16,850	16,900	2 531	2 531	2 531	2 531
16,900	16,950	2 539	2 539	2 539	2 539
16,950	17,000	2 546	2 546	2 546	2 546

If Form 1040A, line 22, is—		And you are—			
At least	But less than	Single	Married filing jointly	Married filing separately	Head of a household
				Your tax is—	
17,000					
17,000	17,050	2 554	2 554	2 554	2 554
17,050	17,100	2 561	2 561	2 561	2 561
17,100	17,150	2 569	2 569	2 569	2 569
17,150	17,200	2 576	2 576	2 576	2 576
17,200	17,250	2 584	2 584	2 584	2 584
17,250	17,300	2 591	2 591	2 591	2 591
17,300	17,350	2 599	2 599	2 599	2 599
17,350	17,400	2 606	2 606	2 606	2 606
17,400	17,450	2 614	2 614	2 614	2 614
17,450	17,500	2 621	2 621	2,621	2 621
17,500	17,550	2 629	2 629	2 629	2 629
17,550	17,600	2,636	2 636	2 636	2 636
17,600	17,650	2 644	2 644	2 644	2 644
17,650	17,700	2,651	2 651	2 651	2 651
17,700	17,750	2 659	2 659	2 659	2,659
17,750	17,800	2 666	2 666	2 666	2 666
17,800	17,850	2 674	2 674	2 674	2 674
17,850	17,900	2 681	2 681	2 681	2,681
17,900	17,950	2 689	2 689	2 689	2 689
17,950	18,000	2 696	2 696	2 696	2 696
18,000					
18,000	18,050	2 704	2 704	2 704	2 704
18,050	18,100	2 711	2 711	2 711	2 711
18,100	18,150	2 719	2 719	2 719	2 719
18,150	18,200	2 726	2 726	2 726	2 726
18,200	18,250	2 734	2 734	2 734	2 734
18,250	18,300	2 741	2 741	2 741	2 741
18,300	18,350	2 749	2 749	2 749	2 749
18,350	18,400	2 756	2 756	2 756	2 756
18,400	18,450	2 764	2 764	2 764	2 764
18,450	18,500	2 771	2 771	2 771	2 771
18,500	18,550	2 779	2 779	2 779	2 779
18,550	18,600	2 786	2 786	2 786	2 786
18,600	18,650	2 794	2 794	2 794	2 794
18,650	18,700	2 801	2 801	2 801	2 801
18,700	18,750	2 809	2 809	2 809	2 809
18,750	18,800	2 816	2 816	2 816	2 816
18,800	18,850	2 824	2 824	2 824	2 824
18,850	18,900	2 831	2 831	2 831	2 831
18,900	18,950	2 839	2 839	2 839	2 839
18,950	19,000	2 846	2 846	2,846	2 846
19,000					
19,000	19,050	2 854	2 854	2 857	2 854
19,050	19,100	2 861	2 861	2 871	2 861
19,100	19,150	2 869	2 869	2 885	2 869
19,150	19,200	2 876	2 876	2 899	2 876
19,200	19,250	2 884	2 884	2 913	2 884
19,250	19,300	2 891	2 891	2 927	2 891
19,300	19,350	2 899	2 899	2 941	2 899
19,350	19,400	2 906	2 906	2 955	2 906
19,400	19,450	2 914	2 914	2 969	2 914
19,450	19,500	2 921	2 921	2 983	2 921
19,500	19,550	2 929	2 929	2 997	2 929
19,550	19,600	2 936	2 936	3 011	2 936
19,600	19,650	2 944	2 944	3 025	2 944
19,650	19,700	2 951	2 951	3 039	2 951
19,700	19,750	2 959	2 959	3 053	2 959
19,750	19,800	2 966	2 966	3 067	2 966
19,800	19,850	2 974	2 974	3 081	2 974
19,850	19,900	2 981	2 981	3 095	2 981
19,900	19,950	2 989	2 989	3 109	2 989
19,950	20,000	2 996	2 996	3 123	2 996

If Form 1040A, line 22, is—		And you are—			
At least	But less than	Single	Married filing jointly	Married filing separately	Head of a household
				Your tax is—	
20,000					
20,000	20,050	3 004	3 004	3 137	3 004
20,050	20,100	3 011	3 011	3 151	3 011
20,100	20,150	3 019	3 019	3 165	3 019
20,150	20,200	3 026	3 026	3 179	3 026
20,200	20,250	3 034	3 034	3 193	3 034
20,250	20,300	3 041	3 041	3 207	3 041
20,300	20,350	3 049	3 049	3 221	3 049
20,350	20,400	3 056	3 056	3 235	3 056
20,400	20,450	3 064	3 064	3 249	3 064
20,450	20,500	3 071	3 071	3 263	3 071
20,500	20,550	3 079	3 079	3 277	3 079
20,550	20,600	3 086	3 086	3 291	3 086
20,600	20,650	3 094	3 094	3 305	3 094
20,650	20,700	3 101	3 101	3 319	3,101
20,700	20,750	3 109	3,109	3 333	3 109
20,750	20,800	3 116	3,116	3,347	3 116
20,800	20,850	3 124	3 124	3 361	3 124
20,850	20,900	3 131	3 131	3 375	3 131
20,900	20,950	3 139	3 139	3 389	3,139
20,950	21,000	3 146	3 146	3,403	3,146
21,000					
21,000	21,050	3 154	3 154	3 417	3 154
21,050	21,100	3 161	3 161	3 431	3,161
21,100	21,150	3 169	3 169	3 445	3,169
21,150	21,200	3 176	3 176	3,459	3,176
21,200	21,250	3 184	3 184	3 473	3,184
21,250	21,300	3 191	3 191	3 487	3,191
21,300	21,350	3 199	3 199	3 501	3,199
21,350	21,400	3 206	3 206	3 515	3 206
21,400	21,450	3 214	3 214	3 529	3 214
21,450	21,500	3 221	3 221	3 543	3 221
21,500	21,550	3 229	3 229	3 557	3 229
21,550	21,600	3 236	3 236	3 571	3 236
21,600	21,650	3 244	3 244	3 585	3 244
21,650	21,700	3 251	3 251	3 599	3 251
21,700	21,750	3 259	3 259	3 613	3 259
21,750	21,800	3 266	3 266	3 627	3 266
21,800	21,850	3 274	3 274	3 641	3,274
21,850	21,900	3 281	3 281	3 655	3 281
21,900	21,950	3 289	3,289	3 669	3 289
21,950	22,000	3 296	3 296	3 683	3 296
22,000					
22,000	22,050	3 304	3 304	3 697	3 304
22,050	22,100	3 311	3 311	3 711	3 311
22,100	22,150	3 319	3 319	3 725	3 319
22,150	22,200	3 326	3 326	3 739	3,326
22,200	22,250	3 334	3 334	3 753	3 334
22,250	22,300	3 341	3,341	3,767	3 341
22,300	22,350	3 349	3 349	3 781	3 349
22,350	22,400	3 356	3 356	3 795	3 356
22,400	22,450	3 364	3 364	3,809	3 364
22,450	22,500	3 371	3 371	3 823	3 371
22,500	22,550	3 379	3 379	3 837	3,379
22,550	22,600	3 386	3 386	3 851	3 386
22,600	22,650	3 394	3 394	3 865	3 394
22,650	22,700	3 401	3 401	3 879	3 401
22,700	22,750	3 409	3 409	3 893	3 409
22,750	22,800	3 420	3 416	3 907	3 416
22,800	22,850	3 434	3 424	3 921	3 424
22,850	22,900	3 448	3 431	3 935	3 431
22,900	22,950	3 462	3 439	3 949	3 439
22,950	23,000	3 476	3 446	3 963	3 446

This column must also be used by a qualifying widow(er)

Continued on next page

Consumer Math Success Kit

34. Income Tax

1994 Tax Table—Continued

23,000 – 25,950

If Form 1040A, line 22, is— At least	But less than	Single	Married filing jointly	Married filing separately	Head of a household
23,000					
23,000	23,050	3 490	3 454	3,977	3,454
23,050	23,100	3 504	3 461	3 991	3,461
23,100	23,150	3 518	3 469	4,005	3 469
23,150	23,200	3 532	3 476	4,019	3 476
23,200	23,250	3 546	3 484	4,033	3 484
23,250	23,300	3 560	3 491	4,047	3 491
23,300	23,350	3 574	3 499	4,061	3,499
23,350	23,400	3 588	3 506	4,075	3 506
23,400	23,450	3 602	3 514	4,089	3 514
23,450	23,500	3 616	3 521	4,103	3 521
23,500	23,550	3 630	3 529	4,117	3,529
23,550	23,600	3 644	3 536	4,131	3 536
23,600	23,650	3 658	3 544	4,145	3 544
23,650	23,700	3 672	3 551	4,159	3 551
23,700	23,750	3 686	3 559	4,173	3,559
23,750	23,800	3 700	3 566	4,187	3 566
23,800	23,850	3 714	3 574	4,201	3 574
23,850	23,900	3 728	3 581	4,215	3,581
23,900	23,950	3 742	3 589	4,229	3,589
23,950	24,000	3 756	3 596	4,243	3 596
24,000					
24,000	24,050	3 770	3 604	4,257	3 604
24,050	24,100	3 784	3 611	4,271	3 611
24,100	24,150	3 798	3 619	4,285	3 619
24,150	24,200	3 812	3 626	4,299	3 626
24,200	24,250	3 826	3 634	4,313	3 634
24,250	24,300	3 840	3 641	4,327	3 641
24,300	24,350	3 854	3 649	4,341	3,649
24,350	24,400	3 868	3 656	4,355	3 656
24,400	24,450	3 882	3 664	4,369	3 664
24,450	24,500	3 896	3 671	4,383	3,671
24,500	24,550	3 910	3 679	4,397	3,679
24,550	24,600	3 924	3 686	4,411	3 686
24,600	24,650	3,938	3,694	4 425	3 694
24,650	24,700	3 952	3 701	4 439	3 701
24,700	24,750	3 966	3,709	4 453	3,709
24,750	24,800	3 980	3,716	4,467	3,716
24,800	24,850	3 994	3 724	4 481	3,724
24,850	24,900	4 008	3 731	4,495	3,731
24,900	24,950	4 022	3,739	4 509	3 739
24,950	25,000	4,036	3 746	4 523	3 746
25,000					
25,000	25,050	4 050	3 754	4 537	3 754
25,050	25,100	4 064	3 761	4 551	3,761
25,100	25,150	4 078	3 769	4 565	3 769
25,150	25,200	4 092	3 776	4 579	3 776
25,200	25,250	4 106	3 784	4,593	3 784
25,250	25,300	4 120	3 791	4 607	3 791
25,300	25,350	4 134	3 799	4 621	3,799
25,350	25,400	4 148	3 806	4 635	3 806
25,400	25,450	4 162	3 814	4 649	3 814
25,450	25,500	4 176	3 821	4 663	3 821
25,500	25,550	4 190	3 829	4 677	3 829
25,550	25,600	4,204	3 836	4 691	3 836
25,600	25,650	4 218	3 844	4 705	3 844
25,650	25,700	4 232	3 851	4 719	3 851
25,700	25,750	4 246	3 859	4 733	3 859
25,750	25,800	4 260	3 866	4 747	3 866
25,800	25,850	4 274	3 874	4 761	3 874
25,850	25,900	4 288	3 881	4 775	3 881
25,900	25,950	4 302	3 889	4 789	3 889
25,950	26,000	4 316	3 896	4 803	3 896

26,000 – 28,950

If Form 1040A, line 22, is— At least	But less than	Single	Married filing jointly	Married filing separately	Head of a household
26,000					
26,000	26,050	4 330	3 904	4 817	3 904
26,050	26,100	4 344	3 911	4 831	3 911
26,100	26,150	4 358	3 919	4 845	3 919
26,150	26,200	4 372	3 926	4,859	3 926
26,200	26,250	4 386	3 934	4 873	3 934
26,250	26,300	4 400	3 941	4,887	3 941
26,300	26,350	4 414	3 949	4 901	3 949
26,350	26,400	4 428	3 956	4 915	3 956
26,400	26,450	4 442	3 964	4 929	3 964
26,450	26,500	4 456	3 971	4,943	3 971
26,500	26,550	4 470	3 979	4 957	3,979
26,550	26,600	4 484	3 986	4 971	3,986
26,600	26,650	4 498	3 994	4 985	3 994
26,650	26,700	4 512	4 001	4 999	4 001
26,700	26,750	4 526	4 009	5 013	4 009
26,750	26,800	4 540	4 016	5,027	4 016
26,800	26,850	4 554	4 024	5 041	4 024
26,850	26,900	4 568	4 031	5 055	4 031
26,900	26,950	4 582	4 039	5 069	4 039
26,950	27,000	4 596	4 046	5 083	4,046
27,000					
27,000	27,050	4 610	4 054	5 097	4 054
27,050	27,100	4 624	4 061	5 111	4 061
27,100	27,150	4 638	4 069	5 125	4 069
27,150	27,200	4,652	4 076	5,139	4 076
27,200	27,250	4 666	4 084	5 153	4 084
27,250	27,300	4 680	4 091	5 167	4,091
27,300	27,350	4 694	4 099	5,181	4 099
27,350	27,400	4 708	4 106	5,195	4 106
27,400	27,450	4 722	4 114	5 209	4 114
27,450	27,500	4 736	4 121	5,223	4,121
27,500	27,550	4 750	4 129	5 237	4,129
27,550	27,600	4 764	4 136	5 251	4 136
27,600	27,650	4 778	4 144	5 265	4 144
27,650	27,700	4 792	4 151	5,279	4 151
27,700	27,750	4,806	4 159	5 293	4 159
27,750	27,800	4 820	4 166	5 307	4 166
27,800	27,850	4 834	4 174	5 321	4 174
27,850	27,900	4 848	4 181	5 335	4,181
27,900	27,950	4 862	4 189	5 349	4 189
27,950	28,000	4,876	4 196	5 363	4 196
28,000					
28,000	28,050	4 890	4 204	5 377	4 204
28,050	28,100	4 904	4 211	5 391	4 211
28,100	28,150	4 918	4 219	5 405	4 219
28,150	28,200	4 932	4 226	5 419	4 226
28,200	28,250	4 946	4 234	5 433	4 234
28,250	28,300	4 960	4 241	5 447	4 241
28,300	28,350	4 974	4 249	5 461	4 249
28,350	28,400	4 988	4 256	5 475	4 256
28,400	28,450	5 002	4 264	5 489	4 264
28,450	28,500	5 016	4 271	5 503	4 271
28,500	28,550	5 030	4 279	5 517	4 279
28,550	28,600	5 044	4 286	5 531	4 286
28,600	28,650	5 058	4 294	5 545	4 294
28,650	28,700	5 072	4 301	5 559	4 301
28,700	28,750	5 086	4 309	5 573	4 309
28,750	28,800	5 100	4 316	5 587	4 316
28,800	28,850	5 114	4 324	5 601	4 324
28,850	28,900	5 128	4 331	5 615	4 331
28,900	28,950	5 142	4 339	5 629	4 339
28,950	29,000	5 156	4 346	5,643	4 346

29,000 – 31,950

If Form 1040A, line 22, is— At least	But less than	Single	Married filing jointly	Married filing separately	Head of a household
29,000					
29,000	29,050	5 170	4 354	5 657	4 354
29,050	29,100	5 184	4 361	5 671	4 361
29,100	29,150	5 198	4 369	5 685	4 369
29,150	29,200	5 212	4 376	5 699	4 376
29,200	29,250	5 226	4 384	5 713	4 384
29,250	29,300	5 240	4 391	5 727	4 391
29,300	29,350	5 254	4 399	5,741	4 399
29,350	29,400	5 268	4 406	5 755	4 406
29,400	29,450	5 282	4 414	5 769	4 414
29,450	29,500	5 296	4 421	5 783	4 421
29,500	29,550	5 310	4 429	5 797	4 429
29,550	29,600	5 324	4 436	5 811	4 436
29,600	29,650	5 338	4 444	5 825	4 444
29,650	29,700	5 352	4 451	5 839	4 451
29,700	29,750	5 366	4 459	5 853	4 459
29,750	29,800	5 380	4 466	5 867	4 466
29,800	29,850	5 394	4 474	5 881	4,474
29,850	29,900	5 408	4 481	5 895	4,481
29,900	29,950	5 422	4 489	5 909	4 489
29,950	30,000	5 436	4 496	5 923	4,496
30,000					
30,000	30,050	5 450	4 504	5 937	4 504
30,050	30,100	5 464	4 511	5 951	4 511
30,100	30,150	5 478	4 519	5 965	4 519
30,150	30,200	5 492	4,526	5 979	4 526
30,200	30,250	5 506	4 534	5 993	4 534
30,250	30,300	5 520	4 541	6 007	4 541
30,300	30,350	5 534	4 549	6 021	4 549
30,350	30,400	5 548	4 556	6 035	4 556
30,400	30,450	5 562	4 564	6 049	4,564
30,450	30,500	5 576	4 571	6 063	4 571
30,500	30,550	5 590	4 579	6 077	4 582
30,550	30,600	5 604	4 586	6 091	4,596
30,600	30,650	5 618	4 594	6 105	4 610
30,650	30,700	5 632	4 601	6 119	4 624
30,700	30,750	5 646	4 609	6 133	4 638
30,750	30,800	5 660	4 616	6 147	4 652
30,800	30,850	5 674	4 624	6 161	4 666
30,850	30,900	5 688	4 631	6 175	4 680
30,900	30,950	5 702	4 639	6 189	4 694
30,950	31,000	5 716	4 646	6 203	4 708
31,000					
31,000	31,050	5 730	4 654	6 217	4 722
31,050	31,100	5 744	4 661	6 231	4 736
31,100	31,150	5 758	4 669	6 245	4 750
31,150	31,200	5 772	4 676	6 259	4 764
31,200	31,250	5 786	4 684	6 273	4 778
31,250	31,300	5 800	4 691	6 287	4 792
31,300	31,350	5 814	4 699	6 301	4 806
31,350	31,400	5 828	4 706	6 315	4 820
31,400	31,450	5 842	4 714	6 329	4 834
31,450	31,500	5 856	4 721	6 343	4 848
31,500	31,550	5 870	4 729	6 357	4 862
31,550	31,600	5 884	4 736	6 371	4 876
31,600	31,650	5 898	4 744	6 385	4 890
31,650	31,700	5 912	4 751	6 399	4 904
31,700	31,750	5 926	4 759	6 413	4 918
31,750	31,800	5 940	4 766	6 427	4 932
31,800	31,850	5 954	4 774	6 441	4 946
31,850	31,900	5 968	4 781	6 455	4 960
31,900	31,950	5 982	4 789	6 469	4 974
31,950	32,000	5 996	4 796	6 483	4 988

This column must also be used by a qualifying widow(er)

Continued on next page

© 1983, 1996 Instructional Horizons. Produced and Distributed by J. Weston Walch, Publisher, Portland, Maine 04104-0658

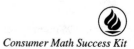

Consumer Math Success Kit

34. Income Tax

1994 Tax Table—Continued

At least	But less than	Single	Married filing jointly	Married filing separately	Head of a household
32,000					
32,000	32,050	6 010	4 804	6 497	5 002
32,050	32,100	6 024	4 811	6 511	5 016
32,100	32,150	6 038	4 819	6 525	5 030
32,150	32,200	6 052	4 826	6 539	5 044
32,200	32,250	6 066	4 834	6 553	5 058
32,250	32,300	6 080	4 841	6 567	5 072
32,300	32,350	6 094	4 849	6 581	5 086
32,350	32,400	6 108	4 856	6 595	5 100
32,400	32,450	6 122	4 864	6 609	5 114
32,450	32,500	6 136	4 871	6 623	5 128
32,500	32,550	6 150	4 879	6 637	5 142
32,550	32,600	6 164	4 886	6 651	5 156
32,600	32,650	6 178	4 894	6 665	5 170
32,650	32,700	6 192	4 901	6 679	5 184
32,700	32,750	6 206	4 909	6 693	5 198
32,750	32,800	6,220	4 916	6 707	5 212
32,800	32,850	6 234	4 924	6 721	5 226
32,850	32,900	6 248	4 931	6 735	5 240
32,900	32,950	6 262	4 939	6 749	5 254
32,950	33,000	6 276	4 946	6 763	5 268
33,000					
33,000	33,050	6 290	4 954	6 777	5 282
33,050	33,100	6 304	4 961	6 791	5 296
33,100	33,150	6 318	4 969	6 805	5 310
33,150	33,200	6 332	4 976	6 819	5 324
33,200	33,250	6 346	4 984	6 833	5 338
33,250	33,300	6 360	4 991	6 847	5 352
33,300	33,350	6 374	4 999	6 861	5 366
33,350	33,400	6 388	5 006	6 875	5 380
33,400	33,450	6 402	5 014	6 889	5 394
33,450	33,500	6 416	5 021	6 903	5 408
33,500	33,550	6 430	5 029	6 917	5 422
33,550	33,600	6 444	5 036	6 931	5 436
33,600	33,650	6 458	5 044	6 945	5 450
33,650	33,700	6 472	5 051	6,959	5 464
33,700	33,750	6 486	5 059	6 973	5 478
33,750	33,800	6 500	5 066	6 987	5 492
33,800	33,850	6 514	5 074	7 001	5 506
33,850	33,900	6 528	5 081	7 015	5 520
33,900	33,950	6 542	5 089	7 029	5 534
33,950	34,000	6 556	5 096	7 043	5 548
34,000					
34,000	34,050	6 570	5 104	7 057	5 562
34,050	34,100	6 584	5 111	7 071	5 576
34,100	34,150	6 598	5 119	7 085	5 590
34,150	34,200	6 612	5 126	7 099	5 604
34,200	34,250	6 626	5 134	7 113	5 618
34,250	34,300	6 640	5 141	7 127	5 632
34,300	34,350	6 654	5 149	7 141	5 646
34,350	34,400	6 668	5 156	7 155	5 660
34,400	34,450	6 682	5 164	7 169	5 674
34,450	34,500	6 696	5 171	7 183	5 688
34,500	34,550	6 710	5 179	7 197	5 702
34,550	34,600	6 724	5 186	7 211	5 716
34,600	34,650	6 738	5 194	7 225	5 730
34,650	34,700	6 752	5 201	7 239	5 744
34,700	34,750	6 766	5 209	7 253	5 758
34,750	34,800	6 780	5 216	7 267	5 772
34,800	34,850	6 794	5 224	7 281	5 786
34,850	34,900	6 808	5 231	7 295	5 800
34,900	34,950	6 822	5 239	7 309	5 814
34,950	35,000	6 836	5 246	7 323	5 828

At least	But less than	Single	Married filing jointly	Married filing separately	Head of a household
35,000					
35,000	35,050	6 850	5 254	7 337	5 842
35,050	35,100	6 864	5 261	7 351	5 856
35,100	35,150	6 878	5 269	7 365	5 870
35,150	35,200	6 892	5 276	7 379	5 884
35,200	35,250	6 906	5 284	7 393	5 898
35,250	35,300	6 920	5 291	7 407	5 912
35,300	35,350	6 934	5 299	7 421	5 926
35,350	35,400	6 948	5 306	7 435	5 940
35,400	35,450	6 962	5 314	7 449	5 954
35,450	35,500	6 976	5 321	7 463	5 968
35,500	35,550	6 990	5 329	7 477	5 982
35,550	35,600	7 004	5 336	7 491	5 996
35,600	35,650	7 018	5 344	7 505	6 010
35,650	35,700	7 032	5 351	7 519	6 024
35,700	35,750	7 046	5 359	7 533	6 038
35,750	35,800	7 060	5 366	7 547	6 052
35,800	35,850	7 074	5 374	7 561	6 066
35,850	35,900	7 088	5 381	7 575	6 080
35,900	35,950	7 102	5 389	7 589	6 094
35,950	36,000	7 116	5 396	7 603	6 108
36,000					
36,000	36,050	7 130	5 404	7 617	6 122
36,050	36,100	7 144	5 411	7 631	6 136
36,100	36,150	7 158	5 419	7 645	6 150
36,150	36,200	7 172	5 426	7 659	6 164
36,200	36,250	7 186	5 434	7 673	6 178
36,250	36,300	7 200	5 441	7 687	6 192
36,300	36,350	7 214	5 449	7 701	6 206
36,350	36,400	7 228	5 456	7 715	6 220
36,400	36,450	7 242	5 464	7 729	6 234
36,450	36,500	7 256	5 471	7 743	6 248
36,500	36,550	7 270	5 479	7 757	6 262
36,550	36,600	7 284	5 486	7 771	6 276
36,600	36,650	7 298	5 494	7 785	6 290
36,650	36,700	7 312	5 501	7 799	6 304
36,700	36,750	7 326	5 509	7 813	6 318
36,750	36,800	7 340	5 516	7 827	6 332
36,800	36,850	7 354	5 524	7 841	6 346
36,850	36,900	7 368	5 531	7 855	6 360
36,900	36,950	7 382	5 539	7 869	6,374
36,950	37,000	7 396	5 546	7 883	6 388
37,000					
37,000	37,050	7 410	5 554	7 897	6 402
37,050	37,100	7 424	5 561	7 911	6 416
37,100	37,150	7 438	5 569	7 925	6 430
37,150	37,200	7 452	5 576	7 939	6 444
37,200	37,250	7 466	5 584	7 953	6 458
37,250	37,300	7 480	5 591	7 967	6 472
37,300	37,350	7 494	5 599	7 981	6 486
37,350	37,400	7 508	5 606	7 995	6 500
37,400	37,450	7 522	5 614	8 009	6 514
37,450	37,500	7 536	5 621	8 023	6 528
37,500	37,550	7 550	5 629	8 037	6 542
37,550	37,600	7 564	5 636	8 051	6 556
37,600	37,650	7 578	5 644	8 065	6 570
37,650	37,700	7 592	5 651	8 079	6 584
37,700	37,750	7 606	5 659	8 093	6 598
37,750	37,800	7 620	5 666	8 107	6 612
37,800	37,850	7 634	5 674	8 121	6 626
37,850	37,900	7 648	5 681	8 135	6 640
37,900	37,950	7 662	5 689	8 149	6 654
37,950	38,000	7 676	5 696	8 163	6 668

At least	But less than	Single	Married filing jointly	Married filing separately	Head of a household
38,000					
38,000	38,050	7 690	5 707	8 177	6 682
38,050	38,100	7,704	5 721	8 191	6 696
38,100	38,150	7 718	5 735	8 205	6 710
38,150	38,200	7 732	5 749	8 219	6 724
38,200	38,250	7 746	5 763	8 233	6 738
38,250	38,300	7 760	5 777	8 247	6 752
38,300	38,350	7 774	5 791	8 261	6 766
38,350	38,400	7 788	5 805	8 275	6 780
38,400	38,450	7 802	5 819	8 289	6 794
38,450	38,500	7 816	5 833	8 303	6 808
38,500	38,550	7 830	5 847	8 317	6 822
38,550	38,600	7 844	5 861	8 331	6 836
38,600	38,650	7 858	5 875	8 345	6 850
38,650	38,700	7 872	5 889	8 359	6 864
38,700	38,750	7 886	5 903	8 373	6 878
38,750	38,800	7 900	5 917	8 387	6 892
38,800	38,850	7 914	5 931	8 401	6 906
38,850	38,900	7 928	5 945	8 415	6 920
38,900	38,950	7 942	5 959	8 429	6 934
38,950	39,000	7 956	5 973	8 443	6 948
39,000					
39,000	39,050	7 970	5 987	8 457	6 962
39,050	39,100	7 984	6 001	8 471	6 976
39,100	39,150	7 998	6 015	8 485	6 990
39,150	39,200	8 012	6 029	8,499	7,004
39,200	39,250	8 026	6 043	8,513	7 018
39,250	39,300	8 040	6 057	8 527	7 032
39,300	39,350	8 054	6 071	8 541	7 046
39,350	39,400	8 068	6 085	8 555	7,060
39,400	39,450	8 082	6 099	8,569	7 074
39,450	39,500	8 096	6 113	8,583	7 088
39,500	39,550	8 110	6 127	8 597	7 102
39,550	39,600	8 124	6 141	8 611	7 116
39,600	39,650	8 138	6 155	8 625	7,130
39,650	39,700	8 152	6 169	8 639	7 144
39,700	39,750	8 166	6 183	8 653	7 158
39,750	39,800	8 180	6 197	8 667	7 172
39,800	39,850	8 194	6 211	8 681	7 186
39,850	39,900	8 208	6 225	8 695	7 200
39,900	39,950	8 222	6 239	8 709	7 214
39,950	40,000	8 236	6 253	8 723	7 228
40,000					
40,000	40,050	8 250	6 267	8 737	7 242
40,050	40,100	8 264	6 281	8 751	7 256
40,100	40,150	8 278	6 295	8 765	7 270
40,150	40,200	8 292	6 309	8 779	7 284
40,200	40,250	8 306	6 323	8 793	7 298
40,250	40,300	8 320	6 337	8 807	7 312
40,300	40,350	8 334	6 351	8 821	7 326
40,350	40,400	8 348	6 365	8 835	7 340
40,400	40,450	8 362	6 379	8 849	7 354
40,450	40,500	8 376	6 393	8 863	7 368
40,500	40,550	8 390	6 407	8 877	7 382
40,550	40,600	8 404	6 421	8 891	7 396
40,600	40,650	8 418	6 435	8 905	7 410
40,650	40,700	8 432	6 449	8 919	7 424
40,700	40,750	8 446	6 463	8 933	7 438
40,750	40,800	8 460	6 477	8 947	7 452
40,800	40,850	8 474	6 491	8 961	7 466
40,850	40,900	8 488	6 505	8 975	7 480
40,900	40,950	8 502	6 519	8 989	7 494
40,950	41,000	8 516	6 533	9 003	7 508

This column must also be used by a qualifying widow(er)

Continued on next page

© 1983, 1996 Instructional Horizons. Produced and Distributed
by J. Weston Walch, Publisher, Portland, Maine 04104-0658

Consumer Math Success Kit

34. Income Tax

1994 Tax Table—*Continued*

If Form 1040A, line 22, is—		And you are—				If Form 1040A, line 22, is—		And you are—				If Form 1040A, line 22, is—		And you are—			
At least	But less than	Single	Married filing jointly	Married filing separately	Head of a house-hold	At least	But less than	Single	Married filing jointly	Married filing separately	Head of a house hold	At least	But less than	Single	Married filing jointly	Married filing sepa rately	Head of a house hold
		Your tax is—						Your tax is—						Your tax is—			
41,000						**44,000**						**47,000**					
41,000	41,050	8 530	6 547	9 017	7 522	44,000	44,050	9 370	7 387	9 857	8 362	47,000	47,050	10 210	8 227	10 730	9 202
41,050	41,100	8 544	6 561	9 031	7 536	44,050	44,100	9 384	7 401	9 871	8 376	47,050	47,100	10 224	8 241	10 746	9 216
41,100	41,150	8 558	6 575	9 045	7 550	44,100	44,150	9 398	7 415	9 885	8 390	47,100	47,150	10 238	8 255	10 761	9 230
41,150	41,200	8 572	6 589	9 059	7 564	44,150	44,200	9 412	7 429	9 899	8 404	47,150	47,200	10 252	8 269	10 777	9 244
41,200	41,250	8 586	6 603	9 073	7 578	44,200	44,250	9 426	7 443	9 913	8 418	47,200	47,250	10 266	8 283	10 792	9 258
41,250	41,300	8 600	6 617	9 087	7 592	44,250	44,300	9 440	7 457	9 927	8 432	47,250	47,300	10 280	8 297	10 808	9 272
41,300	41,350	8 614	6 631	9 101	7 606	44,300	44,350	9 454	7 471	9 941	8 446	47,300	47,350	10 294	8 311	10 823	9 286
41,350	41,400	8 628	6 645	9 115	7 620	44,350	44,400	9 468	7 485	9 955	8 460	47,350	47,400	10 308	8 325	10 839	9 300
41,400	41,450	8 642	6 659	9 129	7 634	44,400	44,450	9 482	7 499	9 969	8 474	47,400	47,450	10 322	8 339	10 854	9 314
41,450	41,500	8 656	6 673	9 143	7 648	44,450	44,500	9 496	7 513	9 983	8 488	47,450	47,500	10 336	8 353	10 870	9 328
41,500	41,550	8 670	6 687	9 157	7 662	44,500	44,550	9 510	7 527	9,997	8 502	47,500	47,550	10 350	8 367	10 885	9 342
41,550	41,600	8 684	6 701	9 171	7 676	44,550	44,600	9 524	7 541	10 011	8 516	47,550	47,600	10 364	8 381	10 901	9 356
41,600	41,650	8 698	6 715	9 185	7 690	44,600	44,650	9 538	7 555	10 025	8 530	47,600	47,650	10 378	8 395	10 916	9 370
41,650	41,700	8 712	6 729	9 199	7 704	44,650	44,700	9 552	7 569	10 039	8 544	47,650	47,700	10 392	8 409	10 932	9 384
41,700	41,750	8,726	6,743	9 213	7,718	44,700	44,750	9 566	7 583	10 053	8 558	47,700	47,750	10 406	8 423	10 947	9 398
41,750	41,800	8 740	6 757	9,227	7,732	44,750	44,800	9 580	7 597	10 067	8 572	47,750	47,800	10 420	8 437	10 963	9 412
41,800	41,850	8 754	6 771	9 241	7 746	44,800	44,850	9 594	7 611	10 081	8 586	47,800	47,850	10 434	8 451	10 978	9 426
41,850	41,900	8 768	6 785	9 255	7,760	44,850	44,900	9 608	7,625	10 095	8 600	47,850	47,900	10 448	8 465	10 994	9 440
41,900	41,950	8 782	6 799	9 269	7 774	44,900	44,950	9 622	7 639	10 109	8 614	47,900	47,950	10 462	8 479	11 009	9 454
41,950	42,000	8 796	6 813	9 283	7,788	44,950	45,000	9 636	7 653	10 123	8 628	47,950	48,000	10 476	8 493	11 025	9 468
42,000						**45,000**						**48,000**					
42,000	42,050	8 810	6 827	9 297	7 802	45,000	45,050	9 650	7 667	10 137	8 642	48,000	48,050	10 490	8 507	11 040	9 482
42,050	42,100	8 824	6 841	9 311	7 816	45,050	45,100	9 664	7 681	10 151	8 656	48,050	48,100	10 504	8 521	11 056	9 496
42,100	42,150	8 838	6 855	9 325	7 830	45,100	45,150	9 678	7 695	10 165	8 670	48,100	48,150	10 518	8 535	11 071	9 510
42,150	42,200	8 852	6 869	9 339	7 844	45,150	45,200	9 692	7 709	10 179	8 684	48,150	48,200	10 532	8 549	11 087	9 524
42,200	42,250	8 866	6 883	9 353	7,858	45,200	45,250	9 706	7 723	10 193	8 698	48,200	48,250	10 546	8 563	11 102	9 538
42,250	42,300	8 880	6 897	9,367	7,872	45,250	45,300	9 720	7 737	10 207	8 712	48,250	48,300	10 560	8 577	11 118	9 552
42,300	42,350	8 894	6 911	9 381	7 886	45,300	45,350	9 734	7 751	10 221	8 726	48,300	48,350	10 574	8 591	11 133	9 566
42,350	42,400	8,908	6 925	9 395	7 900	45,350	45,400	9 748	7 765	10 235	8 740	48,350	48,400	10 588	8 605	11 149	9 580
42,400	42,450	8,922	6 939	9 409	7 914	45,400	45,450	9 762	7 779	10,249	8 754	48,400	48,450	10 602	8 619	11 164	9 594
42,450	42,500	8,936	6 953	9 423	7 928	45,450	45,500	9 776	7 793	10 263	8 768	48,450	48,500	10 616	8 633	11 180	9 608
42,500	42,550	8 950	6 967	9 437	7 942	45,500	45,550	9 790	7,807	10,277	8 782	48,500	48,550	10 630	8 647	11 195	9 622
42,550	42,600	8,964	6 981	9 451	7,956	45,550	45,600	9 804	7 821	10 291	8 796	48,550	48,600	10 644	8 661	11 211	9 636
42,600	42,650	8 978	6 995	9 465	7,970	45,600	45,650	9 818	7 835	10 305	8 810	48,600	48,650	10 658	8 675	11 226	9 650
42,650	42,700	8 992	7,009	9 479	7 984	45,650	45,700	9 832	7 849	10 319	8 824	48,650	48,700	10 672	8 689	11 242	9 664
42,700	42,750	9 006	7 023	9 493	7 998	45,700	45,750	9 846	7 863	10 333	8,838	48,700	48,750	10 686	8 703	11 257	9 678
42,750	42,800	9,020	7 037	9 507	8 012	45,750	45,800	9 860	7 877	10,347	8,852	48,750	48,800	10 700	8 717	11 273	9 692
42,800	42,850	9 034	7 051	9 521	8 026	45,800	45,850	9 874	7 891	10 361	8 866	48,800	48,850	10 714	8 731	11 288	9 706
42,850	42,900	9 048	7 065	9,535	8 040	45,850	45,900	9 888	7 905	10 375	8 880	48,850	48,900	10 728	8 745	11 304	9 720
42,900	42,950	9 062	7 079	9 549	8 054	45,900	45,950	9 902	7 919	10 389	8 894	48,900	48,950	10 742	8 759	11 319	9 734
42,950	43,000	9,076	7 093	9 563	8 068	45,950	46,000	9 916	7 933	10 405	8 908	48,950	49,000	10 756	8 773	11 335	9 748
43,000						**46,000**						**49,000**					
43,000	43,050	9 090	7 107	9 577	8 082	46,000	46,050	9 930	7 947	10 420	8 922	49,000	49,050	10 770	8 787	11 350	9 762
43,050	43,100	9 104	7 121	9 591	8 096	46,050	46,100	9 944	7 961	10 436	8 936	49,050	49,100	10 784	8 801	11 366	9 776
43,100	43,150	9 118	7 135	9 605	8 110	46,100	46,150	9 958	7 975	10 451	8 950	49,100	49,150	10 798	8 815	11 381	9 790
43,150	43,200	9 132	7 149	9 619	8 124	46,150	46,200	9 972	7 989	10 467	8 964	49,150	49,200	10 812	8 829	11 397	9 804
43,200	43,250	9 146	7 163	9 633	8 138	46,200	46,250	9 986	8 003	10 482	8 978	49,200	49,250	10 826	8 843	11 412	9 818
43,250	43,300	9 160	7 177	9 647	8 152	46,250	46,300	10 000	8 017	10 498	8 992	49,250	49,300	10 840	8 857	11 428	9 832
43,300	43,350	9 174	7 191	9 661	8 166	46,300	46,350	10 014	8 031	10 513	9 006	49,300	49,350	10 854	8 871	11 443	9 846
43,350	43,400	9 188	7 205	9 675	8 180	46,350	46,400	10 028	8 045	10 529	9 020	49,350	49,400	10 868	8 885	11 459	9 860
43,400	43,450	9 202	7 219	9 689	8 194	46,400	46,450	10 042	8 059	10 544	9 034	49,400	49,450	10 882	8 899	11 474	9 874
43,450	43,500	9 216	7 233	9 703	8 208	46,450	46,500	10 056	8 073	10 560	9 048	49,450	49,500	10 896	8 913	11 490	9 888
43,500	43,550	9 230	7 247	9 717	8 222	46,500	46,550	10 070	8 087	10 575	9 062	49,500	49,550	10 910	8 927	11 505	9 902
43,550	43,600	9 244	7 261	9 731	8 236	46,550	46,600	10 084	8 101	10 591	9 076	49,550	49,600	10 924	8 941	11 521	9 916
43,600	43,650	9 258	7 275	9 745	8 250	46,600	46,650	10 098	8 115	10 606	9 090	49,600	49,650	10 938	8 955	11 536	9 930
43,650	43,700	9 272	7 289	9 759	8 264	46,650	46,700	10 112	8 129	10 622	9 104	49,650	49,700	10 952	8 969	11 552	9 944
43,700	43,750	9 286	7 303	9 773	8 278	46,700	46,750	10 126	8 143	10 637	9 118	49,700	49,750	10 966	8 983	11 567	9 958
43,750	43,800	9 300	7 317	9 787	8 292	46,750	46,800	10 140	8 157	10 653	9 132	49,750	49,800	10 980	8 997	11 583	9 972
43,800	43,850	9 314	7 331	9 801	8 306	46,800	46,850	10 154	8 171	10 668	9 146	49,800	49,850	10 994	9 011	11 598	9 986
43,850	43,900	9 328	7 345	9 815	8 320	46,850	46,900	10 168	8 185	10 684	9 160	49,850	49,900	11 008	9 025	11 614	10 000
43,900	43,950	9 342	7 359	9 829	8 334	46,900	46,950	10 182	8 199	10 699	9 174	49,900	49,950	11 022	9 039	11 629	10 014
43,950	44,000	9 356	7 373	9 843	8 348	46,950	47,000	10 196	8 213	10 715	9 188	49,950	50,000	11 036	9 053	11 645	10 028

This column must also be used by a qualifying widow(er)　　　　　　　50,000 or over — use Form 1040

© 1983, 1996 Instructional Horizons. Produced and Distributed by J. Weston Walch, Publisher, Portland, Maine 04104-0658

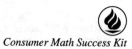

Consumer Math Success Kit

34. Income Tax

● **Extra Solved Example 2:** Sandy Aronson had the following income last year: salary: $29,486.22; interest from savings account: $325.30; dividends: $281.60. He made payments of $250.00 to his IRA. He had $2083.14 withheld from his pay for federal income tax. He received a state tax refund of $144.60. He is unmarried and claims one exemption. (Complete Form 1040 on pages 164–165 for Sandy.)

Solution: First, Sandy must fill in the personal information on the top half of the page—name, address, Social Security number, marital status, number of exemptions. He has checked the "Presidential Election Campaign" box, indicating $3 of his tax money is to go to this fund. He must check the box on Line 1, indicating he is single, and the box at 6a, claiming a personal exemption for himself. Then he must write the number 1 in the boxes on Lines 6a and 6e.

Line 7: Income from salary: $29,486.22

Line 8a: Taxable interest income: $325.30

Line 9: Dividend income: $281.60

Line 10: State tax refund: $144.60

Lines 11–21: Sandy has nothing to enter on these lines.

Line 22: $29,486.22 + $325.30 + $281.60 + $144.60 = $30,237.72

Line 23a: $250.00

Lines 23b–29: He has nothing to enter on these lines.

Line 30: $250.00

Line 31: $30,237.72 – $250.00 = $29,987.72

Line 32: $29,987.72

Line 33: He has nothing to enter on this line.

Line 34: Personal deduction: If he completed Schedule A, he would use the figure obtained there; he is not using Schedule A, so he should enter the standard deduction for a single person, $3800.00, on Line 34.

Line 35: $29,987.72 – $3800.00 = $26,187.72

Line 36: Line 32 is less than $83,850, so he must multiply $2450 by 1, the number he entered on Line 6e; then he should enter $2450.00 on Line 36.

Line 37: $26,187.72 – $2450.00 = $23,737.72; this is Sandy's taxable income.

Line 38: Sandy uses the Tax Table to determine his tax; he should check box *a* of Line 38 for the Tax Table; $3686.00, and that is the number to enter on Line 38.

Line 39: He has nothing to enter on this line.

Line 40: $3686.00

Lines 41–45: He has nothing to enter on these lines.

Line 46: $3686.00

Lines 47–52: He has nothing to enter on these lines.

Line 53: $3686.00

Line 54: Federal income tax withheld: $2083.14

Lines 55–59: He has nothing to enter on these lines.

Line 60: $2083.14

Lines 61–63: He has nothing to enter on these lines.

Line 64: His employer did not withhold enough income tax for him, so he owes a balance of: $3686.00 – $2083.14 = $1602.86, the number to enter on Line 64.

Line 65: The IRS could charge him a penalty for not having enough income tax withheld from his regular pay, so he should be sure to notify his employer of the underwithholding.

© 1983, 1996 Instructional Horizons. Produced and Distributed by J. Weston Walch, Publisher, Portland, Maine 04104-0658

Consumer Math Success Kit

34. Income Tax

Form **1040**	Department of the Treasury—Internal Revenue Service **1994**	(5)	IRS Use Only—Do not write or staple in this space.

U.S. Individual Income Tax Return 1994

For the year Jan. 1–Dec. 31, 1994, or other tax year beginning , 1994, ending 19 OMB No. 1545-0074

Label (See instructions on page 12)

Your first name and initial: Sander J.   Last name: Aronson

If a joint return, spouse's first name and initial   Last name

Your social security number: 55J 34 2878

Spouse's social security number

Use the IRS label. Otherwise, please print or type

Home address (number and street) If you have a P O box see page 12: 1422 Westvale Drive   Apt no 101

City, town or post office, state and ZIP code If you have a foreign address, see page 12: Cathscart PA 01952

For Privacy Act and Paperwork Reduction Act Notice, see page 4.

Presidential Election Campaign (See page 12.)

	Yes	No	Note: Checking "Yes" will not change your tax or reduce your refund.
Do you want $3 to go to this fund?	X		
If a joint return, does your spouse want $3 to go to this fund?			

Filing Status (See page 12)

Check only one box

1. [X] Single
2. [ ] Married filing joint return (even if only one had income)
3. [ ] Married filing separate return. Enter spouse's social security no. above and full name here. ▶
4. [ ] Head of household (with qualifying person). (See page 13.) If the qualifying person is a child but not your dependent, enter this child's name here. ▶
5. [ ] Qualifying widow(er) with dependent child (year spouse died ▶ 19). (See page 13.)

Exemptions (See page 13)

6a [X] Yourself. If your parent (or someone else) can claim you as a dependent on his or her tax return, do not check box 6a. But be sure to check the box on line 33b on page 2

b [ ] Spouse

c Dependents:

(1) Name (first initial and last name)	(2) Check if under age 1	(3) If age 1 or older, dependent's social security number	(4) Dependent's relationship to you	(5) No. of months lived in your home in 1994

No. of boxes checked on 6a and 6b: 1

No. of your children on 6c who:
• lived with you
• didn't live with you due to divorce or separation (see page 14)

Dependents on 6c not entered above

If more than six dependents, see page 14

d If your child didn't live with you but is claimed as your dependent under a pre-1985 agreement, check here ▶ [ ]

e Total number of exemptions claimed

Add numbers entered on lines above ▶ 1

Income

Attach Copy B of your Forms W-2, W-2G, and 1099-R here

If you did not get a W-2, see page 15

Enclose, but do not attach, any payment with your return

7	Wages, salaries, tips, etc. Attach Form(s) W-2	7	29,486 22
8a	Taxable interest income (see page 15). Attach Schedule B if over $400	8a	325 30
b	Tax-exempt interest (see page 16). DON'T include on line 8a	8b	
9	Dividend income. Attach Schedule B if over $400	9	281 60
10	Taxable refunds, credits, or offsets of state and local income taxes (see page 16)	10	144 60
11	Alimony received	11	-0-
12	Business income or (loss). Attach Schedule C or C-EZ	12	-0-
13	Capital gain or (loss). If required, attach Schedule D (see page 16)	13	-0-
14	Other gains or (losses). Attach Form 4797	14	-0-
15a	Total IRA distributions 15a b Taxable amount (see page 17)	15b	-0-
16a	Total pensions and annuities 16a b Taxable amount (see page 17)	16b	-0-
17	Rental real estate, royalties, partnerships, S corporations, trusts, etc. Attach Schedule E	17	-0-
18	Farm income or (loss). Attach Schedule F	18	-0-
19	Unemployment compensation (see page 18)	19	-0-
20a	Social security benefits 20a b Taxable amount (see page 18)	20b	-0-
21	Other income. List type and amount—see page 18	21	-0-
22	Add the amounts in the far right column for lines 7 through 21. This is your total income ▶	22	30,237 72

Adjustments to Income

Caution: See instructions ▶

23a	Your IRA deduction (see page 19)	23a	250 00
b	Spouse's IRA deduction (see page 19)	23b	
24	Moving expenses. Attach Form 3903 or 3903-F	24	
25	One-half of self-employment tax	25	
26	Self-employed health insurance deduction (see page 21)	26	
27	Keogh retirement plan and self-employed SEP deduction	27	
28	Penalty on early withdrawal of savings	28	
29	Alimony paid. Recipient's SSN ▶	29	
30	Add lines 23a through 29. These are your total adjustments ▶	30	250 00

Adjusted Gross Income

31	Subtract line 30 from line 22. This is your adjusted gross income. If less than $25,296 and a child lived with you (less than $9,000 if a child didn't live with you), see "Earned Income Credit" on page 27 ▶	31	29,987 72

Cat. No. 11320B

Form **1040** (1994)

34. Income Tax

Form 1040 (1994) Page 2

Tax Computation (See page 23)	32	Amount from line 31 (adjusted gross income)	32	29,987 72
	33a	Check if: ☐ You were 65 or older, ☐ Blind; ☐ Spouse was 65 or older, ☐ Blind. Add the number of boxes checked above and enter the total here . . . ▶ 33a		
	b	If your parent (or someone else) can claim you as a dependent, check here . ▶ 33b ☐		
	c	If you are married filing separately and your spouse itemizes deductions or you are a dual-status alien, see page 23 and check here . . . . ▶ 33c ☐		
	34	Enter the larger of your: Itemized deductions from Schedule A, line 29, OR Standard deduction shown below for your filing status. But if you checked any box on line 33a or b, go to page 23 to find your standard deduction. If you checked box 33c, your standard deduction is zero. • Single—$3,800 • Head of household—$5,600 • Married filing jointly or Qualifying widow(er)—$6,350 • Married filing separately—$3,175	34	3,800 00
	35	Subtract line 34 from line 32	35	26,187 72
	36	If line 32 is $83,850 or less, multiply $2,450 by the total number of exemptions claimed on line 6e. If line 32 is over $83,850, see the worksheet on page 24 for the amount to enter	36	2,450 00
If you want the IRS to figure your tax, see page 24	37	**Taxable income.** Subtract line 36 from line 35. If line 36 is more than line 35, enter -0-	37	23,737 72
	38	Tax. Check if from a ☒ Tax Table, b ☐ Tax Rate Schedules, c ☐ Capital Gain Tax Worksheet, or d ☐ Form 8615 (see page 24). Amount from Form(s) 8814 ▶ e _____	38	3,686 00
	39	Additional taxes. Check if from a ☐ Form 4970 b ☐ Form 4972	39	-0-
	40	Add lines 38 and 39 . . . . ▶	40	3,686 00
Credits (See page 24)	41	Credit for child and dependent care expenses. Attach Form 2441	41	
	42	Credit for the elderly or the disabled. Attach Schedule R .	42	
	43	Foreign tax credit. Attach Form 1116	43	
	44	Other credits (see page 25). Check if from a ☐ Form 3800 b ☐ Form 8396 c ☐ Form 8801 d ☐ Form (specify) _____	44	
	45	Add lines 41 through 44	45	-0-
	46	Subtract line 45 from line 40. If line 45 is more than line 40, enter -0- . . . ▶	46	3,686 00
Other Taxes (See page 25)	47	Self-employment tax. Attach Schedule SE	47	
	48	Alternative minimum tax. Attach Form 6251	48	
	49	Recapture taxes. Check if from a ☐ Form 4255 b ☐ Form 8611 c ☐ Form 8828	49	
	50	Social security and Medicare tax on tip income not reported to employer. Attach Form 4137	50	
	51	Tax on qualified retirement plans, including IRAs. If required, attach Form 5329 .	51	
	52	Advance earned income credit payments from Form W-2 . .	52	
	53	Add lines 46 through 52. This is your **total tax** . . . . ▶	53	3,686 00
Payments Attach Forms W-2, W-2G, and 1099-R on the front	54	Federal income tax withheld. If any is from Form(s) 1099, check ▶ ☐	54	2,083 14
	55	1994 estimated tax payments and amount applied from 1993 return .	55	
	56	**Earned income credit.** If required, attach Schedule EIC (see page 27). Nontaxable earned income: amount ▶ _____ and type ▶ _____	56	
	57	Amount paid with Form 4868 (extension request)	57	
	58	Excess social security and RRTA tax withheld (see page 32) .	58	
	59	Other payments. Check if from a ☐ Form 2439 b ☐ Form 4136	59	
	60	Add lines 54 through 59. These are your **total payments** . . . . . ▶	60	2,083 14
Refund or Amount You Owe	61	If line 60 is more than line 53, subtract line 53 from line 60. This is the amount you OVERPAID . ▶	61	
	62	Amount of line 61 you want REFUNDED TO YOU. . . . . ▶	62	
	63	Amount of line 61 you want APPLIED TO YOUR 1995 ESTIMATED TAX ▶ 63		
	64	If line 53 is more than line 60, subtract line 60 from line 53. This is the **AMOUNT YOU OWE.** For details on how to pay, including what to write on your payment, see page 32 .	64	1,602 86
	65	Estimated tax penalty (see page 33). Also include on line 64	65	

Sign Here
Keep a copy of this return for your records

Under penalties of perjury, I declare that I have examined this return and accompanying schedules and statements, and to the best of my knowledge and belief, they are true, correct, and complete. Declaration of preparer (other than taxpayer) is based on all information of which preparer has any knowledge.

Your signature	Date 03/24/95	Your occupation TEACHER
Spouse's signature If a joint return BOTH must sign	Date	Spouse's occupation

Paid Preparer's Use Only

Preparer's signature	Date	Check if self-employed ☐	Preparer's social security no
Firm's name (or yours if self-employed) and address		E.I. No.	
		ZIP code	

34. Income Tax

Section 6.

1994 Tax Table

Use if your taxable income is less than $100,000
If $100,000 or more, use the Tax Rate Schedules

Example Mr and Mrs Brown are filing a joint return Their taxable income on line 37 of Form 1040 is $25,300 First, they find the $25,300–25,350 income line Next, they find the column for married filing jointly and read down the column The amount shown where the income line and filing status column meet is $3,799 This is the tax amount they must enter on line 38 of their Form 1040

Sample Table

At least	But less than	Single	Married filing jointly	Married filing sepa rately	Head of a house-hold
		Your tax is—			
25,200	25,250	4 106	3 784	4,593	3,784
25,250	25,300	4 120	3,791	4 607	3 791
25,300	25,350	4 134	(3,799)	4 621	3,799
25,350	25,400	4,148	3,806	4,635	3,806

If line 37 (taxable income) is— At least	But less than	And you are— Single	Married filing jointly*	Married filing sepa rately	Head of a house hold
		Your tax is—			
0	5	0	0	0	0
5	15	2	2	2	2
15	25	3	3	3	3
25	50	6	6	6	6
50	75	9	9	9	9
75	100	13	13	13	13
100	125	17	17	17	17
125	150	21	21	21	21
150	175	24	24	24	24
175	200	28	28	28	28
200	225	32	32	32	32
225	250	36	36	36	36
250	275	39	39	39	39
275	300	43	43	43	43
300	325	47	47	47	47
325	350	51	51	51	51
350	375	54	54	54	54
375	400	58	58	58	58
400	425	62	62	62	62
425	450	66	66	66	66
450	475	69	69	69	69
475	500	73	73	73	73
500	525	77	77	77	77
525	550	81	81	81	81
550	575	84	84	84	84
575	600	88	88	88	88
600	625	92	92	92	92
625	650	96	96	96	96
650	675	99	99	99	99
675	700	103	103	103	103
700	725	107	107	107	107
725	750	111	111	111	111
750	775	114	114	114	114
775	800	118	118	118	118
800	825	122	122	122	122
825	850	126	126	126	126
850	875	129	129	129	129
875	900	133	133	133	133
900	925	137	137	137	137
925	950	141	141	141	141
950	975	144	144	144	144
975	1,000	148	148	148	148
1,000					
1,000	1,025	152	152	152	152
1,025	1,050	156	156	156	156
1,050	1,075	159	159	159	159
1,075	1,100	163	163	163	163
1,100	1,125	167	167	167	167
1,125	1,150	171	171	171	171
1,150	1,175	174	174	174	174
1,175	1,200	178	178	178	178
1,200	1,225	182	182	182	182
1,225	1,250	186	186	186	186
1,250	1,275	189	189	189	189
1,275	1,300	193	193	193	193

If line 37 (taxable income) is— At least	But less than	And you are— Single	Married filing jointly*	Married filing sepa rately	Head of a house hold
		Your tax is—			
1,300	1,325	197	197	197	197
1,325	1,350	201	201	201	201
1,350	1,375	204	204	204	204
1,375	1,400	208	208	208	208
1,400	1,425	212	212	212	212
1,425	1,450	216	216	216	216
1,450	1,475	219	219	219	219
1,475	1,500	223	223	223	223
1,500	1,525	227	227	227	227
1,525	1,550	231	231	231	231
1,550	1,575	234	234	234	234
1,575	1,600	238	238	238	238
1,600	1,625	242	242	242	242
1,625	1,650	246	246	246	246
1,650	1,675	249	249	249	249
1,675	1,700	253	253	253	253
1,700	1,725	257	257	257	257
1,725	1,750	261	261	261	261
1,750	1,775	264	264	264	264
1,775	1,800	268	268	268	268
1,800	1,825	272	272	272	272
1,825	1,850	276	276	276	276
1,850	1,875	279	279	279	279
1,875	1,900	283	283	283	283
1,900	1,925	287	287	287	287
1,925	1,950	291	291	291	291
1,950	1,975	294	294	294	294
1,975	2,000	298	298	298	298
2,000					
2,000	2,025	302	302	302	302
2,025	2,050	306	306	306	306
2,050	2,075	309	309	309	309
2,075	2,100	313	313	313	313
2,100	2,125	317	317	317	317
2,125	2,150	321	321	321	321
2,150	2,175	324	324	324	324
2,175	2,200	328	328	328	328
2,200	2,225	332	332	332	332
2,225	2,250	336	336	336	336
2,250	2,275	339	339	339	339
2,275	2,300	343	343	343	343
2,300	2,325	347	347	347	347
2,325	2,350	351	351	351	351
2,350	2,375	354	354	354	354
2,375	2,400	358	358	358	358
2,400	2,425	362	362	362	362
2,425	2,450	366	366	366	366
2,450	2,475	369	369	369	369
2,475	2,500	373	373	373	373
2,500	2,525	377	377	377	377
2,525	2,550	381	381	381	381
2,550	2,575	384	384	384	384
2,575	2,600	388	388	388	388
2,600	2,625	392	392	392	392
2,625	2,650	396	396	396	396
2,650	2,675	399	399	399	399
2,675	2,700	403	403	403	403

If line 37 (taxable income) is— At least	But less than	And you are— Single	Married filing jointly*	Married filing sepa rately	Head of a house hold
		Your tax is—			
2,700	2,725	407	407	407	407
2,725	2,750	411	411	411	411
2,750	2,775	414	414	414	414
2,775	2,800	418	418	418	418
2,800	2,825	422	422	422	422
2,825	2,850	426	426	426	426
2,850	2,875	429	429	429	429
2,875	2,900	433	433	433	433
2,900	2,925	437	437	437	437
2,925	2,950	441	441	441	441
2,950	2,975	444	444	444	444
2,975	3,000	448	448	448	448
3,000					
3,000	3,050	454	454	454	454
3,050	3,100	461	461	461	461
3,100	3,150	469	469	469	469
3,150	3,200	476	476	476	476
3,200	3,250	484	484	484	484
3,250	3,300	491	491	491	491
3,300	3,350	499	499	499	499
3,350	3,400	506	506	506	506
3,400	3,450	514	514	514	514
3,450	3,500	521	521	521	521
3,500	3,550	529	529	529	529
3,550	3,600	536	536	536	536
3,600	3,650	544	544	544	544
3,650	3,700	551	551	551	551
3,700	3,750	559	559	559	559
3,750	3,800	566	566	566	566
3,800	3,850	574	574	574	574
3,850	3,900	581	581	581	581
3,900	3,950	589	589	589	589
3,950	4,000	596	596	596	596
4,000					
4,000	4,050	604	604	604	604
4,050	4,100	611	611	611	611
4,100	4,150	619	619	619	619
4,150	4,200	626	626	626	626
4,200	4,250	634	634	634	634
4,250	4,300	641	641	641	641
4,300	4,350	649	649	649	649
4,350	4,400	656	656	656	656
4,400	4,450	664	664	664	664
4,450	4,500	671	671	671	671
4,500	4,550	679	679	679	679
4,550	4,600	686	686	686	686
4,600	4,650	694	694	694	694
4,650	4,700	701	701	701	701
4,700	4,750	709	709	709	709
4,750	4,800	716	716	716	716
4,800	4,850	724	724	724	724
4,850	4,900	731	731	731	731
4,900	4,950	739	739	739	739
4,950	5,000	746	746	746	746

Continued on next page

* This column must also be used by a qualifying widow(er)

© 1983, 1996 Instructional Horizons. Produced and Distributed by J. Weston Walch, Publisher, Portland, Maine 04104-0658

34. Income Tax

1994 Tax Table—*Continued*

5,000 – 7,999

If line 37 (taxable income) is— At least	But less than	Single	Married filing jointly	Married filing separately	Head of a household
5,000					
5,000	5,050	754	754	754	754
5,050	5,100	761	761	761	761
5,100	5,150	769	769	769	769
5,150	5,200	776	776	776	776
5,200	5,250	784	784	784	784
5,250	5,300	791	791	791	791
5,300	5,350	799	799	799	799
5,350	5,400	806	806	806	806
5,400	5,450	814	814	814	814
5,450	5,500	821	821	821	821
5,500	5,550	829	829	829	829
5,550	5,600	836	836	836	836
5,600	5,650	844	844	844	844
5,650	5,700	851	851	851	851
5,700	5,750	859	859	859	859
5,750	5,800	866	866	866	866
5,800	5,850	874	874	874	874
5,850	5,900	881	881	881	881
5,900	5,950	889	889	889	889
5,950	6,000	896	896	896	896
6,000					
6,000	6,050	904	904	904	904
6,050	6,100	911	911	911	911
6,100	6,150	919	919	919	919
6,150	6,200	926	926	926	926
6,200	6,250	934	934	934	934
6,250	6,300	941	941	941	941
6,300	6,350	949	949	949	949
6,350	6,400	956	956	956	956
6,400	6,450	964	964	964	964
6,450	6,500	971	971	971	971
6,500	6,550	979	979	979	979
6,550	6,600	986	986	986	986
6,600	6,650	994	994	994	994
6,650	6,700	1,001	1,001	1,001	1,001
6,700	6,750	1,009	1,009	1,009	1,009
6,750	6,800	1,016	1,016	1,016	1,016
6,800	6,850	1,024	1,024	1,024	1,024
6,850	6,900	1,031	1,031	1,031	1,031
6,900	6,950	1,039	1,039	1,039	1,039
6,950	7,000	1,046	1,046	1,046	1,046
7,000					
7,000	7,050	1,054	1,054	1,054	1,054
7,050	7,100	1,061	1,061	1,061	1,061
7,100	7,150	1,069	1,069	1,069	1,069
7,150	7,200	1,076	1,076	1,076	1,076
7,200	7,250	1,084	1,084	1,084	1,084
7,250	7,300	1,091	1,091	1,091	1,091
7,300	7,350	1,099	1,099	1,099	1,099
7,350	7,400	1,106	1,106	1,106	1,106
7,400	7,450	1,114	1,114	1,114	1,114
7,450	7,500	1,121	1,121	1,121	1,121
7,500	7,550	1,129	1,129	1,129	1,129
7,550	7,600	1,136	1,136	1,136	1,136
7,600	7,650	1,144	1,144	1,144	1,144
7,650	7,700	1,151	1,151	1,151	1,151
7,700	7,750	1,159	1,159	1,159	1,159
7,750	7,800	1,166	1,166	1,166	1,166
7,800	7,850	1,174	1,174	1,174	1,174
7,850	7,900	1,181	1,181	1,181	1,181
7,900	7,950	1,189	1,189	1,189	1,189
7,950	8,000	1,196	1,196	1,196	1,196

8,000 – 10,999

If line 37 (taxable income) is— At least	But less than	Single	Married filing jointly	Married filing separately	Head of a household
8,000					
8,000	8,050	1,204	1,204	1,204	1,204
8,050	8,100	1,211	1,211	1,211	1,211
8,100	8,150	1,219	1,219	1,219	1,219
8,150	8,200	1,226	1,226	1,226	1,226
8,200	8,250	1,234	1,234	1,234	1,234
8,250	8,300	1,241	1,241	1,241	1,241
8,300	8,350	1,249	1,249	1,249	1,249
8,350	8,400	1,256	1,256	1,256	1,256
8,400	8,450	1,264	1,264	1,264	1,264
8,450	8,500	1,271	1,271	1,271	1,271
8,500	8,550	1,279	1,279	1,279	1,279
8,550	8,600	1,286	1,286	1,286	1,286
8,600	8,650	1,294	1,294	1,294	1,294
8,650	8,700	1,301	1,301	1,301	1,301
8,700	8,750	1,309	1,309	1,309	1,309
8,750	8,800	1,316	1,316	1,316	1,316
8,800	8,850	1,324	1,324	1,324	1,324
8,850	8,900	1,331	1,331	1,331	1,331
8,900	8,950	1,339	1,339	1,339	1,339
8,950	9,000	1,346	1,346	1,346	1,346
9,000					
9,000	9,050	1,354	1,354	1,354	1,354
9,050	9,100	1,361	1,361	1,361	1,361
9,100	9,150	1,369	1,369	1,369	1,369
9,150	9,200	1,376	1,376	1,376	1,376
9,200	9,250	1,384	1,384	1,384	1,384
9,250	9,300	1,391	1,391	1,391	1,391
9,300	9,350	1,399	1,399	1,399	1,399
9,350	9,400	1,406	1,406	1,406	1,406
9,400	9,450	1,414	1,414	1,414	1,414
9,450	9,500	1,421	1,421	1,421	1,421
9,500	9,550	1,429	1,429	1,429	1,429
9,550	9,600	1,436	1,436	1,436	1,436
9,600	9,650	1,444	1,444	1,444	1,444
9,650	9,700	1,451	1,451	1,451	1,451
9,700	9,750	1,459	1,459	1,459	1,459
9,750	9,800	1,466	1,466	1,466	1,466
9,800	9,850	1,474	1,474	1,474	1,474
9,850	9,900	1,481	1,481	1,481	1,481
9,900	9,950	1,489	1,489	1,489	1,489
9,950	10,000	1,496	1,496	1,496	1,496
10,000					
10,000	10,050	1,504	1,504	1,504	1,504
10,050	10,100	1,511	1,511	1,511	1,511
10,100	10,150	1,519	1,519	1,519	1,519
10,150	10,200	1,526	1,526	1,526	1,526
10,200	10,250	1,534	1,534	1,534	1,534
10,250	10,300	1,541	1,541	1,541	1,541
10,300	10,350	1,549	1,549	1,549	1,549
10,350	10,400	1,556	1,556	1,556	1,556
10,400	10,450	1,564	1,564	1,564	1,564
10,450	10,500	1,571	1,571	1,571	1,571
10,500	10,550	1,579	1,579	1,579	1,579
10,550	10,600	1,586	1,586	1,586	1,586
10,600	10,650	1,594	1,594	1,594	1,594
10,650	10,700	1,601	1,601	1,601	1,601
10,700	10,750	1,609	1,609	1,609	1,609
10,750	10,800	1,616	1,616	1,616	1,616
10,800	10,850	1,624	1,624	1,624	1,624
10,850	10,900	1,631	1,631	1,631	1,631
10,900	10,950	1,639	1,639	1,639	1,639
10,950	11,000	1,646	1,646	1,646	1,646

11,000 – 13,999

If line 37 (taxable income) is— At least	But less than	Single	Married filing jointly	Married filing separately	Head of a household
11,000					
11,000	11,050	1,654	1,654	1,654	1,654
11,050	11,100	1,661	1,661	1,661	1,661
11,100	11,150	1,669	1,669	1,669	1,669
11,150	11,200	1,676	1,676	1,676	1,676
11,200	11,250	1,684	1,684	1,684	1,684
11,250	11,300	1,691	1,691	1,691	1,691
11,300	11,350	1,699	1,699	1,699	1,699
11,350	11,400	1,706	1,706	1,706	1,706
11,400	11,450	1,714	1,714	1,714	1,714
11,450	11,500	1,721	1,721	1,721	1,721
11,500	11,550	1,729	1,729	1,729	1,729
11,550	11,600	1,736	1,736	1,736	1,736
11,600	11,650	1,744	1,744	1,744	1,744
11,650	11,700	1,751	1,751	1,751	1,751
11,700	11,750	1,759	1,759	1,759	1,759
11,750	11,800	1,766	1,766	1,766	1,766
11,800	11,850	1,774	1,774	1,774	1,774
11,850	11,900	1,781	1,781	1,781	1,781
11,900	11,950	1,789	1,789	1,789	1,789
11,950	12,000	1,796	1,796	1,796	1,796
12,000					
12,000	12,050	1,804	1,804	1,804	1,804
12,050	12,100	1,811	1,811	1,811	1,811
12,100	12,150	1,819	1,819	1,819	1,819
12,150	12,200	1,826	1,826	1,826	1,826
12,200	12,250	1,834	1,834	1,834	1,834
12,250	12,300	1,841	1,841	1,841	1,841
12,300	12,350	1,849	1,849	1,849	1,849
12,350	12,400	1,856	1,856	1,856	1,856
12,400	12,450	1,864	1,864	1,864	1,864
12,450	12,500	1,871	1,871	1,871	1,871
12,500	12,550	1,879	1,879	1,879	1,879
12,550	12,600	1,886	1,886	1,886	1,886
12,600	12,650	1,894	1,894	1,894	1,894
12,650	12,700	1,901	1,901	1,901	1,901
12,700	12,750	1,909	1,909	1,909	1,909
12,750	12,800	1,916	1,916	1,916	1,916
12,800	12,850	1,924	1,924	1,924	1,924
12,850	12,900	1,931	1,931	1,931	1,931
12,900	12,950	1,939	1,939	1,939	1,939
12,950	13,000	1,946	1,946	1,946	1,946
13,000					
13,000	13,050	1,954	1,954	1,954	1,954
13,050	13,100	1,961	1,961	1,961	1,961
13,100	13,150	1,969	1,969	1,969	1,969
13,150	13,200	1,976	1,976	1,976	1,976
13,200	13,250	1,984	1,984	1,984	1,984
13,250	13,300	1,991	1,991	1,991	1,991
13,300	13,350	1,999	1,999	1,999	1,999
13,350	13,400	2,006	2,006	2,006	2,006
13,400	13,450	2,014	2,014	2,014	2,014
13,450	13,500	2,021	2,021	2,021	2,021
13,500	13,550	2,029	2,029	2,029	2,029
13,550	13,600	2,036	2,036	2,036	2,036
13,600	13,650	2,044	2,044	2,044	2,044
13,650	13,700	2,051	2,051	2,051	2,051
13,700	13,750	2,059	2,059	2,059	2,059
13,750	13,800	2,066	2,066	2,066	2,066
13,800	13,850	2,074	2,074	2,074	2,074
13,850	13,900	2,081	2,081	2,081	2,081
13,900	13,950	2,089	2,089	2,089	2,089
13,950	14,000	2,096	2,096	2,096	2,096

This column must also be used by a qualifying widow(er)

Continued on next page

© 1983, 1996 Instructional Horizons. Produced and Distributed by J. Weston Walch, Publisher, Portland, Maine 04104-0658   *167*   *Consumer Math Success Kit*

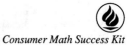

34. Income Tax

1994 Tax Table—Continued

If line 37 (taxable income) is—		And you are—			
At least	But less than	Single	Married filing jointly	Married filing separately	Head of a household
		Your tax is—			

14,000

At least	But less than	Single	Married jointly	Married sep.	Head
14,000	14,050	2 104	2 104	2 104	2,104
14,050	14,100	2 111	2,111	2 111	2,111
14,100	14,150	2 119	2,119	2 119	2 119
14,150	14,200	2 126	2 126	2 126	2 126
14,200	14,250	2,134	2,134	2,134	2,134
14,250	14,300	2,141	2,141	2,141	2,141
14,300	14,350	2,149	2,149	2,149	2,149
14,350	14,400	2 156	2,156	2,156	2,156
14,400	14,450	2,164	2,164	2,164	2,164
14,450	14,500	2,171	2,171	2,171	2,171
14,500	14,550	2 179	2,179	2 179	2,179
14,550	14,600	2 186	2 186	2 186	2,186
14,600	14,650	2 194	2,194	2,194	2,194
14,650	14,700	2 201	2,201	2 201	2,201
14,700	14,750	2 209	2,209	2,209	2,209
14,750	14,800	2 216	2,216	2,216	2,216
14,800	14,850	2 224	2,224	2,224	2,224
14,850	14,900	2,231	2,231	2 231	2,231
14,900	14,950	2,239	2,239	2 239	2 239
14,950	15,000	2,246	2,246	2,246	2,246

15,000

At least	But less than	Single	Married jointly	Married sep.	Head
15,000	15,050	2 254	2,254	2 254	2,254
15,050	15,100	2,261	2,261	2 261	2,261
15,100	15,150	2 269	2 269	2 269	2,269
15,150	15,200	2,276	2 276	2,276	2,276
15,200	15,250	2,284	2,284	2,284	2,284
15,250	15,300	2,291	2,291	2,291	2,291
15,300	15,350	2,299	2,299	2,299	2,299
15,350	15,400	2,306	2,306	2,306	2,306
15,400	15,450	2,314	2,314	2,314	2,314
15,450	15,500	2,321	2,321	2,321	2,321
15,500	15,550	2,329	2,329	2,329	2,329
15,550	15,600	2,336	2,336	2,336	2,336
15,600	15,650	2,344	2,344	2,344	2,344
15,650	15,700	2,351	2,351	2 351	2,351
15,700	15,750	2,359	2,359	2,359	2,359
15,750	15,800	2,366	2,366	2 366	2,366
15,800	15,850	2,374	2,374	2,374	2,374
15,850	15,900	2,381	2,381	2,381	2,381
15,900	15,950	2,389	2,389	2,389	2,389
15,950	16,000	2,396	2,396	2,396	2,396

16,000

At least	But less than	Single	Married jointly	Married sep.	Head
16,000	16,050	2,404	2,404	2,404	2,404
16,050	16,100	2,411	2,411	2 411	2,411
16,100	16,150	2,419	2,419	2,419	2,419
16,150	16,200	2,426	2,426	2,426	2,426
16,200	16,250	2,434	2,434	2,434	2,434
16,250	16,300	2,441	2,441	2,441	2,441
16,300	16,350	2,449	2,449	2,449	2,449
16,350	16,400	2,456	2,456	2,456	2,456
16,400	16,450	2,464	2,464	2,464	2,464
16,450	16,500	2,471	2,471	2,471	2,471
16,500	16,550	2,479	2,479	2,479	2,479
16,550	16,600	2,486	2,486	2,486	2,486
16,600	16,650	2,494	2,494	2,494	2,494
16,650	16,700	2,501	2,501	2,501	2,501
16,700	16,750	2 509	2,509	2,509	2,509
16,750	16,800	2,516	2,516	2,516	2,516
16,800	16,850	2,524	2,524	2,524	2,524
16,850	16,900	2 531	2,531	2 531	2,531
16,900	16,950	2,539	2,539	2,539	2,539
16,950	17,000	2,546	2,546	2,546	2,546

17,000

At least	But less than	Single	Married jointly	Married sep.	Head
17,000	17,050	2 554	2 554	2 554	2 554
17,050	17,100	2 561	2,561	2 561	2,561
17,100	17,150	2 569	2,569	2 569	2,569
17,150	17,200	2 576	2,576	2 576	2 576
17,200	17,250	2 584	2,584	2 584	2 584
17,250	17,300	2 591	2,591	2 591	2,591
17,300	17,350	2 599	2,599	2 599	2,599
17,350	17,400	2 606	2,606	2,606	2,606
17,400	17,450	2 614	2,614	2,614	2,614
17,450	17,500	2 621	2,621	2,621	2,621
17,500	17,550	2 629	2 629	2,629	2,629
17,550	17,600	2 636	2,636	2 636	2,636
17,600	17,650	2 644	2,644	2 644	2,644
17,650	17,700	2 651	2,651	2 651	2,651
17,700	17,750	2 659	2,659	2,659	2,659
17,750	17,800	2 666	2,666	2 666	2 666
17,800	17,850	2 674	2 674	2 674	2,674
17,850	17,900	2 681	2,681	2,681	2,681
17,900	17,950	2 689	2,689	2 689	2,689
17,950	18,000	2 696	2,696	2,696	2,696

18,000

At least	But less than	Single	Married jointly	Married sep.	Head
18,000	18,050	2 704	2 704	2 704	2,704
18,050	18,100	2 711	2,711	2 711	2 711
18,100	18,150	2 719	2 719	2 719	2,719
18,150	18,200	2 726	2,726	2 726	2,726
18,200	18,250	2 734	2 734	2 734	2,734
18,250	18,300	2 741	2,741	2 741	2,741
18,300	18,350	2 749	2,749	2 749	2,749
18,350	18,400	2,756	2,756	2 756	2,756
18,400	18,450	2,764	2 764	2 764	2,764
18,450	18,500	2 771	2,771	2 771	2,771
18,500	18,550	2 779	2,779	2 779	2,779
18,550	18,600	2 786	2,786	2 786	2,786
18,600	18,650	2,794	2,794	2,794	2,794
18,650	18,700	2 801	2 801	2,801	2,801
18,700	18,750	2,809	2,809	2,809	2,809
18,750	18,800	2,816	2,816	2,816	2,816
18,800	18,850	2 824	2,824	2 824	2,824
18,850	18,900	2 831	2,831	2,831	2,831
18,900	18,950	2 839	2,839	2,839	2,839
18,950	19,000	2 846	2,846	2,846	2,846

19,000

At least	But less than	Single	Married jointly	Married sep.	Head
19,000	19,050	2 854	2,854	2,857	2,854
19,050	19,100	2 861	2,861	2,871	2,861
19,100	19,150	2,869	2,869	2,885	2,869
19,150	19,200	2,876	2,876	2,899	2,876
19,200	19,250	2 884	2,884	2,913	2,884
19,250	19,300	2 891	2,891	2 927	2,891
19,300	19,350	2 899	2,899	2,941	2,899
19,350	19,400	2 906	2,906	2,955	2,906
19,400	19,450	2,914	2 914	2,969	2,914
19,450	19,500	2 921	2,921	2,983	2,921
19,500	19,550	2,929	2,929	2,997	2,929
19,550	19,600	2,936	2,936	3,011	2,936
19,600	19,650	2 944	2,944	3,025	2,944
19,650	19,700	2 951	2,951	3,039	2,951
19,700	19,750	2 959	2,959	3,053	2,959
19,750	19,800	2 966	2,966	3,067	2,966
19,800	19,850	2 974	2,974	3,081	2,974
19,850	19,900	2 981	2,981	3,095	2,981
19,900	19,950	2 989	2,989	3 109	2,989
19,950	20,000	2 996	2,996	3,123	2 996

20,000

At least	But less than	Single	Married jointly	Married sep.	Head
20,000	20,050	3 004	3 004	3 137	3 004
20,050	20,100	3 011	3 011	3 151	3,011
20,100	20,150	3 019	3,019	3 165	3 019
20,150	20,200	3 026	3,026	3 179	3 026
20,200	20,250	3 034	3 034	3 193	3 034
20,250	20,300	3 041	3 041	3 207	3 041
20,300	20,350	3 049	3,049	3 221	3 049
20,350	20,400	3 056	3,056	3 235	3 056
20,400	20,450	3 064	3 064	3,249	3 064
20,450	20,500	3 071	3,071	3 263	3 071
20,500	20,550	3 079	3 079	3 277	3,079
20,550	20,600	3 086	3,086	3 291	3,086
20,600	20,650	3 094	3,094	3 305	3,094
20,650	20,700	3 101	3,101	3 319	3,101
20,700	20,750	3 109	3,109	3 333	3,109
20,750	20,800	3 116	3,116	3 347	3 116
20,800	20,850	3 124	3 124	3 361	3,124
20,850	20,900	3 131	3,131	3 375	3 131
20,900	20,950	3 139	3,139	3 389	3,139
20,950	21,000	3 146	3,146	3 403	3,146

21,000

At least	But less than	Single	Married jointly	Married sep.	Head
21,000	21,050	3 154	3,154	3 417	3,154
21,050	21,100	3 161	3,161	3 431	3,161
21,100	21,150	3 169	3 169	3 445	3,169
21,150	21,200	3 176	3,176	3 459	3,176
21,200	21,250	3 184	3,184	3 473	3,184
21,250	21,300	3 191	3,191	3 487	3,191
21,300	21,350	3 199	3,199	3 501	3,199
21,350	21,400	3 206	3,206	3 515	3,206
21,400	21,450	3 214	3,214	3 529	3,214
21,450	21,500	3 221	3,221	3 543	3,221
21,500	21,550	3 229	3,229	3 557	3,229
21,550	21,600	3 236	3,236	3 571	3,236
21,600	21,650	3 244	3,244	3 585	3,244
21,650	21,700	3 251	3,251	3 599	3,251
21,700	21,750	3 259	3,259	3 613	3,259
21,750	21,800	3 266	3 266	3 627	3 266
21,800	21,850	3 274	3,274	3 641	3,274
21,850	21,900	3 281	3 281	3 655	3,281
21,900	21,950	3 289	3,289	3 669	3,289
21,950	22,000	3 296	3,296	3 683	3,296

22,000

At least	But less than	Single	Married jointly	Married sep.	Head
22,000	22,050	3,304	3,304	3,697	3,304
22,050	22,100	3 311	3,311	3,711	3,311
22,100	22,150	3 319	3,319	3,725	3,319
22,150	22,200	3 326	3,326	3,739	3,326
22,200	22,250	3,334	3,334	3,753	3,334
22,250	22,300	3,341	3,341	3,767	3,341
22,300	22,350	3,349	3,349	3,781	3,349
22,350	22,400	3,356	3,356	3,795	3 356
22,400	22,450	3 364	3,364	3,809	3,364
22,450	22,500	3 371	3,371	3,823	3,371
22,500	22,550	3 379	3,379	3,837	3,379
22,550	22,600	3 386	3,386	3,851	3,386
22,600	22,650	3 394	3,394	3,865	3,394
22,650	22,700	3 401	3,401	3,879	3,401
22,700	22,750	3 409	3,409	3,893	3,409
22,750	22,800	3 420	3,416	3,907	3,416
22,800	22,850	3 434	3,424	3 921	3,424
22,850	22,900	3 448	3 431	3 935	3,431
22,900	22,950	3 462	3,439	3 949	3,439
22,950	23,000	3 476	3,446	3 963	3,446

* This column must also be used by a qualifying widow(er)

Continued on next page

© 1983, 1996 Instructional Horizons. Produced and Distributed by J. Weston Walch, Publisher, Portland, Maine 04104-0658

Consumer Math Success Kit

34. Income Tax

1994 Tax Table—Continued

If line 37 (taxable income) is—		And you are—			
At least	But less than	Single	Married filing jointly	Married filing separately	Head of a household
					Your tax is—

23,000

At least	But less than	Single	Married filing jointly	Married filing separately	Head of a household
23,000	23,050	3,490	3,454	3,977	3,454
23,050	23,100	3,504	3,461	3,991	3,461
23,100	23,150	3,518	3,469	4,005	3,469
23,150	23,200	3,532	3,476	4,019	3,476
23,200	23,250	3,546	3,484	4,033	3,484
23,250	23,300	3,560	3,491	4,047	3,491
23,300	23,350	3,574	3,499	4,061	3,499
23,350	23,400	3,588	3,506	4,075	3,506
23,400	23,450	3,602	3,514	4,089	3,514
23,450	23,500	3,616	3,521	4,103	3,521
23,500	23,550	3,630	3,529	4,117	3,529
23,550	23,600	3,644	3,536	4,131	3,536
23,600	23,650	3,658	3,544	4,145	3,544
23,650	23,700	3,672	3,551	4,159	3,551
23,700	23,750	3,686	3,559	4,173	3,559
23,750	23,800	3,700	3,566	4,187	3,566
23,800	23,850	3,714	3,574	4,201	3,574
23,850	23,900	3,728	3,581	4,215	3,581
23,900	23,950	3,742	3,589	4,229	3,589
23,950	24,000	3,756	3,596	4,243	3,596

24,000

At least	But less than	Single	Married filing jointly	Married filing separately	Head of a household
24,000	24,050	3,770	3,604	4,257	3,604
24,050	24,100	3,784	3,611	4,271	3,611
24,100	24,150	3,798	3,619	4,285	3,619
24,150	24,200	3,812	3,626	4,299	3,626
24,200	24,250	3,826	3,634	4,313	3,634
24,250	24,300	3,840	3,641	4,327	3,641
24,300	24,350	3,854	3,649	4,341	3,649
24,350	24,400	3,868	3,656	4,355	3,656
24,400	24,450	3,882	3,664	4,369	3,664
24,450	24,500	3,896	3,671	4,383	3,671
24,500	24,550	3,910	3,679	4,397	3,679
24,550	24,600	3,924	3,686	4,411	3,686
24,600	24,650	3,938	3,694	4,425	3,694
24,650	24,700	3,952	3,701	4,439	3,701
24,700	24,750	3,966	3,709	4,453	3,709
24,750	24,800	3,980	3,716	4,467	3,716
24,800	24,850	3,994	3,724	4,481	3,724
24,850	24,900	4,008	3,731	4,495	3,731
24,900	24,950	4,022	3,739	4,509	3,739
24,950	25,000	4,036	3,746	4,523	3,746

25,000

At least	But less than	Single	Married filing jointly	Married filing separately	Head of a household
25,000	25,050	4,050	3,754	4,537	3,754
25,050	25,100	4,064	3,761	4,551	3,761
25,100	25,150	4,078	3,769	4,565	3,769
25,150	25,200	4,092	3,776	4,579	3,776
25,200	25,250	4,106	3,784	4,593	3,784
25,250	25,300	4,120	3,791	4,607	3,791
25,300	25,350	4,134	3,799	4,621	3,799
25,350	25,400	4,148	3,806	4,635	3,806
25,400	25,450	4,162	3,814	4,649	3,814
25,450	25,500	4,176	3,821	4,663	3,821
25,500	25,550	4,190	3,829	4,677	3,829
25,550	25,600	4,204	3,836	4,691	3,836
25,600	25,650	4,218	3,844	4,705	3,844
25,650	25,700	4,232	3,851	4,719	3,851
25,700	25,750	4,246	3,859	4,733	3,859
25,750	25,800	4,260	3,866	4,747	3,866
25,800	25,850	4,274	3,874	4,761	3,874
25,850	25,900	4,288	3,881	4,775	3,881
25,900	25,950	4,302	3,889	4,789	3,889
25,950	26,000	4,316	3,896	4,803	3,896

26,000

At least	But less than	Single	Married filing jointly	Married filing separately	Head of a household
26,000	26,050	4,330	3,904	4,817	3,904
26,050	26,100	4,344	3,911	4,831	3,911
26,100	26,150	4,358	3,919	4,845	3,919
26,150	26,200	4,372	3,926	4,859	3,926
26,200	26,250	4,386	3,934	4,873	3,934
26,250	26,300	4,400	3,941	4,887	3,941
26,300	26,350	4,414	3,949	4,901	3,949
26,350	26,400	4,428	3,956	4,915	3,956
26,400	26,450	4,442	3,964	4,929	3,964
26,450	26,500	4,456	3,971	4,943	3,971
26,500	26,550	4,470	3,979	4,957	3,979
26,550	26,600	4,484	3,986	4,971	3,986
26,600	26,650	4,498	3,994	4,985	3,994
26,650	26,700	4,512	4,001	4,999	4,001
26,700	26,750	4,526	4,009	5,013	4,009
26,750	26,800	4,540	4,016	5,027	4,016
26,800	26,850	4,554	4,024	5,041	4,024
26,850	26,900	4,568	4,031	5,055	4,031
26,900	26,950	4,582	4,039	5,069	4,039
26,950	27,000	4,596	4,046	5,083	4,046

27,000

At least	But less than	Single	Married filing jointly	Married filing separately	Head of a household
27,000	27,050	4,610	4,054	5,097	4,054
27,050	27,100	4,624	4,061	5,111	4,061
27,100	27,150	4,638	4,069	5,125	4,069
27,150	27,200	4,652	4,076	5,139	4,076
27,200	27,250	4,666	4,084	5,153	4,084
27,250	27,300	4,680	4,091	5,167	4,091
27,300	27,350	4,694	4,099	5,181	4,099
27,350	27,400	4,708	4,106	5,195	4,106
27,400	27,450	4,722	4,114	5,209	4,114
27,450	27,500	4,736	4,121	5,223	4,121
27,500	27,550	4,750	4,129	5,237	4,129
27,550	27,600	4,764	4,136	5,251	4,136
27,600	27,650	4,778	4,144	5,265	4,144
27,650	27,700	4,792	4,151	5,279	4,151
27,700	27,750	4,806	4,159	5,293	4,159
27,750	27,800	4,820	4,166	5,307	4,166
27,800	27,850	4,834	4,174	5,321	4,174
27,850	27,900	4,848	4,181	5,335	4,181
27,900	27,950	4,862	4,189	5,349	4,189
27,950	28,000	4,876	4,196	5,363	4,196

28,000

At least	But less than	Single	Married filing jointly	Married filing separately	Head of a household
28,000	28,050	4,890	4,204	5,377	4,204
28,050	28,100	4,904	4,211	5,391	4,211
28,100	28,150	4,918	4,219	5,405	4,219
28,150	28,200	4,932	4,226	5,419	4,226
28,200	28,250	4,946	4,234	5,433	4,234
28,250	28,300	4,960	4,241	5,447	4,241
28,300	28,350	4,974	4,249	5,461	4,249
28,350	28,400	4,988	4,256	5,475	4,256
28,400	28,450	5,002	4,264	5,489	4,264
28,450	28,500	5,016	4,271	5,503	4,271
28,500	28,550	5,030	4,279	5,517	4,279
28,550	28,600	5,044	4,286	5,531	4,286
28,600	28,650	5,058	4,294	5,545	4,294
28,650	28,700	5,072	4,301	5,559	4,301
28,700	28,750	5,086	4,309	5,573	4,309
28,750	28,800	5,100	4,316	5,587	4,316
28,800	28,850	5,114	4,324	5,601	4,324
28,850	28,900	5,128	4,331	5,615	4,331
28,900	28,950	5,142	4,339	5,629	4,339
28,950	29,000	5,156	4,346	5,643	4,346

29,000

At least	But less than	Single	Married filing jointly	Married filing separately	Head of a household
29,000	29,050	5,170	4,354	5,657	4,354
29,050	29,100	5,184	4,361	5,671	4,361
29,100	29,150	5,198	4,369	5,685	4,369
29,150	29,200	5,212	4,376	5,699	4,376
29,200	29,250	5,226	4,384	5,713	4,384
29,250	29,300	5,240	4,391	5,727	4,391
29,300	29,350	5,254	4,399	5,741	4,399
29,350	29,400	5,268	4,406	5,755	4,406
29,400	29,450	5,282	4,414	5,769	4,414
29,450	29,500	5,296	4,421	5,783	4,421
29,500	29,550	5,310	4,429	5,797	4,429
29,550	29,600	5,324	4,436	5,811	4,436
29,600	29,650	5,338	4,444	5,825	4,444
29,650	29,700	5,352	4,451	5,839	4,451
29,700	29,750	5,366	4,459	5,853	4,459
29,750	29,800	5,380	4,466	5,867	4,466
29,800	29,850	5,394	4,474	5,881	4,474
29,850	29,900	5,408	4,481	5,895	4,481
29,900	29,950	5,422	4,489	5,909	4,489
29,950	30,000	5,436	4,496	5,923	4,496

30,000

At least	But less than	Single	Married filing jointly	Married filing separately	Head of a household
30,000	30,050	5,450	4,504	5,937	4,504
30,050	30,100	5,464	4,511	5,951	4,511
30,100	30,150	5,478	4,519	5,965	4,519
30,150	30,200	5,492	4,526	5,979	4,526
30,200	30,250	5,506	4,534	5,993	4,534
30,250	30,300	5,520	4,541	6,007	4,541
30,300	30,350	5,534	4,549	6,021	4,549
30,350	30,400	5,548	4,556	6,035	4,556
30,400	30,450	5,562	4,564	6,049	4,564
30,450	30,500	5,576	4,571	6,063	4,571
30,500	30,550	5,590	4,579	6,077	4,582
30,550	30,600	5,604	4,586	6,091	4,596
30,600	30,650	5,618	4,594	6,105	4,610
30,650	30,700	5,632	4,601	6,119	4,624
30,700	30,750	5,646	4,609	6,133	4,638
30,750	30,800	5,660	4,616	6,147	4,652
30,800	30,850	5,674	4,624	6,161	4,666
30,850	30,900	5,688	4,631	6,175	4,680
30,900	30,950	5,702	4,639	6,189	4,694
30,950	31,000	5,716	4,646	6,203	4,708

31,000

At least	But less than	Single	Married filing jointly	Married filing separately	Head of a household
31,000	31,050	5,730	4,654	6,217	4,722
31,050	31,100	5,744	4,661	6,231	4,736
31,100	31,150	5,758	4,669	6,245	4,750
31,150	31,200	5,772	4,676	6,259	4,764
31,200	31,250	5,786	4,684	6,273	4,778
31,250	31,300	5,800	4,691	6,287	4,792
31,300	31,350	5,814	4,699	6,301	4,806
31,350	31,400	5,828	4,706	6,315	4,820
31,400	31,450	5,842	4,714	6,329	4,834
31,450	31,500	5,856	4,721	6,343	4,848
31,500	31,550	5,870	4,729	6,357	4,862
31,550	31,600	5,884	4,736	6,371	4,876
31,600	31,650	5,898	4,744	6,385	4,890
31,650	31,700	5,912	4,751	6,399	4,904
31,700	31,750	5,926	4,759	6,413	4,918
31,750	31,800	5,940	4,766	6,427	4,932
31,800	31,850	5,954	4,774	6,441	4,946
31,850	31,900	5,968	4,781	6,455	4,960
31,900	31,950	5,982	4,789	6,469	4,974
31,950	32,000	5,996	4,796	6,483	4,988

This column must also be used by a qualifying widow(er)

Continued on next page

© 1983, 1996 Instructional Horizons. Produced and Distributed by J. Weston Walch, Publisher, Portland, Maine 04104-0658

Consumer Math Success Kit

34. Income Tax

1994 Tax Table—*Continued*

If line 37 (taxable income) is— At least	But less than	Single	Married filing jointly	Married filing separately	Head of a household
32,000					
32,000	32,050	6 010	4,804	6 497	5,002
32,050	32,100	6,024	4,811	6 511	5,016
32,100	32,150	6 038	4,819	6 525	5,030
32,150	32,200	6 052	4,826	6 539	5,044
32,200	32,250	6 066	4 834	6,553	5,058
32,250	32,300	6 080	4,841	6 567	5,072
32,300	32,350	6 094	4,849	6,581	5,086
32,350	32,400	6 108	4,856	6 595	5,100
32,400	32,450	6,122	4,864	6 609	5,114
32,450	32,500	6 136	4,871	6 623	5,128
32,500	32,550	6,150	4,879	6 637	5,142
32,550	32,600	6 164	4,886	6 651	5,156
32,600	32,650	6 178	4 894	6 665	5,170
32,650	32,700	6 192	4,901	6 679	5,184
32,700	32,750	6 206	4,909	6 693	5,198
32,750	32,800	6 220	4,916	6 707	5,212
32,800	32,850	6 234	4,924	6 721	5,226
32,850	32,900	6 248	4,931	6 735	5,240
32,900	32,950	6 262	4,939	6 749	5,254
32,950	33,000	6 276	4,946	6 763	5,268
33,000					
33,000	33,050	6 290	4,954	6,777	5,282
33,050	33,100	6 304	4,961	6 791	5,296
33,100	33,150	6,318	4,969	6 805	5,310
33,150	33,200	6 332	4,976	6,819	5,324
33,200	33,250	6,346	4,984	6,833	5,338
33,250	33,300	6 360	4,991	6 847	5,352
33,300	33,350	6,374	4,999	6,861	5,366
33,350	33,400	6,388	5,006	6,875	5,380
33,400	33,450	6,402	5,014	6,889	5,394
33,450	33,500	6,416	5,021	6,903	5,408
33,500	33,550	6,430	5,029	6,917	5,422
33,550	33,600	6 444	5,036	6,931	5,436
33,600	33,650	6,458	5,044	6 945	5,450
33,650	33,700	6 472	5,051	6 959	5,464
33,700	33,750	6,486	5,059	6 973	5,478
33,750	33,800	6,500	5,066	6,987	5,492
33,800	33,850	6 514	5,074	7,001	5,506
33,850	33,900	6 528	5,081	7 015	5,520
33,900	33,950	6 542	5,089	7,029	5,534
33,950	34,000	6 556	5,096	7 043	5,548
34,000					
34,000	34,050	6 570	5,104	7 057	5,562
34,050	34,100	6 584	5,111	7 071	5,576
34,100	34,150	6,598	5,119	7 085	5,590
34,150	34,200	6 612	5,126	7,099	5,604
34,200	34,250	6,626	5,134	7,113	5,618
34,250	34,300	6,640	5,141	7,127	5,632
34,300	34,350	6 654	5,149	7 141	5,646
34,350	34,400	6,668	5,156	7 155	5,660
34,400	34,450	6,682	5,164	7 169	5,674
34,450	34,500	6,696	5,171	7,183	5,688
34,500	34,550	6,710	5,179	7,197	5,702
34,550	34,600	6 724	5,186	7,211	5,716
34,600	34,650	6 738	5,194	7 225	5,730
34,650	34,700	6 752	5,201	7 239	5,744
34,700	34,750	6 766	5,209	7 253	5,758
34,750	34,800	6 780	5 216	7 267	5,772
34,800	34,850	6 794	5,224	7 281	5 786
34,850	34,900	6 808	5,231	7 295	5,800
34,900	34,950	6 822	5,239	7 309	5,814
34,950	35,000	6 836	5,246	7 323	5,828

If line 37 (taxable income) is— At least	But less than	Single	Married filing jointly	Married filing separately	Head of a household
35,000					
35,000	35,050	6 850	5,254	7 337	5,842
35,050	35,100	6 864	5,261	7 351	5,856
35,100	35,150	6 878	5,269	7 365	5,870
35,150	35,200	6 892	5,276	7 379	5,884
35,200	35,250	6 906	5,284	7 393	5,898
35,250	35,300	6 920	5,291	7 407	5,912
35,300	35,350	6 934	5,299	7 421	5,926
35,350	35,400	6 948	5,306	7 435	5,940
35,400	35,450	6 962	5 314	7 449	5,954
35,450	35,500	6 976	5,321	7,463	5,968
35,500	35,550	6 990	5,329	7 477	5,982
35,550	35,600	7 004	5,336	7 491	5,996
35,600	35,650	7 018	5 344	7,505	6,010
35,650	35,700	7 032	5,351	7 519	6,024
35,700	35,750	7 046	5,359	7 533	6,038
35,750	35,800	7 060	5,366	7 547	6,052
35,800	35,850	7 074	5,374	7 561	6,066
35,850	35,900	7 088	5,381	7 575	6,080
35,900	35,950	7 102	5,389	7,589	6,094
35,950	36,000	7 116	5 396	7 603	6,108
36,000					
36,000	36,050	7 130	5,404	7,617	6,122
36,050	36,100	7 144	5,411	7,631	6,136
36,100	36,150	7 158	5 419	7 645	6,150
36,150	36,200	7 172	5,426	7,659	6,164
36,200	36,250	7 186	5,434	7,673	6,178
36,250	36,300	7 200	5,441	7,687	6,192
36,300	36,350	7 214	5,449	7,701	6,206
36,350	36,400	7 228	5,456	7,715	6,220
36,400	36,450	7,242	5,464	7,729	6,234
36,450	36,500	7 256	5,471	7,743	6,248
36,500	36,550	7,270	5,479	7,757	6,262
36,550	36,600	7,284	5,486	7,771	6,276
36,600	36,650	7,298	5 494	7 785	6,290
36,650	36,700	7 312	5,501	7 799	6,304
36,700	36,750	7 326	5,509	7 813	6,318
36,750	36,800	7 340	5,516	7,827	6,332
36,800	36,850	7 354	5,524	7,841	6,346
36,850	36,900	7 368	5,531	7 855	6,360
36,900	36,950	7 382	5,539	7 869	6,374
36,950	37,000	7 396	5,546	7 883	6,388
37,000					
37,000	37,050	7 410	5,554	7 897	6,402
37,050	37,100	7 424	5,561	7 911	6,416
37,100	37,150	7 438	5,569	7 925	6,430
37,150	37,200	7 452	5,576	7 939	6,444
37,200	37,250	7 466	5,584	7,953	6,458
37,250	37,300	7 480	5,591	7,967	6,472
37,300	37,350	7 494	5,599	7,981	6,486
37,350	37,400	7 508	5,606	7,995	6,500
37,400	37,450	7,522	5,614	8,009	6,514
37,450	37,500	7,536	5,621	8,023	6,528
37,500	37,550	7,550	5,629	8,037	6,542
37,550	37,600	7,564	5,636	8 051	6,556
37,600	37,650	7 578	5,644	8 065	6,570
37,650	37,700	7 592	5,651	8 079	6,584
37,700	37,750	7 606	5,659	8 093	6,598
37,750	37,800	7 620	5,666	8 107	6,612
37,800	37,850	7 634	5,674	8 121	6,626
37,850	37,900	7 648	5,681	8 135	6,640
37,900	37,950	7 662	5,689	8,149	6,654
37,950	38,000	7 676	5 696	8 163	6 668

If line 37 (taxable income) is— At least	But less than	Single	Married filing jointly	Married filing separately	Head of a household
38,000					
38,000	38,050	7 690	5,707	8 177	6,682
38,050	38,100	7 704	5,721	8 191	6,696
38,100	38,150	7 718	5,735	8 205	6 710
38,150	38,200	7 732	5,749	8 219	6 724
38,200	38,250	7 746	5,763	8 233	6,738
38,250	38,300	7 760	5,777	8 247	6,752
38,300	38,350	7 774	5,791	8 261	6,766
38,350	38,400	7 788	5,805	8 275	6,780
38,400	38,450	7 802	5,819	8 289	6,794
38,450	38,500	7 816	5,833	8 303	6,808
38,500	38,550	7 830	5,847	8 317	6,822
38,550	38,600	7 844	5,861	8 331	6,836
38,600	38,650	7 858	5,875	8 345	6,850
38,650	38,700	7 872	5,889	8 359	6,864
38,700	38,750	7 886	5,903	8 373	6,878
38,750	38,800	7 900	5,917	8 387	6,892
38,800	38,850	7 914	5,931	8 401	6,906
38,850	28,900	7 928	5,945	8 415	6,920
38,900	38,950	7 942	5,959	8 429	6,934
38,950	39,000	7 956	5,973	8 443	6,948
39,000					
39,000	39,050	7,970	5,987	8 457	6,962
39,050	39,100	7 984	6,001	8 471	6,976
39,100	39,150	7 998	6,015	8 485	6,990
39,150	39,200	8,012	6 029	8 499	7,004
39,200	39,250	8 026	6,043	8 513	7,018
39,250	39,300	8 040	6,057	8 527	7,032
39,300	39,350	8 054	6,071	8 541	7,046
39,350	39,400	8 068	6,085	8 555	7,060
39,400	39,450	8,082	6,099	8 569	7,074
39,450	39,500	8,096	6 113	8 583	7,088
39,500	39,550	8,110	6,127	8 597	7,102
39,550	39,600	8 124	6,141	8 611	7,116
39,600	39,650	8,138	6,155	8 625	7,130
39,650	39,700	8,152	6,169	8 639	7,144
39,700	39,750	8 166	6,183	8 653	7,158
39,750	39,800	8 180	6,197	8 667	7,172
39,800	39,850	8 194	6,211	8 681	7,186
39,850	39,900	8,208	6,225	8 695	7,200
39,900	39,950	8 222	6,239	8 709	7,214
39,950	40,000	8 236	6 253	8 723	7,228
40,000					
40,000	40,050	8 250	6,267	8 737	7,242
40,050	40,100	8 264	6,281	8 751	7,256
40,100	40,150	8 278	6,295	8 765	7,270
40,150	40,200	8 292	6,309	8 779	7,284
40,200	40,250	8,306	6,323	8 793	7,298
40,250	40,300	8 320	6,337	8 807	7,312
40,300	40,350	8 334	6,351	8 821	7,326
40,350	40,400	8 348	6,365	8 835	7,340
40,400	40,450	8 362	6,379	8 849	7,354
40,450	40,500	8 376	6,393	8 863	7,368
40,500	40,550	8 390	6,407	8 877	7,382
40,550	40,600	8 404	6,421	8,891	7,396
40,600	40,650	8 418	6,435	8 905	7,410
40,650	40,700	8,432	6,449	8 919	7,424
40,700	40,750	8,446	6,463	8 933	7,438
40,750	40,800	8 460	6,477	8 947	7,452
40,800	40,850	8 474	6,491	8 961	7,466
40,850	40,900	8 488	6,505	8 975	7,480
40,900	40,950	8,502	6,519	8 989	7,494
40,950	41,000	8 516	6,533	9 003	7,508

This column must also be used by a qualifying widow(er)

Continued on next page

Consumer Math Success Kit

34. Income Tax

1994 Tax Table—*Continued*

If line 37 (taxable income) is—		And you are—			
At least	But less than	Single	Married filing jointly	Married filing separately	Head of a household
			Your tax is—		

41,000

At least	But less than	Single	Married filing jointly	Married filing separately	Head of a household
41,000	41,050	8,530	6,547	9,017	7,522
41,050	41,100	8,544	6,561	9,031	7,536
41,100	41,150	8,558	6,575	9,045	7,550
41,150	41,200	8,572	6,589	9,059	7,564
41,200	41,250	8,586	6,603	9,073	7,578
41,250	41,300	8,600	6,617	9,087	7,592
41,300	41,350	8,614	6,631	9,101	7,606
41,350	41,400	8,628	6,645	9,115	7,620
41,400	41,450	8,642	6,659	9,129	7,634
41,450	41,500	8,656	6,673	9,143	7,648
41,500	41,550	8,670	6,687	9,157	7,662
41,550	41,600	8,684	6,701	9,171	7,676
41,600	41,650	8,698	6,715	9,185	7,690
41,650	41,700	8,712	6,729	9,199	7,704
41,700	41,750	8,726	6,743	9,213	7,718
41,750	41,800	8,740	6,757	9,227	7,732
41,800	41,850	8,754	6,771	9,241	7,746
41,850	41,900	8,768	6,785	9,255	7,760
41,900	41,950	8,782	6,799	9,269	7,774
41,950	42,000	8,796	6,813	9,283	7,788

42,000

At least	But less than	Single	Married filing jointly	Married filing separately	Head of a household
42,000	42,050	8,810	6,827	9,297	7,802
42,050	42,100	8,824	6,841	9,311	7,816
42,100	42,150	8,838	6,855	9,325	7,830
42,150	42,200	8,852	6,869	9,339	7,844
42,200	42,250	8,866	6,883	9,353	7,858
42,250	42,300	8,880	6,897	9,367	7,872
42,300	42,350	8,894	6,911	9,381	7,886
42,350	42,400	8,908	6,925	9,395	7,900
42,400	42,450	8,922	6,939	9,409	7,914
42,450	42,500	8,936	6,953	9,423	7,928
42,500	42,550	8,950	6,967	9,437	7,942
42,550	42,600	8,964	6,981	9,451	7,956
42,600	42,650	8,978	6,995	9,465	7,970
42,650	42,700	8,992	7,009	9,479	7,984
42,700	42,750	9,006	7,023	9,493	7,998
42,750	42,800	9,020	7,037	9,507	8,012
42,800	42,850	9,034	7,051	9,521	8,026
42,850	42,900	9,048	7,065	9,535	8,040
42,900	42,950	9,062	7,079	9,549	8,054
42,950	43,000	9,076	7,093	9,563	8,068

43,000

At least	But less than	Single	Married filing jointly	Married filing separately	Head of a household
43,000	43,050	9,090	7,107	9,577	8,082
43,050	43,100	9,104	7,121	9,591	8,096
43,100	43,150	9,118	7,135	9,605	8,110
43,150	43,200	9,132	7,149	9,619	8,124
43,200	43,250	9,146	7,163	9,633	8,138
43,250	43,300	9,160	7,177	9,647	8,152
43,300	43,350	9,174	7,191	9,661	8,166
43,350	43,400	9,188	7,205	9,675	8,180
43,400	43,450	9,202	7,219	9,689	8,194
43,450	43,500	9,216	7,233	9,703	8,208
43,500	43,550	9,230	7,247	9,717	8,222
43,550	43,600	9,244	7,261	9,731	8,236
43,600	43,650	9,258	7,275	9,745	8,250
43,650	43,700	9,272	7,289	9,759	8,264
43,700	43,750	9,286	7,303	9,773	8,278
43,750	43,800	9,300	7,317	9,787	8,292
43,800	43,850	9,314	7,331	9,801	8,306
43,850	43,900	9,328	7,345	9,815	8,320
43,900	43,950	9,342	7,359	9,829	8,334
43,950	44,000	9,356	7,373	9,843	8,348

44,000

At least	But less than	Single	Married filing jointly	Married filing separately	Head of a household
44,000	44,050	9,370	7,387	9,857	8,362
44,050	44,100	9,384	7,401	9,871	8,376
44,100	44,150	9,398	7,415	9,885	8,390
44,150	44,200	9,412	7,429	9,899	8,404
44,200	44,250	9,426	7,443	9,913	8,418
44,250	44,300	9,440	7,457	9,927	8,432
44,300	44,350	9,454	7,471	9,941	8,446
44,350	44,400	9,468	7,485	9,955	8,460
44,400	44,450	9,482	7,499	9,969	8,474
44,450	44,500	9,496	7,513	9,983	8,488
44,500	44,550	9,510	7,527	9,997	8,502
44,550	44,600	9,524	7,541	10,011	8,516
44,600	44,650	9,538	7,555	10,025	8,530
44,650	44,700	9,552	7,569	10,039	8,544
44,700	44,750	9,566	7,583	10,053	8,558
44,750	44,800	9,580	7,597	10,067	8,572
44,800	44,850	9,594	7,611	10,081	8,586
44,850	44,900	9,608	7,625	10,095	8,600
44,900	44,950	9,622	7,639	10,109	8,614
44,950	45,000	9,636	7,653	10,123	8,628

45,000

At least	But less than	Single	Married filing jointly	Married filing separately	Head of a household
45,000	45,050	9,650	7,667	10,137	8,642
45,050	45,100	9,664	7,681	10,151	8,656
45,100	45,150	9,678	7,695	10,165	8,670
45,150	45,200	9,692	7,709	10,179	8,684
45,200	45,250	9,706	7,723	10,193	8,698
45,250	45,300	9,720	7,737	10,207	8,712
45,300	45,350	9,734	7,751	10,221	8,726
45,350	45,400	9,748	7,765	10,235	8,740
45,400	45,450	9,762	7,779	10,249	8,754
45,450	45,500	9,776	7,793	10,263	8,768
45,500	45,550	9,790	7,807	10,277	8,782
45,550	45,600	9,804	7,821	10,291	8,796
45,600	45,650	9,818	7,835	10,305	8,810
45,650	45,700	9,832	7,849	10,319	8,824
45,700	45,750	9,846	7,863	10,333	8,838
45,750	45,800	9,860	7,877	10,347	8,852
45,800	45,850	9,874	7,891	10,361	8,866
45,850	45,900	9,888	7,905	10,375	8,880
45,900	45,950	9,902	7,919	10,389	8,894
45,950	46,000	9,916	7,933	10,405	8,908

46,000

At least	But less than	Single	Married filing jointly	Married filing separately	Head of a household
46,000	46,050	9,930	7,947	10,420	8,922
46,050	46,100	9,944	7,961	10,436	8,936
46,100	46,150	9,958	7,975	10,451	8,950
46,150	46,200	9,972	7,989	10,467	8,964
46,200	46,250	9,986	8,003	10,482	8,978
46,250	46,300	10,000	8,017	10,498	8,992
46,300	46,350	10,014	8,031	10,513	9,006
46,350	46,400	10,028	8,045	10,529	9,020
46,400	46,450	10,042	8,059	10,544	9,034
46,450	46,500	10,056	8,073	10,560	9,048
46,500	46,550	10,070	8,087	10,575	9,062
46,550	46,600	10,084	8,101	10,591	9,076
46,600	46,650	10,098	8,115	10,606	9,090
46,650	46,700	10,112	8,129	10,622	9,104
46,700	46,750	10,126	8,143	10,637	9,118
46,750	46,800	10,140	8,157	10,653	9,132
46,800	46,850	10,154	8,171	10,668	9,146
46,850	46,900	10,168	8,185	10,684	9,160
46,900	46,950	10,182	8,199	10,699	9,174
46,950	47,000	10,196	8,213	10,715	9,188

47,000

At least	But less than	Single	Married filing jointly	Married filing separately	Head of a household
47,000	47,050	10,210	8,227	10,730	9,202
47,050	47,100	10,224	8,241	10,746	9,216
47,100	47,150	10,238	8,255	10,761	9,230
47,150	47,200	10,252	8,269	10,777	9,244
47,200	47,250	10,266	8,283	10,792	9,258
47,250	47,300	10,280	8,297	10,808	9,272
47,300	47,350	10,294	8,311	10,823	9,286
47,350	47,400	10,308	8,325	10,839	9,300
47,400	47,450	10,322	8,339	10,854	9,314
47,450	47,500	10,336	8,353	10,870	9,328
47,500	47,550	10,350	8,367	10,885	9,342
47,550	47,600	10,364	8,381	10,901	9,356
47,600	47,650	10,378	8,395	10,916	9,370
47,650	47,700	10,392	8,409	10,932	9,384
47,700	47,750	10,406	8,423	10,947	9,398
47,750	47,800	10,420	8,437	10,963	9,412
47,800	47,850	10,434	8,451	10,978	9,426
47,850	47,900	10,448	8,465	10,994	9,440
47,900	47,950	10,462	8,479	11,009	9,454
47,950	48,000	10,476	8,493	11,025	9,468

48,000

At least	But less than	Single	Married filing jointly	Married filing separately	Head of a household
48,000	48,050	10,490	8,507	11,040	9,482
48,050	48,100	10,504	8,521	11,056	9,496
48,100	48,150	10,518	8,535	11,071	9,510
48,150	48,200	10,532	8,549	11,087	9,524
48,200	48,250	10,546	8,563	11,102	9,538
48,250	48,300	10,560	8,577	11,118	9,552
48,300	48,350	10,574	8,591	11,133	9,566
48,350	48,400	10,588	8,605	11,149	9,580
48,400	48,450	10,602	8,619	11,164	9,594
48,450	48,500	10,616	8,633	11,180	9,608
48,500	48,550	10,630	8,647	11,195	9,622
48,550	48,600	10,644	8,661	11,211	9,636
48,600	48,650	10,658	8,675	11,226	9,650
48,650	48,700	10,672	8,689	11,242	9,664
48,700	48,750	10,686	8,703	11,257	9,678
48,750	48,800	10,700	8,717	11,273	9,692
48,800	48,850	10,714	8,731	11,288	9,706
48,850	48,900	10,728	8,745	11,304	9,720
48,900	48,950	10,742	8,759	11,319	9,734
48,950	49,000	10,756	8,773	11,335	9,748

49,000

At least	But less than	Single	Married filing jointly	Married filing separately	Head of a household
49,000	49,050	10,770	8,787	11,350	9,762
49,050	49,100	10,784	8,801	11,366	9,776
49,100	49,150	10,798	8,815	11,381	9,790
49,150	49,200	10,812	8,829	11,397	9,804
49,200	49,250	10,826	8,843	11,412	9,818
49,250	49,300	10,840	8,857	11,428	9,832
49,300	49,350	10,854	8,871	11,443	9,846
49,350	49,400	10,868	8,885	11,459	9,860
49,400	49,450	10,882	8,899	11,474	9,874
49,450	49,500	10,896	8,913	11,490	9,888
49,500	49,550	10,910	8,927	11,505	9,902
49,550	49,600	10,924	8,941	11,521	9,916
49,600	49,650	10,938	8,955	11,536	9,930
49,650	49,700	10,952	8,969	11,552	9,944
49,700	49,750	10,966	8,983	11,567	9,958
49,750	49,800	10,980	8,997	11,583	9,972
49,800	49,850	10,994	9,011	11,598	9,986
49,850	49,900	11,008	9,025	11,614	10,000
49,900	49,950	11,022	9,039	11,629	10,014
49,950	50,000	11,036	9,053	11,645	10,028

This column must also be used by a qualifying widow(er)

Continued on next page

© 1983, 1996 Instructional Horizons. Produced and Distributed by J. Weston Walch, Publisher, Portland, Maine 04104-0658

Consumer Math Success Kit

34. Income Tax

1994 Tax Table—*Continued*

50,000

At least	But less than	Single	Married filing jointly	Married filing separately	Head of a household
50,000	50,050	11 050	9 067	11 660	10 042
50,050	50,100	11 064	9 081	11 676	10,056
50,100	50,150	11 078	9 095	11 691	10,070
50,150	50,200	11 092	9,109	11 707	10,084
50,200	50,250	11 106	9,123	11 722	10 098
50,250	50,300	11 120	9,137	11 738	10,112
50,300	50,350	11 134	9,151	11 753	10,126
50,350	50,400	11,148	9,165	11 769	10,140
50,400	50,450	11 162	9 179	11,784	10,154
50,450	50,500	11,176	9 193	11 800	10,168
50,500	50,550	11 190	9,207	11 815	10,182
50,550	50,600	11 204	9,221	11 831	10,196
50,600	50,650	11 218	9,235	11 846	10 210
50,650	50,700	11 232	9 249	11 862	10,224
50,700	50,750	11 246	9,263	11 877	10,238
50,750	50,800	11 260	9 277	11,893	10,252
50,800	50,850	11 274	9,291	11 908	10,266
50,850	50,900	11,288	9,305	11 924	10,280
50,900	50,950	11 302	9,319	11 939	10,294
50,950	51,000	11 316	9 333	11 955	10,308

51,000

At least	But less than	Single	Married filing jointly	Married filing separately	Head of a household
51,000	51,050	11,330	9,347	11 970	10,322
51,050	51,100	11,344	9,361	11,986	10,336
51,100	51,150	11,358	9,375	12,001	10,350
51,150	51,200	11,372	9,389	12 017	10,364
51,200	51,250	11,386	9,403	12,032	10,378
51,250	51,300	11 400	9,417	12,048	10,392
51,300	51,350	11 414	9,431	12,063	10,406
51,350	51,400	11 428	9,445	12,079	10,420
51,400	51,450	11,442	9,459	12 094	10,434
51,450	51,500	11,456	9,473	12,110	10,448
51,500	51,550	11,470	9,487	12,125	10,462
51,550	51,600	11 484	9,501	12 141	10,476
51,600	51,650	11 498	9,515	12,156	10,490
51,650	51,700	11 512	9,529	12 172	10,504
51,700	51,750	11 526	9,543	12 187	10,518
51,750	51,800	11,540	9,557	12 203	10,532
51,800	51,850	11,554	9,571	12 218	10,546
51,850	51,900	11,568	9,585	12 234	10,560
51,900	51,950	11 582	9,599	12,249	10,574
51,950	52,000	11,596	9,613	12 265	10,588

52,000

At least	But less than	Single	Married filing jointly	Married filing separately	Head of a household
52,000	52,050	11 610	9,627	12 280	10,602
52,050	52,100	11 624	9,641	12,296	10,616
52,100	52,150	11,638	9,655	12,311	10,630
52,150	52,200	11,652	9,669	12,327	10,644
52,200	52,250	11,666	9,683	12 342	10,658
52,250	52,300	11,680	9,697	12,358	10,672
52,300	52,350	11,694	9,711	12,373	10,686
52,350	52,400	11,708	9,725	12,389	10,700
52,400	52,450	11,722	9,739	12,404	10,714
52,450	52,500	11 736	9,753	12 420	10,728
52,500	52,550	11,750	9,767	12,435	10,742
52,550	52,600	11,764	9,781	12,451	10 756
52,600	52,650	11,778	9,795	12,466	10,770
52,650	52,700	11 792	9,809	12,482	10,784
52,700	52,750	11 806	9,823	12,497	10,798
52,750	52,800	11,820	9,837	12,513	10,812
52,800	52,850	11 834	9,851	12 528	10,826
52,850	52,900	11 848	9,865	12 544	10,840
52,900	52,950	11 862	9,879	12 559	10,854
52,950	53,000	11,876	9,893	12 575	10,868

53,000

At least	But less than	Single	Married filing jointly	Married filing separately	Head of a household
53,000	53,050	11 890	9 907	12 590	10,882
53,050	53,100	11 904	9,921	12 606	10 896
53,100	53,150	11 918	9,935	12 621	10,910
53,150	53,200	11 932	9 949	12 637	10,924
53,200	53,250	11 946	9,963	12 652	10 938
53,250	53,300	11 960	9,977	12 668	10 952
53,300	53,350	11 974	9,991	12 683	10,966
53,350	53,400	11 988	10 005	12,699	10,980
53,400	53,450	12 002	10 019	12,714	10,994
53,450	53,500	12 016	10 033	12 730	11,008
53,500	53,550	12 030	10 047	12 745	11,022
53,550	53,600	12 044	10,061	12 761	11,036
53,600	53,650	12 058	10,075	12 776	11,050
53,650	53,700	12 072	10,089	12 792	11,064
53,700	53,750	12 086	10,103	12,807	11,078
53,750	53,800	12 100	10,117	12 823	11,092
53,800	53,850	12 114	10,131	12 838	11,106
53,850	53,900	12 128	10 145	12 854	11,120
53,900	53,950	12 142	10,159	12 869	11,134
53,950	54,000	12 156	10 173	12 885	11,148

54,000

At least	But less than	Single	Married filing jointly	Married filing separately	Head of a household
54,000	54,050	12 170	10,187	12,900	11 162
54,050	54,100	12 184	10,201	12 916	11,176
54,100	54,150	12 198	10,215	12 931	11,190
54,150	54,200	12 212	10,229	12 947	11,204
54,200	54,250	12 226	10,243	12,962	11,218
54,250	54,300	12 240	10,257	12 978	11,232
54,300	54,350	12 254	10,271	12 993	11,246
54,350	54,400	12 268	10,285	13 009	11,260
54,400	54,450	12 282	10,299	13 024	11,274
54,450	54,500	12 296	10,313	13 040	11 288
54,500	54,550	12 310	10,327	13 055	11 302
54,550	54,600	12 324	10,341	13 071	11 316
54,600	54,650	12 338	10 355	13 086	11,330
54,650	54,700	12 352	10,369	13 102	11,344
54,700	54,750	12 366	10,383	13 117	11,358
54,750	54,800	12 380	10,397	13,133	11,372
54,800	54,850	12 394	10,411	13 148	11,386
54,850	54,900	12 408	10,425	13 164	11,400
54,900	54,950	12,422	10,439	13 179	11,414
54,950	55,000	12 436	10,453	13 195	11,428

55,000

At least	But less than	Single	Married filing jointly	Married filing separately	Head of a household
55,000	55,050	12 450	10,467	13 210	11,442
55,050	55,100	12 464	10,481	13 226	11,456
55,100	55,150	12,478	10,495	13,241	11,470
55,150	55,200	12,494	10,509	13,257	11,484
55,200	55,250	12 509	10,523	13,272	11,498
55,250	55,300	12 525	10,537	13,288	11,512
55,300	55,350	12 540	10,551	13,303	11,526
55,350	55,400	12 555	10,565	13 319	11,540
55,400	55,450	12 571	10,579	13 334	11,554
55,450	55,500	12 587	10,593	13,350	11,568
55,500	55,550	12 602	10,607	13 365	11,582
55,550	55,600	12 618	10,621	13,381	11,596
55,600	55,650	12 633	10,635	13 396	11,610
55,650	55,700	12 649	10,649	13 412	11,624
55,700	55,750	12 664	10 663	13 427	11,638
55,750	55,800	12 680	10,677	13 443	11,652
55,800	55,850	12 695	10 691	13 458	11,666
55,850	55,900	12 711	10,705	13 474	11 680
55,900	55,950	12 726	10 719	13 489	11,694
55,950	56,000	12 742	10 733	13 505	11,708

56,000

At least	But less than	Single	Married filing jointly	Married filing separately	Head of a household
56,000	56,050	12 757	10 747	13 520	11 722
56,050	56,100	12 773	10 761	13 536	11 736
56,100	56,150	12 788	10 775	13 551	11,750
56,150	56,200	12 804	10,789	13 567	11,764
56,200	56,250	12 819	10,803	13 582	11,778
56,250	56,300	12 835	10,817	13 598	11,792
56,300	56,350	12 850	10 831	13,613	11,806
56,350	56,400	12 866	10,845	13 629	11,820
56,400	56,450	12 881	10,859	13 644	11,834
56,450	56,500	12 897	10,873	13 660	11,848
56,500	56,550	12 912	10 887	13 675	11,862
56,550	56,600	12 928	10 901	13 691	11,876
56,600	56,650	12 943	10,915	13 706	11,890
56,650	56,700	12 959	10,929	13 722	11,904
56,700	56,750	12 974	10,943	13 737	11,918
56,750	56,800	12 990	10,957	13 753	11,932
56,800	56,850	13 005	10 971	13 768	11,946
56,850	56,900	13,021	10,985	13 784	11,960
56,900	56,950	13 036	10,999	13 799	11,974
56,950	57,000	13 052	11,013	13 815	11,988

57,000

At least	But less than	Single	Married filing jointly	Married filing separately	Head of a household
57,000	57,050	13 067	11,027	13,830	12,002
57,050	57,100	13 083	11,041	13 846	12,016
57,100	57,150	13 098	11,055	13 861	12,030
57,150	57,200	13 114	11,069	13 877	12,044
57,200	57,250	13 129	11,083	13 892	12,058
57,250	57,300	13 145	11,097	13 908	12,072
57,300	57,350	13 160	11,111	13 923	12,086
57,350	57,400	13 176	11,125	13 939	12,100
57,400	57,450	13 191	11,139	13 954	12,114
57,450	57,500	13 207	11 153	13 970	12,128
57,500	57,550	13 222	11 167	13,985	12,142
57,550	57,600	13 238	11,181	14 001	12,156
57,600	57,650	13 253	11,195	14 016	12,170
57,650	57,700	13 269	11 209	14 032	12,184
57,700	57,750	13 284	11,223	14,047	12,198
57,750	57,800	13 300	11,237	14 063	12,212
57,800	57,850	13 315	11,251	14 078	12,226
57,850	57,900	13 331	11,265	14 094	12,240
57,900	57,950	13 346	11,279	14 109	12,254
57,950	58,000	13 362	11,293	14 125	12,268

58,000

At least	But less than	Single	Married filing jointly	Married filing separately	Head of a household
58,000	58,050	13,377	11,307	14 140	12,282
58,050	58,100	13,393	11,321	14,156	12,296
58,100	58,150	13,408	11,335	14 171	12,310
58,150	58,200	13 424	11,349	14,187	12,324
58,200	58,250	13 439	11,363	14,202	12,338
58,250	58,300	13,455	11,377	14 218	12,352
58,300	58,350	13,470	11,391	14 233	12,366
58,350	58,400	13,486	11,405	14 249	12,380
58,400	58,450	13 501	11,419	14,264	12,394
58,450	58,500	13,517	11,433	14 280	12,408
58,500	58,550	13 532	11,447	14 295	12,422
58,550	58,600	13,548	11,461	14,311	12,436
58,600	58,650	13,563	11,475	14 326	12,450
58,650	58,700	13 579	11,489	14 342	12,464
58,700	58,750	13 594	11,503	14,357	12,478
58,750	58,800	13,610	11,517	14 373	12,492
58,800	58,850	13,625	11,531	14 388	12,506
58,850	58,900	13 641	11 545	14 404	12,520
58,900	58,950	13 656	11,559	14 419	12,534
58,950	59,000	13 672	11,573	14,435	12,548

This column must also be used by a qualifying widow(er)

Continued on next page

© 1983, 1996 Instructional Horizons. Produced and Distributed by J. Weston Walch, Publisher, Portland, Maine 04104-0658

Consumer Math Success Kit

34. Income Tax

1994 Tax Table—*Continued*

If line 37 (taxable income) is—		And you are—			
At least	But less than	Single	Married filing jointly	Married filing sepa rately	Head of a house hold
		Your tax is—			
59,000					
59,000	59,050	13 687	11 587	14 450	12,562
59,050	59,100	13 703	11 601	14 466	12 576
59,100	59,150	13 718	11 615	14 481	12 590
59,150	59,200	13 734	11 629	14 497	12,604
59,200	59,250	13 749	11 643	14 512	12 618
59,250	59,300	13 765	11 657	14 528	12,632
59,300	59,350	13 780	11 671	14 543	12,646
59,350	59,400	13 796	11,685	14 559	12 660
59,400	59,450	13 811	11,699	14 574	12 674
59,450	59,500	13 827	11,713	14 590	12,688
59,500	59,550	13 842	11 727	14 605	12,702
59,550	59,600	13 858	11 741	14 621	12,716
59,600	59,650	13 873	11,755	14 636	12,730
59,650	59,700	13 889	11 769	14 652	12,744
59,700	59,750	13,904	11,783	14 667	12,758
59,750	59,800	13 920	11,797	14 683	12,772
59,800	59,850	13 935	11 811	14 698	12,786
59,850	59,900	13 951	11,825	14 714	12,800
59,900	59,950	13 966	11 839	14 729	12,814
59,950	60,000	13 982	11 853	14 745	12 828
60,000					
60,000	60,050	13 997	11,867	14 760	12,842
60,050	60,100	14 013	11 881	14 776	12 856
60,100	60,150	14 028	11,895	14 791	12 870
60,150	60,200	14 044	11 909	14 807	12 884
60,200	60,250	14,059	11 923	14,822	12,898
60,250	60,300	14 075	11 937	14 838	12 912
60,300	60,350	14 090	11,951	14 853	12,926
60,350	60,400	14 106	11 965	14 869	12,940
60,400	60,450	14,121	11 979	14 884	12,954
60,450	60,500	14 137	11,993	14 900	12 968
60,500	60,550	14 152	12,007	14 915	12,982
60,550	60,600	14 168	12 021	14 931	12 996
60,600	60,650	14 183	12 035	14 946	13,010
60,650	60,700	14 199	12,049	14 962	13,024
60,700	60,750	14 214	12 063	14 977	13 038
60,750	60,800	14 230	12,077	14 993	13,052
60,800	60,850	14 245	12 091	15 008	13,066
60,850	60,900	14,261	12 105	15,024	13,080
60,900	60,950	14 276	12 119	15 039	13,094
60,950	61,000	14 292	12 133	15 055	13,108
61,000					
61,000	61,050	14 307	12,147	15 070	13,122
61,050	61,100	14 323	12 161	15 086	13 136
61,100	61,150	14 338	12 175	15 101	13,150
61,150	61,200	14 354	12,189	15 117	13,164
61,200	61,250	14 369	12 203	15 132	13,178
61,250	61,300	14 385	12 217	15 148	13,192
61,300	61,350	14 400	12,231	15 163	13,206
61,350	61,400	14 416	12,245	15 179	13,220
61,400	61,450	14 431	12 259	15 194	13,234
61,450	61,500	14 447	12 273	15 210	13,248
61,500	61,550	14 462	12,287	15 225	13,262
61,550	61,600	14 478	12 301	15 241	13,276
61,600	61,650	14 493	12,315	15 256	13 290
61,650	61,700	14 509	12 329	15 272	13,304
61,700	61,750	14 524	12 343	15 287	13,318
61,750	61,800	14 540	12 357	15 303	13 332
61,800	61,850	14 555	12,371	15 318	13,346
61,850	61,900	14 571	12 385	15 334	13,360
61,900	61,950	14 586	12,399	15 349	13 374
61,950	62,000	14 602	12 413	15 365	13 388
62,000					
62,000	62,050	14 617	12 427	15 380	13,402
62,050	62,100	14 633	12 441	15 396	13,416
62,100	62,150	14 648	12 455	15 411	13 430
62,150	62,200	14 664	12 469	15 427	13 444
62,200	62,250	14 679	12,483	15 442	13 458
62,250	62,300	14 695	12 497	15 458	13 472
62,300	62,350	14 710	12 511	15 473	13,486
62,350	62,400	14 726	12 525	15 489	13 500
62,400	62,450	14 741	12 539	15 504	13 514
62,450	62,500	14 757	12 553	15 520	13,528
62,500	62,550	14 772	12 567	15 535	13,542
62,550	62,600	14 788	12 581	15 551	13 556
62,600	62,650	14 803	12 595	15 566	13,570
62,650	62,700	14 819	12 609	15 582	13,584
62,700	62,750	14 834	12 623	15 597	13,598
62,750	62,800	14 850	12 637	15 613	13,612
62,800	62,850	14 865	12 651	15 628	13 626
62,850	62,900	14 881	12 665	15 644	13 640
62,900	62,950	14 896	12 679	15 659	13 654
62,950	63,000	14 912	12 693	15 675	13 668
63,000					
63,000	63,050	14 927	12 707	15 690	13 682
63,050	63,100	14 943	12 721	15 706	13 696
63,100	63,150	14 958	12 735	15 721	13 710
63,150	63,200	14 974	12 749	15 737	13 724
63,200	63,250	14 989	12 763	15 752	13 738
63,250	63,300	15 005	12 777	15 768	13 752
63,300	63,350	15 020	12 791	15 783	13,766
63,350	63,400	15 036	12,805	15 799	13 780
63,400	63,450	15 051	12 819	15 814	13 794
63,450	63,500	15 067	12 833	15 830	13,808
63,500	63,550	15 082	12 847	15 845	13 822
63,550	63,600	15 098	12,861	15 861	13,836
63,600	63,650	15 113	12 875	15 876	13 850
63,650	63,700	15 129	12 889	15 892	13,864
63,700	63,750	15 144	12 903	15 907	13,878
63,750	63,800	15 160	12 917	15 923	13 892
63,800	63,850	15 175	12 931	15 938	13 906
63,850	63,900	15 191	12 945	15 954	13 920
63,900	63,950	15 206	12 959	15 969	13,934
63,950	64,000	15 222	12,973	15 985	13 948
64,000					
64,000	64,050	15 237	12 987	16 000	13 962
64,050	64,100	15 253	13 001	16 016	13 976
64,100	64,150	15 268	13,015	16 031	13 990
64,150	64,200	15 284	13,029	16 047	14,004
64,200	64,250	15 299	13,043	16 062	14 018
64,250	64,300	15 315	13,057	16 078	14,032
64,300	64,350	15 330	13 071	16 093	14,046
64,350	64,400	15 346	13 085	16 109	14,060
64,400	64,450	15 361	13 099	16 124	14,074
64,450	64,500	15 377	13,113	16 140	14,088
64,500	64,550	15 392	13 127	16 155	14,102
64,550	64,600	15 408	13 141	16 171	14,116
64,600	64,650	15 423	13,155	16 186	14,130
64,650	64,700	15 439	13 169	16 202	14,144
64,700	64,750	15 454	13,183	16 217	14,158
64,750	64,800	15 470	13 197	16,233	14,172
64,800	64,850	15 485	13 211	16 248	14,186
64,850	64,900	15 501	13 225	16 264	14,200
64,900	64,950	15 516	13,239	16 279	14 214
64,950	65,000	15 532	13 253	16 295	14 228
65,000					
65,000	65,050	15 547	13 267	16 310	14 242
65,050	65,100	15 563	13 281	16 326	14 256
65,100	65,150	15 578	13 295	16 341	14 270
65,150	65,200	15 594	13 309	16 357	14 284
65,200	65,250	15 609	13 323	16 372	14 298
65,250	65,300	15 625	13 337	16 388	14 312
65,300	65,350	15 640	13 351	16 403	14 326
65,350	65,400	15 656	13 365	16 419	14 340
65,400	65,450	15 671	13 379	16 434	14 354
65,450	65,500	15 687	13 393	16 450	14 368
65,500	65,550	15 702	13 407	16 465	14 382
65,550	65,600	15 718	13 421	16 481	14 396
65,600	65,650	15 733	13 435	16 496	14 410
65,650	65,700	15 749	13 449	16 512	14 424
65,700	65,750	15 764	13 463	16 527	14 438
65,750	65,800	15 780	13 477	16 543	14 452
65,800	65,850	15 795	13 491	16 558	14 466
65,850	65,900	15 811	13 505	16 574	14 480
65,900	65,950	15 826	13 519	16 589	14 494
65,950	66,000	15 842	13 533	16 605	14 508
66,000					
66,000	66,050	15 857	13 547	16 620	14 522
66,050	66,100	15 873	13 561	16 636	14 536
66,100	66,150	15 888	13 575	16 651	14 550
66,150	66,200	15 904	13 589	16 667	14 564
66,200	66,250	15 919	13 603	16 682	14 578
66,250	66,300	15 935	13 617	16 698	14 592
66,300	66,350	15 950	13 631	16 713	14 606
66,350	66,400	15 966	13 645	16 729	14 620
66,400	66,450	15 981	13 659	16 744	14 634
66,450	66,500	15 997	13 673	16 760	14 648
66,500	66,550	16 012	13 687	16 775	14 662
66,550	66,600	16 028	13 701	16 791	14 676
66,600	66,650	16 043	13,715	16 806	14 690
66,650	66,700	16 059	13,729	16 822	14 704
66,700	66,750	16 074	13 743	16 837	14 718
66,750	66,800	16 090	13 757	16 853	14 732
66,800	66,850	16 105	13 771	16 868	14 746
66,850	66,900	16 121	13 785	16 884	14 760
66,900	66,950	16 136	13 799	16 899	14 774
66,950	67,000	16 152	13 813	16 915	14 788
67,000					
67,000	67,050	16 167	13 827	16 930	14 802
67,050	67,100	16 183	13 841	16 946	14 816
67,100	67,150	16 198	13 855	16 961	14 830
67,150	67,200	16 214	13,869	16 977	14 844
67,200	67,250	16 229	13 883	16 992	14,858
67,250	67,300	16 245	13 897	17 008	14,872
67,300	67,350	16 260	13 911	17 023	14,886
67,350	67,400	16 276	13 925	17 039	14 900
67,400	67,450	16 291	13 939	17 054	14 914
67,450	67,500	16 307	13,953	17 070	14 928
67,500	67,550	16 322	13 967	17 085	14 942
67,550	67,600	16 338	13,981	17 101	14 956
67,600	67,650	16 353	13,995	17 116	14 970
67,650	67,700	16 369	14 009	17 132	14,984
67,700	67,750	16 384	14 023	17 147	14 998
67,750	67,800	16 400	14 037	17 163	15 012
67,800	67,850	16 415	14 051	17 178	15 026
67,850	67,900	16 431	14,065	17 194	15 040
67,900	67,950	16 446	14 079	17 209	15 054
67,950	68,000	16 462	14 093	17 225	15,068

This column must also be used by a qualifying widow(er)

Continued on next page

173

Consumer Math Success Kit

34. Income Tax

1994 Tax Table—*Continued*

Left column group

If line 37 (taxable income) is— At least	But less than	Single	Married filing jointly	Married filing separately	Head of a household
68,000					
68,000	68,050	16,477	14,107	17,240	15,082
68,050	68,100	16 493	14,121	17 256	15,096
68,100	68,150	16,508	14,135	17 271	15,110
68,150	68,200	16 524	14 149	17,287	15,124
68,200	68,250	16,539	14,163	17,302	15,138
68,250	68,300	16 555	14,177	17,318	15,152
68,300	68,350	16,570	14,191	17 333	15,166
68,350	68,400	16 586	14,205	17,349	15,180
68,400	68,450	16,601	14,219	17,364	15,194
68,450	68,500	16,617	14,233	17,380	15,208
68,500	68,550	16,632	14,247	17 395	15,222
68,550	68,600	16 648	14,261	17,411	15,236
68,600	68,650	16,663	14,275	17,426	15,250
68,650	68,700	16 679	14,289	17,442	15,264
68,700	68,750	16 694	14,303	17 457	15,278
68,750	68,800	16,710	14,317	17 473	15,292
68,800	68,850	16,725	14,331	17,488	15,306
68,850	68,900	16,741	14,345	17,504	15,320
68,900	68,950	16,756	14,359	17,519	15,334
68,950	69,000	16,772	14,373	17,535	15,348
69,000					
69,000	69,050	16,787	14,387	17,550	15,362
69,050	69,100	16,803	14,401	17 566	15,376
69,100	69,150	16,818	14,415	17,581	15,390
69,150	69,200	16 834	14,429	17 597	15,404
69,200	69,250	16,849	14,443	17,612	15,418
69,250	69,300	16,865	14,457	17,628	15,432
69,300	69,350	16,880	14,471	17,643	15,446
69,350	69,400	16,896	14,485	17,659	15,460
69,400	69,450	16,911	14,499	17,674	15,474
69,450	69,500	16,927	14,513	17,690	15,488
69,500	69,550	16,942	14,527	17,705	15,502
69,550	69,600	16,958	14,541	17,721	15,516
69,600	69,650	16,973	14,555	17,736	15,530
69,650	69,700	16,989	14,569	17,752	15,544
69,700	69,750	17,004	14,583	17 767	15 558
69,750	69,800	17,020	14,597	17,783	15,572
69,800	69,850	17 035	14,611	17 798	15,586
69,850	69,900	17,051	14,625	17,814	15,600
69,900	69,950	17,066	14,639	17 829	15,614
69,950	70,000	17,082	14,653	17,845	15,628
70,000					
70,000	70,050	17,097	14,667	17,861	15,642
70,050	70,100	17,113	14,681	17,879	15,656
70,100	70,150	17,128	14,695	17,897	15,670
70,150	70,200	17,144	14,709	17,915	15,684
70,200	70,250	17,159	14,723	17,933	15,698
70,250	70,300	17,175	14,737	17,951	15,712
70,300	70,350	17,190	14,751	17,969	15,726
70,350	70,400	17,206	14,765	17,987	15,740
70,400	70,450	17,221	14,779	18,005	15,754
70,450	70,500	17,237	14 793	18,023	15,768
70,500	70,550	17,252	14,807	18,041	15,782
70,550	70,600	17 268	14,821	18,059	15,796
70,600	70,650	17,283	14,835	18,077	15,810
70,650	70,700	17,299	14,849	18,095	15,824
70,700	70,750	17 314	14,863	18 113	15,838
70,750	70,800	17,330	14,877	18,131	15,852
70,800	70,850	17 345	14,891	18 149	15,866
70,850	70,900	17,361	14,905	18,167	15,880
70,900	70,950	17,376	14,919	18,185	15,894
70,950	71,000	17,392	14,933	18,203	15,908

Middle column group

If line 37 (taxable income) is— At least	But less than	Single	Married filing jointly	Married filing separately	Head of a household
71,000					
71,000	71,050	17 407	14,947	18,221	15,922
71,050	71,100	17,423	14,961	18 239	15,936
71,100	71,150	17,438	14 975	18,257	15,950
71,150	71,200	17 454	14,989	18,275	15,964
71,200	71,250	17,469	15,003	18 293	15,978
71,250	71,300	17,485	15,017	18,311	15,992
71,300	71,350	17 500	15 031	18 329	16,006
71,350	71,400	17,516	15 045	18,347	16,020
71,400	71,450	17 531	15,059	18 365	16,034
71,450	71,500	17,547	15 073	18,383	16,048
71,500	71,550	17 562	15,087	18,401	16,062
71,550	71,600	17 578	15,101	18 419	16,076
71,600	71,650	17 593	15 115	18 437	16,090
71,650	71,700	17 609	15,129	18 455	16,104
71,700	71,750	17 624	15,143	18 473	16,118
71,750	71,800	17 640	15,157	18 491	16,132
71,800	71,850	17 655	15 171	18,509	16,146
71,850	71,900	17 671	15,185	18,527	16,160
71,900	71,950	17 686	15,199	18,545	16,174
71,950	72,000	17 702	15,213	18 563	16,188
72,000					
72,000	72,050	17 717	15,227	18 581	16,202
72,050	72,100	17,733	15 241	18 599	16,216
72,100	72,150	17 748	15,255	18,617	16,230
72,150	72,200	17 764	15,269	18 635	16,244
72,200	72,250	17 779	15,283	18,653	16,258
72,250	72,300	17,795	15,297	18,671	16,272
72,300	72,350	17 810	15,311	18,689	16,286
72,350	72,400	17,826	15 325	18,707	16,300
72,400	72,450	17 841	15,339	18,725	16,314
72,450	72,500	17,857	15,353	18,743	16,328
72,500	72,550	17,872	15,367	18,761	16,342
72,550	72,600	17 888	15,381	18,779	16,356
72,600	72,650	17,903	15,395	18,797	16,370
72,650	72,700	17,919	15,409	18,815	16,384
72,700	72,750	17,934	15,423	18,833	16,398
72,750	72,800	17,950	15 437	18,851	16,412
72,800	72,850	17,965	15,451	18 869	16,426
72,850	72,900	17,981	15,465	18,887	16,440
72,900	72,950	17 996	15,479	18,905	16,454
72,950	73,000	18 012	15 493	18,923	16,468
73,000					
73,000	73,050	18 027	15,507	18,941	16,482
73,050	73,100	18,043	15,521	18,959	16,496
73,100	73,150	18,058	15,535	18,977	16,510
73,150	73,200	18,074	15,549	18,995	16,524
73,200	73,250	18,089	15,563	19,013	16,538
73,250	73,300	18,105	15,577	19 031	16,552
73,300	73,350	18,120	15,591	19,049	16,566
73,350	73,400	18,136	15,605	19,067	16,580
73,400	73,450	18 151	15,619	19,085	16,594
73,450	73,500	18 167	15,633	19 103	16,608
73,500	73,550	18 182	15,647	19,121	16,622
73,550	73,600	18 198	15,661	19,139	16,636
73,600	73,650	18,213	15,675	19,157	16,650
73,650	73,700	18,229	15,689	19,175	16,664
73,700	73,750	18 244	15,703	19,193	16,678
73,750	73,800	18 260	15,717	19,211	16,692
73,800	73,850	18 275	15,731	19,229	16,706
73,850	73,900	18 291	15 745	19,247	16,720
73,900	73,950	18 306	15,759	19,265	16,734
73,950	74,000	18,322	15,773	19,283	16,748

Right column group

If line 37 (taxable income) is— At least	But less than	Single	Married filing jointly	Married filing separately	Head of a household
74,000					
74,000	74,050	18 337	15 787	19 301	16 762
74,050	74,100	18 353	15,801	19 319	16,776
74,100	74,150	18 368	15,815	19 337	16,790
74,150	74,200	18 384	15,829	19,355	16,804
74,200	74,250	18 399	15 843	19 373	16,818
74,250	74,300	18 415	15,857	19 391	16 832
74,300	74,350	18,430	15 871	19 409	16,846
74,350	74,400	18 446	15,885	19 427	16 860
74,400	74,450	18 461	15 899	19 445	16,874
74,450	74,500	18 477	15 913	19 463	16,888
74,500	74,550	18 492	15,927	19 481	16,902
74,550	74,600	18 508	15,941	19,499	16,916
74,600	74,650	18 523	15 955	19 517	16,930
74,650	74,700	18 539	15,969	19 535	16,944
74,700	74,750	18 554	15 983	19 553	16,958
74,750	74,800	18 570	15,997	19,571	16,972
74,800	74,850	18 585	16 011	19 589	16,986
74,850	74,900	18,601	16 025	19 607	17,000
74,900	74,950	18 616	16,039	19 625	17 014
74,950	75,000	18,632	16 053	19 643	17,028
75,000					
75,000	75,050	18 647	16 067	19 661	17,042
75,050	75,100	18 663	16,081	19 679	17,056
75,100	75,150	18 678	16,095	19 697	17,070
75,150	75,200	18 694	16,109	19 715	17 084
75,200	75,250	18 709	16,123	19 733	17 098
75,250	75,300	18,725	16,137	19 751	17,112
75,300	75,350	18,740	16,151	19,769	17,126
75,350	75,400	18 756	16,165	19 787	17,140
75,400	75,450	18 771	16,179	19 805	17,154
75,450	75,500	18,787	16,193	19,823	17,168
75,500	75,550	18 802	16,207	19 841	17 182
75,550	75,600	18,818	16,221	19,859	17,196
75,600	75,650	18,833	16,235	19 877	17,210
75,650	75,700	18,849	16,249	19 895	17,224
75,700	75,750	18,864	16,263	19,913	17,238
75,750	75,800	18,880	16,277	19 931	17,252
75,800	75,850	18,895	16,291	19 949	17,266
75,850	75,900	18,911	16,305	19,967	17,280
75,900	75,950	18,926	16,319	19 985	17,294
75,950	76,000	18,942	16,333	20 003	17,308
76,000					
76,000	76,050	18,957	16,347	20,021	17,322
76,050	76,100	18,973	16,361	20,039	17,336
76,100	76,150	18,988	16,375	20,057	17,350
76,150	76,200	19 004	16,389	20,075	17,364
76,200	76,250	19,019	16,403	20,093	17,378
76,250	76,300	19,035	16,417	20,111	17,392
76,300	76,350	19,050	16,431	20 129	17,406
76,350	76,400	19,066	16,445	20 147	17,420
76,400	76,450	19,081	16,459	20,165	17,434
76,450	76,500	19,097	16,473	20,183	17,448
76,500	76,550	19 112	16,487	20,201	17,462
76,550	76,600	19,128	16,501	20,219	17,476
76,600	76,650	19,143	16,515	20 237	17,490
76,650	76,700	19,159	16,529	20,255	17,504
76,700	76,750	19,174	16,543	20 273	17,518
76,750	76,800	19 190	16,557	20,291	17,532
76,800	76,850	19,205	16,571	20,309	17,546
76,850	76,900	19 221	16,585	20,327	17,560
76,900	76,950	19,236	16,599	20,345	17,574
76,950	77,000	19 252	16,613	20 363	17 588

This column must also be used by a qualifying widow(er)

Continued on next page

© 1983, 1996 Instructional Horizons. Produced and Distributed by J. Weston Walch, Publisher, Portland, Maine 04104-0658

Consumer Math Success Kit

34. Income Tax

1994 Tax Table—*Continued*

77,000

If line 37 (taxable income) is— At least	But less than	And you are— Single	Married filing jointly	Married filing separately	Head of a household
		Your tax is—			
77,000	77,050	19 267	16,627	20 381	17,602
77,050	77,100	19,283	16,641	20 399	17,616
77,100	77,150	19 298	16,655	20,417	17,630
77,150	77,200	19 314	16,669	20,435	17,644
77,200	77,250	19,329	16,683	20,453	17,658
77,250	77,300	19,345	16 697	20,471	17,672
77,300	77,350	19,360	16,711	20,489	17,686
77,350	77,400	19,376	16,725	20 507	17 700
77,400	77,450	19,391	16,739	20,525	17,714
77,450	77,500	19,407	16 753	20 543	17,728
77,500	77,550	19 422	16 767	20 561	17,742
77,550	77,600	19 438	16,781	20,579	17 756
77,600	77,650	19 453	16,795	20 597	17,770
77,650	77,700	19,469	16 809	20,615	17,784
77,700	77,750	19 484	16,823	20 633	17,798
77,750	77,800	19 500	16,837	20 651	17,812
77,800	77,850	19 515	16,851	20 669	17,826
77,850	77,900	19 531	16,865	20 687	17,840
77,900	77,950	19 546	16,879	20 705	17,854
77,950	78,000	19 562	16,893	20,723	17,868

78,000

At least	But less than	Single	Married filing jointly	Married filing separately	Head of a household
78,000	78,050	19 577	16,907	20,741	17,882
78,050	78,100	19 593	16,921	20,759	17,896
78,100	78,150	19 608	16,935	20,777	17,910
78,150	78,200	19,624	16,949	20,795	17,924
78,200	78,250	19,639	16,963	20,813	17,938
78,250	78,300	19,655	16,977	20,831	17,952
78,300	78,350	19,670	16,991	20,849	17,966
78,350	78,400	19,686	17,005	20,867	17,980
78,400	78,450	19,701	17,019	20,885	17,994
78,450	78,500	19,717	17,033	20,903	18,008
78,500	78,550	19 732	17 047	20,921	18,022
78,550	78,600	19,748	17,061	20,939	18,036
78,600	78,650	19,763	17,075	20,957	18,050
78,650	78,700	19,779	17,089	20,975	18,064
78,700	78,750	19,794	17,103	20 993	18,079
78,750	78,800	19 810	17,117	21,011	18,094
78,800	78,850	19,825	17,131	21,029	18,110
78,850	78,900	19,841	17,145	21,047	18,125
78,900	78,950	19,856	17,159	21,065	18,141
78,950	79,000	19,872	17,173	21,083	18,156

79,000

At least	But less than	Single	Married filing jointly	Married filing separately	Head of a household
79,000	79,050	19,887	17,187	21 101	18,172
79,050	79,100	19,903	17,201	21,119	18,187
79,100	79,150	19,918	17,215	21,137	18,203
79,150	79,200	19,934	17,229	21,155	18,218
79,200	79,250	19,949	17,243	21,173	18,234
79,250	79,300	19,965	17,257	21,191	18,249
79,300	79,350	19,980	17,271	21,209	18,265
79,350	79,400	19,996	17,285	21,227	18,280
79,400	79,450	20,011	17,299	21,245	18,296
79,450	79,500	20,027	17,313	21,263	18,311
79,500	79,550	20,042	17,327	21,281	18,327
79,550	79,600	20,058	17,341	21,299	18,342
79,600	79,650	20,073	17,355	21,317	18,358
79,650	79,700	20,089	17,369	21,335	18,373
79,700	79,750	20,104	17,383	21,353	18,389
79,750	79,800	20,120	17,397	21,371	18,404
79,800	79,850	20,135	17,411	21 389	18,420
79,850	79,900	20,151	17,425	21,407	18,435
79,900	79,950	20,166	17,439	21,425	18,451
79,950	80,000	20,182	17,453	21,443	18,466

80,000

At least	But less than	Single	Married filing jointly	Married filing separately	Head of a household
80,000	80,050	20 197	17,467	21 461	18,482
80,050	80,100	20 213	17,481	21 479	18,497
80,100	80,150	20 228	17,495	21,497	18,513
80,150	80,200	20 244	17 509	21,515	18,528
80,200	80,250	20 259	17,523	21,533	18,544
80,250	80,300	20 275	17,537	21,551	18,559
80,300	80,350	20 290	17,551	21 569	18 575
80,350	80,400	20 306	17,565	21 587	18,590
80,400	80,450	20 321	17,579	21,605	18 606
80,450	80,500	20 337	17,593	21,623	18,621
80,500	80,550	20 352	17,607	21 641	18,637
80,550	80,600	20 368	17,621	21 659	18,652
80,600	80,650	20 383	17,635	21 677	18,668
80,650	80,700	20 399	17,649	21 695	18,683
80,700	80,750	20 414	17,663	21 713	18,699
80,750	80,800	20 430	17,677	21 731	18,714
80,800	80,850	20 445	17,691	21,749	18 730
80,850	80,900	20 461	17,705	21 767	18,745
80,900	80,950	20 476	17,719	21,785	18,761
80,950	81,000	20 492	17,733	21,803	18,776

81,000

At least	But less than	Single	Married filing jointly	Married filing separately	Head of a household
81,000	81,050	20,507	17,747	21,821	18,792
81,050	81,100	20 523	17,761	21,839	18,807
81,100	81,150	20 538	17,775	21,857	18,823
81,150	81,200	20 554	17,789	21,875	18,838
81,200	81,250	20,569	17,803	21,893	18,854
81,250	81,300	20,585	17,817	21,911	18,869
81,300	81,350	20,600	17,831	21,929	18,885
81,350	81,400	20,616	17,845	21,947	18,900
81,400	81,450	20,631	17,859	21,965	18,916
81,450	81,500	20,647	17,873	21,983	18,931
81,500	81,550	20,662	17,887	22,001	18,947
81,550	81,600	20,678	17,901	22,019	18,962
81,600	81,650	20,693	17,915	22,037	18,978
81,650	81,700	20,709	17,929	22,055	18,993
81,700	81,750	20,724	17,943	22 073	19,009
81,750	81,800	20,740	17,957	22,091	19,024
81,800	81,850	20 755	17,971	22,109	19,040
81,850	81,900	20,771	17,985	22,127	19,055
81,900	81,950	20 786	17,999	22,145	19,071
81,950	82,000	20 802	18,013	22,163	19,086

82,000

At least	But less than	Single	Married filing jointly	Married filing separately	Head of a household
82,000	82,050	20,817	18,027	22,181	19,102
82,050	82,100	20,833	18,041	22,199	19,117
82,100	82,150	20,848	18,055	22,217	19,133
82,150	82,200	20,864	18,069	22,235	19,148
82,200	82,250	20,879	18,083	22,253	19,164
82,250	82,300	20,895	18,097	22,271	19,179
82,300	82,350	20,910	18,111	22,289	19,195
82,350	82,400	20,926	18,125	22,307	19,210
82,400	82,450	20,941	18,139	22,325	19,226
82,450	82,500	20,957	18,153	22,343	19,241
82,500	82,550	20,972	18,167	22,361	19,257
82,550	82,600	20,988	18,181	22,379	19,272
82,600	82,650	21,003	18,195	22,397	19,288
82,650	82,700	21,019	18,209	22,415	19,303
82,700	82,750	21,034	18,223	22,433	19,319
82,750	82,800	21,050	18,237	22,451	19,334
82,800	82,850	21,065	18,251	22,469	19,350
82,850	82,900	21,081	18,265	22,487	19,365
82,900	82,950	21,096	18,279	22,505	19,381
82,950	83,000	21,112	18 293	22,523	19,396

83,000

At least	But less than	Single	Married filing jointly	Married filing separately	Head of a household
83,000	83,050	21 127	18 307	22 541	19,412
83,050	83,100	21 143	18,321	22 559	19,427
83,100	83,150	21,158	18 335	22,577	19,443
83,150	83,200	21 174	18,349	22,595	19;458
83,200	83,250	21 189	18 363	22,613	19,474
83,250	83,300	21 205	18,377	22 631	19 489
83,300	83,350	21 220	18,391	22,649	19,505
83,350	83,400	21 236	18,405	22 667	19 520
83,400	83,450	21 251	18,419	22 685	19,536
83,450	83,500	21 267	18 433	22 703	19,551
83,500	83,550	21 282	18,447	22 721	19,567
83,550	83,600	21 298	18 461	22 739	19 582
83,600	83,650	21 313	18 475	22 757	19,598
83,650	83,700	21 329	18,489	22,775	19,613
83,700	83,750	21 344	18 503	22,793	19,629
83,750	83,800	21 360	18,517	22 811	19,644
83,800	83,850	21 375	18,531	22 829	19,660
83,850	83,900	21 391	18 545	22 847	19,675
83,900	83,950	21 406	18,559	22 865	19,691
83,950	84,000	21 422	18 573	22,883	19,706

84,000

At least	But less than	Single	Married filing jointly	Married filing separately	Head of a household
84,000	84,050	21,437	18,587	22,901	19,722
84,050	84,100	21 453	18,601	22,919	19,737
84,100	84,150	21,468	18,615	22,937	19,753
84,150	84,200	21 484	18,629	22,955	19,768
84,200	84,250	21,499	18,643	22,973	19,784
84,250	84,300	21 515	18,657	22,991	19,799
84,300	84,350	21 530	18,671	23,009	19,815
84,350	84,400	21,546	18,685	23,027	19,830
84,400	84,450	21 561	18,699	23,045	19,846
84,450	84,500	21 577	18,713	23,063	19,861
84,500	84,550	21 592	18,727	23,081	19,877
84,550	84,600	21 608	18 741	23,099	19,892
84,600	84,650	21 623	18,755	23,117	19,908
84,650	84,700	21 639	18,769	23,135	19,923
84,700	84,750	21 654	18,783	23,153	19,939
84,750	84,800	21 670	18,797	23,171	19,954
84,800	84,850	21 685	18,811	23,189	19,970
84,850	84,900	21 701	18,825	23,207	19,985
84,900	84,950	21,716	18,839	23,225	20,001
84,950	85,000	21,732	18,853	23,243	20,016

85,000

At least	But less than	Single	Married filing jointly	Married filing separately	Head of a household
85,000	85,050	21,747	18,867	23,261	20,032
85,050	85,100	21,763	18,881	23,279	20,047
85,100	85,150	21 778	13,895	23,297	20,063
85,150	85,200	21 794	18,909	23,315	20,078
85,200	85,250	21,809	18,923	23,333	20,094
85,250	85,300	21 825	18,937	23,351	20,109
85,300	85,350	21,840	18,951	23,369	20,125
85,350	85,400	21,856	18,965	23,387	20,140
85,400	85,450	21,871	18,979	23,405	20,156
85,450	85,500	21,887	18,993	23,423	20,171
85,500	85,550	21 902	19,007	23,441	20,187
85,550	85,600	21,918	19,021	23,459	20,202
85,600	85,650	21,933	19,035	23,477	20,218
85,650	85,700	21,949	19,049	23,495	20,233
85,700	85,750	21 964	19,063	23,513	20,249
85,750	85,800	21,980	19,077	23,531	20,264
85,800	85,850	21,995	19,091	23,549	20,280
85,850	85,900	22,011	19,105	23,567	20,295
85,900	85,950	22 026	19 119	23,585	20,311
85,950	86,000	22 042	19,133	23,603	20,326

This column must also be used by a qualifying widow(er)

Continued on next page

© 1983, 1996 Instructional Horizons. Produced and Distributed by J. Weston Walch, Publisher, Portland, Maine 04104-0658

Consumer Math Success Kit

34. Income Tax

1994 Tax Table—*Continued*

If line 37 (taxable income) is— At least	But less than	Single	Married filing jointly	Married filing separately	Head of a household
86,000					
86,000	86,050	22,057	19,147	23,621	20,342
86,050	86,100	22,073	19,161	23,639	20,357
86,100	86,150	22,088	19,175	23,657	20,373
86,150	86,200	22,104	19,189	23,675	20,388
86,200	86,250	22,119	19,203	23,693	20,404
86,250	86,300	22,135	19,217	23,711	20,419
86,300	86,350	22,150	19,231	23,729	20,435
86,350	86,400	22,166	19,245	23,747	20,450
86,400	86,450	22,181	19,259	23,765	20,466
86,450	86,500	22,197	19,273	23,783	20,481
86,500	86,550	22,212	19,287	23,801	20,497
86,550	86,600	22,228	19,301	23,819	20,512
86,600	86,650	22,243	19,315	23,837	20,528
86,650	86,700	22,259	19,329	23,855	20,543
86,700	86,750	22,274	19,343	23,873	20,559
86,750	86,800	22,290	19,357	23,891	20,574
86,800	86,850	22,305	19,371	23,909	20,590
86,850	86,900	22,321	19,385	23,927	20,605
86,900	86,950	22,336	19,399	23,945	20,621
86,950	87,000	22,352	19,413	23,963	20,636
87,000					
87,000	87,050	22,367	19,427	23,981	20,652
87,050	87,100	22,383	19,441	23,999	20,667
87,100	87,150	22,398	19,455	24,017	20,683
87,150	87,200	22,414	19,469	24,035	20,698
87,200	87,250	22,429	19,483	24,053	20,714
87,250	87,300	22,445	19,497	24,071	20,729
87,300	87,350	22,460	19,511	24,089	20,745
87,350	87,400	22,476	19,525	24,107	20,760
87,400	87,450	22,491	19,539	24,125	20,776
87,450	87,500	22,507	19,553	24,143	20,791
87,500	87,550	22,522	19,567	24,161	20,807
87,550	87,600	22,538	19,581	24,179	20,822
87,600	87,650	22,553	19,595	24,197	20,838
87,650	87,700	22,569	19,609	24,215	20,853
87,700	87,750	22,584	19,623	24,233	20,869
87,750	87,800	22,600	19,637	24,251	20,884
87,800	87,850	22,615	19,651	24,269	20,900
87,850	87,900	22,631	19,665	24,287	20,915
87,900	87,950	22,646	19,679	24,305	20,931
87,950	88,000	22,662	19,693	24,323	20,946
88,000					
88,000	88,050	22,677	19,707	24,341	20,962
88,050	88,100	22,693	19,721	24,359	20,977
88,100	88,150	22,708	19,735	24,377	20,993
88,150	88,200	22,724	19,749	24,395	21,008
88,200	88,250	22,739	19,763	24,413	21,024
88,250	88,300	22,755	19,777	24,431	21,039
88,300	88,350	22,770	19,791	24,449	21,055
88,350	88,400	22,786	19,805	24,467	21,070
88,400	88,450	22,801	19,819	24,485	21,086
88,450	88,500	22,817	19,833	24,503	21,101
88,500	88,550	22,832	19,847	24,521	21,117
88,550	88,600	22,848	19,861	24,539	21,132
88,600	88,650	22,863	19,875	24,557	21,148
88,650	88,700	22,879	19,889	24,575	21,163
88,700	88,750	22,894	19,903	24,593	21,179
88,750	88,800	22,910	19,917	24,611	21,194
88,800	88,850	22,925	19,931	24,629	21,210
88,850	88,900	22,941	19,945	24,647	21,225
88,900	88,950	22,956	19,959	24,665	21,241
88,950	89,000	22,972	19,973	24,683	21,256

If line 37 (taxable income) is— At least	But less than	Single	Married filing jointly	Married filing separately	Head of a household
89,000					
89,000	89,050	22,987	19,987	24,701	21,272
89,050	89,100	23,003	20,001	24,719	21,287
89,100	89,150	23,018	20,015	24,737	21,303
89,150	89,200	23,034	20,029	24,755	21,318
89,200	89,250	23,049	20,043	24,773	21,334
89,250	89,300	23,065	20,057	24,791	21,349
89,300	89,350	23,080	20,071	24,809	21,365
89,350	89,400	23,096	20,085	24,827	21,380
89,400	89,450	23,111	20,099	24,845	21,396
89,450	89,500	23,127	20,113	24,863	21,411
89,500	89,550	23,142	20,127	24,881	21,427
89,550	89,600	23,158	20,141	24,899	21,442
89,600	89,650	23,173	20,155	24,917	21,458
89,650	89,700	23,189	20,169	24,935	21,473
89,700	89,750	23,204	20,183	24,953	21,489
89,750	89,800	23,220	20,197	24,971	21,504
89,800	89,850	23,235	20,211	24,989	21,520
89,850	89,900	23,251	20,225	25,007	21,535
89,900	89,950	23,266	20,239	25,025	21,551
89,950	90,000	23,282	20,253	25,043	21,566
90,000					
90,000	90,050	23,297	20,267	25,061	21,582
90,050	90,100	23,313	20,281	25,079	21,597
90,100	90,150	23,328	20,295	25,097	21,613
90,150	90,200	23,344	20,309	25,115	21,628
90,200	90,250	23,359	20,323	25,133	21,644
90,250	90,300	23,375	20,337	25,151	21,659
90,300	90,350	23,390	20,351	25,169	21,675
90,350	90,400	23,406	20,365	25,187	21,690
90,400	90,450	23,421	20,379	25,205	21,706
90,450	90,500	23,437	20,393	25,223	21,721
90,500	90,550	23,452	20,407	25,241	21,737
90,550	90,600	23,468	20,421	25,259	21,752
90,600	90,650	23,483	20,435	25,277	21,768
90,650	90,700	23,499	20,449	25,295	21,783
90,700	90,750	23,514	20,463	25,313	21,799
90,750	90,800	23,530	20,477	25,331	21,814
90,800	90,850	23,545	20,491	25,349	21,830
90,850	90,900	23,561	20,505	25,367	21,845
90,900	90,950	23,576	20,519	25,385	21,861
90,950	91,000	23,592	20,533	25,403	21,876
91,000					
91,000	91,050	23,607	20,547	25,421	21,892
91,050	91,100	23,623	20,561	25,439	21,907
91,100	91,150	23,638	20,575	25,457	21,923
91,150	91,200	23,654	20,589	25,475	21,938
91,200	91,250	23,669	20,603	25,493	21,954
91,250	91,300	23,685	20,617	25,511	21,969
91,300	91,350	23,700	20,631	25,529	21,985
91,350	91,400	23,716	20,645	25,547	22,000
91,400	91,450	23,731	20,659	25,565	22,016
91,450	91,500	23,747	20,673	25,583	22,031
91,500	91,550	23,762	20,687	25,601	22,047
91,550	91,600	23,778	20,701	25,619	22,062
91,600	91,650	23,793	20,715	25,637	22,078
91,650	91,700	23,809	20,729	25,655	22,093
91,700	91,750	23,824	20,743	25,673	22,109
91,750	91,800	23,840	20,757	25,691	22,124
91,800	91,850	23,855	20,771	25,709	22,140
91,850	91,900	23,871	20,786	25,727	22,155
91,900	91,950	23,886	20,801	25,745	22,171
91,950	92,000	23,902	20,817	25,763	22,186

If line 37 (taxable income) is— At least	But less than	Single	Married filing jointly	Married filing separately	Head of a household
92,000					
92,000	92,050	23,917	20,832	25,781	22,202
92,050	92,100	23,933	20,848	25,799	22,217
92,100	92,150	23,948	20,863	25,817	22,233
92,150	92,200	23,964	20,879	25,835	22,248
92,200	92,250	23,979	20,894	25,853	22,264
92,250	92,300	23,995	20,910	25,871	22,279
92,300	92,350	24,010	20,925	25,889	22,295
92,350	92,400	24,026	20,941	25,907	22,310
92,400	92,450	24,041	20,956	25,925	22,326
92,450	92,500	24,057	20,972	25,943	22,341
92,500	92,550	24,072	20,987	25,961	22,357
92,550	92,600	24,088	21,003	25,979	22,372
92,600	92,650	24,103	21,018	25,997	22,388
92,650	92,700	24,119	21,034	26,015	22,403
92,700	92,750	24,134	21,049	26,033	22,419
92,750	92,800	24,150	21,065	26,051	22,434
92,800	92,850	24,165	21,080	26,069	22,450
92,850	92,900	24,181	21,096	26,087	22,465
92,900	92,950	24,196	21,111	26,105	22,481
92,950	93,000	24,212	21,127	26,123	22,496
93,000					
93,000	93,050	24,227	21,142	26,141	22,512
93,050	93,100	24,243	21,158	26,159	22,527
93,100	93,150	24,258	21,173	26,177	22,543
93,150	93,200	24,274	21,189	26,195	22,558
93,200	93,250	24,289	21,204	26,213	22,574
93,250	93,300	24,305	21,220	26,231	22,589
93,300	93,350	24,320	21,235	26,249	22,605
93,350	93,400	24,336	21,251	26,267	22,620
93,400	93,450	24,351	21,266	26,285	22,636
93,450	93,500	24,367	21,282	26,303	22,651
93,500	93,550	24,382	21,297	26,321	22,667
93,550	93,600	24,398	21,313	26,339	22,682
93,600	93,650	24,413	21,328	26,357	22,698
93,650	93,700	24,429	21,344	26,375	22,713
93,700	93,750	24,444	21,359	26,393	22,729
93,750	93,800	24,460	21,375	26,411	22,744
93,800	93,850	24,475	21,390	26,429	22,760
93,850	93,900	24,491	21,406	26,447	22,775
93,900	93,950	24,506	21,421	26,465	22,791
93,950	94,000	24,522	21,437	26,483	22,806
94,000					
94,000	94,050	24,537	21,452	26,501	22,822
94,050	94,100	24,553	21,468	26,519	22,837
94,100	94,150	24,568	21,483	26,537	22,853
94,150	94,200	24,584	21,499	26,555	22,868
94,200	94,250	24,599	21,514	26,573	22,884
94,250	94,300	24,615	21,530	26,591	22,899
94,300	94,350	24,630	21,545	26,609	22,915
94,350	94,400	24,646	21,561	26,627	22,930
94,400	94,450	24,661	21,576	26,645	22,946
94,450	94,500	24,677	21,592	26,663	22,961
94,500	94,550	24,692	21,607	26,681	22,977
94,550	94,600	24,708	21,623	26,699	22,992
94,600	94,650	24,723	21,638	26,717	23,008
94,650	94,700	24,739	21,654	26,735	23,023
94,700	94,750	24,754	21,669	26,753	23,039
94,750	94,800	24,770	21,685	26,771	23,054
94,800	94,850	24,785	21,700	26,789	23,070
94,850	94,900	24,801	21,716	26,807	23,085
94,900	94,950	24,816	21,731	26,825	23,101
94,950	95,000	24,832	21,747	26,843	23,116

This column must also be used by a qualifying widow(er)

Continued on next page

© 1983, 1996 Instructional Horizons. Produced and Distributed by J. Weston Walch, Publisher, Portland, Maine 04104-0658

Consumer Math Success Kit

34. Income Tax

1994 Tax Table—Continued

If line 37 (taxable income) is—		And you are—				If line 37 (taxable income) is—		And you are—			
At least	But less than	Single	Married filing jointly	Married filing separately	Head of a house-hold	At least	But less than	Single	Married filing jointly	Married filing separately	Head of a house-hold
		Your tax is—						Your tax is—			
95,000						**98,000**					
95,000	95,050	24,847	21,762	26,861	23,132	98,000	98,050	25,777	22,692	27,941	24,062
95,050	95,100	24,863	21,778	26,879	23,147	98,050	98,100	25,793	22,708	27,959	24,077
95,100	95,150	24,878	21,793	26,897	23,163	98,100	98,150	25,808	22,723	27,977	24,093
95,150	95,200	24,894	21,809	26,915	23,178	98,150	98,200	25,824	22,739	27,995	24,108
95,200	95,250	24,909	21,824	26,933	23,194	98,200	98,250	25,839	22,754	28,013	24,124
95,250	95,300	24,925	21,840	26,951	23,209	98,250	98,300	25,855	22,770	28,031	24,139
95,300	95,350	24,940	21,855	26,969	23,225	98,300	98,350	25,870	22,785	28,049	24,155
95,350	95,400	24,956	21,871	26,987	23,240	98,350	98,400	25,886	22,801	28,067	24,170
95,400	95,450	24,971	21,886	27,005	23,256	98,400	98,450	25,901	22,816	28,085	24,186
95,450	95,500	24,987	21,902	27,023	23,271	98,450	98,500	25,917	22,832	28,103	24,201
95,500	95,550	25,002	21,917	27,041	23,287	98,500	98,550	25,932	22,847	28,121	24,217
95,550	95,600	25,018	21,933	27,059	23,302	98,550	98,600	25,948	22,863	28,139	24,232
95,600	95,650	25,033	21,948	27,077	23,318	98,600	98,650	25,963	22,878	28,157	24,248
95,650	95,700	25,049	21,964	27,095	23,333	98,650	98,700	25,979	22,894	28,175	24,263
95,700	95,750	25,064	21,979	27,113	23,349	98,700	98,750	25,994	22,909	28,193	24,279
95,750	95,800	25,080	21,995	27,131	23,364	98,750	98,800	26,010	22,925	28,211	24,294
95,800	95,850	25,095	22,010	27,149	23,380	98,800	98,850	26,025	22,940	28,229	24,310
95,850	95,900	25,111	22,026	27,167	23,395	98,850	98,900	26,041	22,956	28,247	24,325
95,900	95,950	25,126	22,041	27,185	23,411	98,900	98,950	26,056	22,971	28,265	24,341
95,950	96,000	25,142	22,057	27,203	23,426	98,950	99,000	26,072	22,987	28,283	24,356
96,000						**99,000**					
96,000	96,050	25,157	22,072	27,221	23,442	99,000	99,050	26,087	23,002	28,301	24,372
96,050	96,100	25,173	22,088	27,239	23,457	99,050	99,100	26,103	23,018	28,319	24,387
96,100	96,150	25,188	22,103	27,257	23,473	99,100	99,150	26,118	23,033	28,337	24,403
96,150	96,200	25,204	22,119	27,275	23,488	99,150	99,200	26,134	23,049	28,355	24,418
96,200	96,250	25,219	22,134	27,293	23,504	99,200	99,250	26,149	23,064	28,373	24,434
96,250	96,300	25,235	22,150	27,311	23,519	99,250	99,300	26,165	23,080	28,391	24,449
96,300	96,350	25,250	22,165	27,329	23,535	99,300	99,350	26,180	23,095	28,409	24,465
96,350	96,400	25,266	22,181	27,347	23,550	99,350	99,400	26,196	23,111	28,427	24,480
96,400	96,450	25,281	22,196	27,365	23,566	99,400	99,450	26,211	23,126	28,445	24,496
96,450	96,500	25,297	22,212	27,383	23,581	99,450	99,500	26,227	23,142	28,463	24,511
96,500	96,550	25,312	22,227	27,401	23,597	99,500	99,550	26,242	23,157	28,481	24,527
96,550	96,600	25,328	22,243	27,419	23,612	99,550	99,600	26,258	23,173	28,499	24,542
96,600	96,650	25,343	22,258	27,437	23,628	99,600	99,650	26,273	23,188	28,517	24,558
96,650	96,700	25,359	22,274	27,455	23,643	99,650	99,700	26,289	23,204	28,535	24,573
96,700	96,750	25,374	22,289	27,473	23,659	99,700	99,750	26,304	23,219	28,553	24,589
96,750	96,800	25,390	22,305	27,491	23,674	99,750	99,800	26,320	23,235	28,571	24,604
96,800	96,850	25,405	22,320	27,509	23,690	99,800	99,850	26,335	23,250	28,589	24,620
96,850	96,900	25,421	22,336	27,527	23,705	99,850	99,900	26,351	23,266	28,607	24,635
96,900	96,950	25,436	22,351	27,545	23,721	99,900	99,950	26,366	23,281	28,625	24,651
96,950	97,000	25,452	22,367	27,563	23,736	99,950	100,000	26,382	23,297	28,643	24,666
97,000											
97,000	97,050	25,467	22,382	27,581	23,752						
97,050	97,100	25,483	22,398	27,599	23,767						
97,100	97,150	25,498	22,413	27,617	23,783						
97,150	97,200	25,514	22,429	27,635	23,798						
97,200	97,250	25,529	22,444	27,653	23,814						
97,250	97,300	25,545	22,460	27,671	23,829						
97,300	97,350	25,560	22,475	27,689	23,845						
97,350	97,400	25,576	22,491	27,707	23,860						
97,400	97,450	25,591	22,506	27,725	23,876						
97,450	97,500	25,607	22,522	27,743	23,891						
97,500	97,550	25,622	22,537	27,761	23,907						
97,550	97,600	25,638	22,553	27,779	23,922						
97,600	97,650	25,653	22,568	27,797	23,938						
97,650	97,700	25,669	22,584	27,815	23,953						
97,700	97,750	25,684	22,599	27,833	23,969						
97,750	97,800	25,700	22,615	27,851	23,984						
97,800	97,850	25,715	22,630	27,869	24,000						
97,850	97,900	25,731	22,646	27,887	24,015						
97,900	97,950	25,746	22,661	27,905	24,031						
97,950	98,000	25,762	22,677	27,923	24,046						

$100,000 or over — use the Tax Rate Schedules on page 53

This column must also be used by a qualifying widow(er)

© 1983, 1996 Instructional Horizons. Produced and Distributed by J. Weston Walch, Publisher, Portland, Maine 04104-0658

Consumer Math Success Kit

34. Income Tax

Tax forms and tables needed to solve these problems are found on pages 149–153, 157–162, and 166–177. Blank forms are provided on pages 179–184.

1. Andrea is single and earned $16,291.40 last year. She received $42.30 in interest from her savings account and had $2904.35 withheld from her pay for federal income tax last year. Complete Form 1040EZ and calculate Andrea's tax this year.

2. Lorraine is married, with two dependent children, and filing separately. Last year she earned $33,065.84 in wages and received $105.20 in interest on her savings account. She had $4044.36 withheld from her pay for federal income tax last year. Complete Form 1040A for Lorraine and determine her tax liability for this year.

3. Dan is a single man with an income of $18,424.69 last year. From this amount, his employer withheld $2689.91 for his federal income tax. Use Form 1040EZ to determine Dan's income tax for this year.

4. Wilson is married with three dependent children. He files form 1040A separately from his wife. Wilson's income and expenses last year consisted of the following items: wages: $34,032.37; unemployment compensation of $1558.22; interest on savings account: $338.22; federal income tax withheld: $3642.17. Complete Wilson's tax return.

5. Jolene is married with no dependents. She files a tax return separately from her husband, with whom she lives. The information you need to calculate her federal income tax using Form 1040 is as follows: salary: $28,642.40; interest from savings account: $395.50; dividend from stocks: $388.99; royalties: $2540.00; IRA deduction: $1750.00; total of deductions itemized on Schedule A: $6952.18; federal tax withheld from pay: $5822.13.

6. Barney is married with one dependent child. He files jointly with his wife and lists a total of three exemptions on his return. Here is the information you need to complete Form 1040 for Barney: salary: $41,399.42; interest on savings account: $198.44; net rents received: $10,905.84; contribution to Keogh plan: $1852.00; credit for child care expenses: $450.00; special credit for investment in community development program (Line 44): $1250.00; total of deductions listed on Schedule A: $10,791.91; federal income tax withheld: $6909.02.

Consumer Math Success Kit

Name _____   Date _____

34. Income Tax

Form
1040EZ

Department of the Treasury—Internal Revenue Service

Income Tax Return for Single and
Joint Filers With No Dependents   1994 (L)

OMB No 1545-0675

Use the
IRS label
(See page 12)
Otherwise,
please print

L A B E L   H E R E

Print your name (first initial last)

If a joint return print spouse's name (first initial last)

Home address (number and street) If you have a P O box see page 12   Apt no

City town or post office state and ZIP code If you have a foreign address see page 12

Your social security number

Spouse's social security number

See instructions on back and in Form 1040EZ booklet.

Presidential
Election
Campaign
(See page 12.)

Note: *Checking "Yes" will not change your tax or reduce your refund.*

Do you want $3 to go to this fund?   ▶

If a joint return, does your spouse want $3 to go to this fund? ▶

Income

Attach
Copy B of
Form(s)
W-2 here
Enclose, but
do not attach,
any payment
with your
return

Note: *You*
must check
Yes or No

1   Total wages, salaries, and tips. This
should be shown in box 1 of your
W-2 form(s). Attach your W-2 form(s).   1

2   Taxable interest income of $400 or less. If the total is
over $400, you cannot use Form 1040EZ.   2

3   Add lines 1 and 2. This is your **adjusted gross income.**
If less than $9,000, see page 15 to find out if you can
claim the earned income credit on line 7.   3

4   Can your parents (or someone else) claim you on their return?
☐ **Yes.** Do worksheet   ☐ **No.** If **single,** enter 6,250.00.
on back; enter   If **married,** enter 11,250.00.
amount from   For an explanation of these
line G here.   amounts, see back of form.   4

5   Subtract line 4 from line 3. If line 4 is larger than
line 3, enter 0. This is your **taxable income.** ▶ 5

Payments
and tax

6   Enter your Federal income tax withheld from box 2 of
your W-2 form(s).   6

7   **Earned income credit** (see page 15). Enter type
and amount of nontaxable earned income below.
Type $ 7

8   Add lines 6 and 7 (don't include nontaxable earned
income). These are your **total payments.**   8

9   **Tax.** Use the amount on **line 5** to find your tax in the
tax table on pages 28–32 of the booklet. Then, enter the
tax from the table on this line.   9

Refund
or
amount
you
owe

10   If line 8 is larger than line 9, subtract line 9 from line 8.
This is your **refund.**   10

11   If line 9 is larger than line 8, subtract line 8 from line 9.
This is the **amount you owe.** See page 20 for details on
how to pay and what to write on your payment.   11

Sign
your
return

Keep a copy
of this form
for your
records

I have read this return. Under penalties of perjury, I declare that to the
best of my knowledge and belief, the return is true, correct, and accurately
lists all amounts and sources of income I received during the tax year.

Your signature   Spouse's signature if joint return

Date   Your occupation   Date   Spouse's occupation

For **Privacy Act and Paperwork Reduction Act Notice,** see page 4   Cat No 12617R   Form 1040EZ (1994)

Consumer Math Success Kit

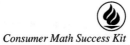

34. Income Tax

1994   **Instructions for Form 1040EZ**

Use this form if	• Your filing status is single or married filing jointly	• You (and your spouse if married) were under 65 on January 1, 1995, and not blind at the end of 1994

• You do not claim any dependents
• Your taxable income (line 5) is less than $50 000
• You had **only** wages, salaries, tips and taxable scholarship or fellowship grants, and your taxable interest income was $400 or less. **But** if you earned tips, including allocated tips, that are not included in box 5 and box 7 of your W-2, you may not be able to use Form 1040EZ. See page 14
• You did not receive any advance earned income credit payments

Caution: *If married and either you or your spouse had total wages of over $60,600, you may not be able to use this form. See page 7*

If you are not sure about your filing status, see page 7. If you have questions about dependents, call Tele-Tax (see page 26) and listen to topic 354. If you **can't use this form**, call Tele-Tax (see page 26) and listen to topic 352

Filling in your return

Because this form is read by a machine, please print your numbers inside the boxes like this:

$$9\ 8\ 7\ 6\ 5\ 4\ 3\ 2\ 1\ 0$$ Do not type your numbers. Do not use dollar signs

If you received a scholarship or fellowship grant or tax-exempt interest income, such as on municipal bonds, see the booklet before filling in the form. Also, see the booklet if you received a Form 1099 INT showing income tax withheld (backup withholding)

Remember, you must report all wages, salaries, and tips even if you don't get a W-2 form from your employer. You must also report all your taxable interest income, including interest from banks, savings and loans, credit unions, etc., even if you don't get a Form 1099-INT

If you paid someone to prepare your return, see page 21

Worksheet for dependents who checked "Yes" on line 4

Use this worksheet to figure the amount to enter on line 4 if someone can claim you (or your spouse if married) as a dependent, even if that person chooses not to do so. To find out if someone can claim you as a dependent, call Tele-Tax (see page 26) and listen to topic 354

A. Enter the amount from line 1 on the front   A. _____

B. Minimum standard deduction   B. ___   600.00

C. Enter the LARGER of line A or line B here   C. _____

D. Maximum standard deduction. If single, enter 3,800 00; if married, enter 6,350 00   D. _____

E. Enter the SMALLER of line C or line D here. This is your standard deduction   E. _____

F. Exemption amount
  • If single enter 0
  • If married and both you and your spouse can be claimed as dependents, enter 0
  • If married and only one of you can be claimed as a dependent, enter 2,450 00   F

G. Add lines E and F. Enter the total here and on line 4 on the front   G   __

If you checked "No" on line 4 because no one can claim you (or your spouse if married) as a dependent, enter on line 4 the amount shown below that applies to you

• Single enter 6 250 00. This is the total of your standard deduction (3,800 00) and personal exemption (2 450 00)

• Married, enter 11 250 00. This is the total of your standard deduction (6,350 00), exemption for yourself (2 450 00), and exemption for your spouse (2,450 00)

Avoid mistakes

See page 21 of the Form 1040EZ booklet for a list of common mistakes to avoid. Errors will delay your refund

---

Mailing your return

Mail your return by **April 17, 1995**. Use the envelope that came with your booklet. If you don't have that envelope see page 33 for the address to use

---

☆ U.S Government Printing Office 1994 375 062

180   *Consumer Math Success Kit*

34. Income Tax

Form **1040A**	Department of the Treasury—Internal Revenue Service **U.S. Individual Income Tax Return** (T) **1994**	IRS Use Only—Do not write or staple in this space.

OMB No 1545-0085

Label
(See page 16)

Use the IRS label Otherwise, please print or type

L A B E L H E R E

Your first name and initial	Last name	Your social security number
If a joint return spouse's first name and initial	Last name	Spouse's social security number
Home address (number and street) If you have a P O box, see page 17	Apt. no	**For Privacy Act and Paperwork Reduction Act Notice, see page 4.**
City town or post office state, and ZIP code If you have a foreign address see page 17		

Presidential Election Campaign Fund (See page 17)
Do you want $3 to go to this fund?
If a joint return, does your spouse want $3 to go to this fund?

Yes No

Note: *Checking "Yes" will not change your tax or reduce your refund.*

Check the box for your filing status
(See page 17)
Check only one box.

1 ☐ Single
2 ☐ Married filing joint return (even if only one had income)
3 ☐ Married filing separate return. Enter spouse's social security number above and full name here ▶ _____
4 ☐ Head of household (with qualifying person) (See page 18) If the qualifying person is a child but not your dependent, enter this child's name here ▶ _____
5 ☐ Qualifying widow(er) with dependent child (year spouse died ▶ 19___). (See page 19.)

Figure your exemptions
(See page 20)

If more than seven dependents, see page 23

6a ☐ **Yourself.** If your parent (or someone else) can claim you as a dependent on his or her tax return, do not check box 6a But be sure to check the box on line 18b on page 2

b ☐ **Spouse**

c **Dependents:**

(1) Name (first initial, and last name)	(2) Check if under age 1	(3) If age 1 or older, dependent's social security number	(4) Dependent's relationship to you	(5) No of months lived in your home in 1994

No of boxes checked on 6a and 6b _____

No. of your children on 6c who:
• lived with you _____
• didn't live with you due to divorce or separation (see page 23) _____

Dependents on 6c not entered above _____

d If your child didn't live with you but is claimed as your dependent under a pre-1985 agreement, check here ▶ ☐
e Total number of exemptions claimed.

Add numbers entered on lines above _____

Figure your total income

Attach Copy B of your Forms W-2 and 1099-R here

If you didn't get a W-2, see page 25

Enclose, but do not attach, any payment with your return

7 Wages, salaries, tips, etc This should be shown in box 1 of your W-2 form(s). Attach Form(s) W-2.   7 _____

8a **Taxable** interest income (see page 25) If over $400, attach Schedule 1.   8a _____
b **Tax-exempt** interest. DO NOT include on line 8a.   8b _____
9 Dividends. If over $400, attach Schedule 1.   9 _____
10a Total IRA distributions.   10a _____   10b Taxable amount (see page 26).   10b _____
11a Total pensions and annuities.   11a _____   11b Taxable amount (see page 27).   11b _____
12 Unemployment compensation (see page 30).   12 _____
13a Social security benefits.   13a _____   13b Taxable amount (see page 31).   13b _____

14 Add lines 7 through 13b (far right column). This is your **total income**. ▶ 14 _____

Figure your adjusted gross income

15a Your IRA deduction (see page 34).   15a _____
b Spouse's IRA deduction (see page 34).   15b _____
c Add lines 15a and 15b. These are your **total adjustments**.   15c _____
16 Subtract line 15c from line 14. This is your **adjusted gross income**. If less than $25,296 and a child lived with you (less than $9,000 if a child didn't live with you), see "Earned income credit" on page 44.   ▶ 16 _____

Cat No 11327A

1994 Form 1040A page 1

Consumer Math Success Kit

34. Income Tax

1994 Form 1040A page 2

Figure your standard deduction, exemption amount, and taxable income	**17**	Enter the amount from line 16.	**17**

18a Check if: ☐ You were 65 or older   ☐ Blind   } Enter number of
☐ Spouse was 65 or older   ☐ Blind   } boxes checked ▶ **18a** ☐

b If your parent (or someone else) can claim you as a dependent, check here . . . . ▶ **18b** ☐

c If you are married filing separately and your spouse files Form 1040 and itemizes deductions, see page 38 and check here. ▶ **18c** ☐

19 Enter the **standard deduction** shown below for your filing status **But if you checked any box on line 18a or b,** go to page 38 to find your standard deduction **If you checked box 18c,** enter -0-
 • Single—$3,800   • Married filing jointly or Qualifying widow(er)—$6,350
 • Head of household—$5,600   • Married filing separately—$3,175   **19**

20 Subtract line 19 from line 17. If line 19 is more than line 17, enter -0-. **20**

21 Multiply $2,450 by the total number of exemptions claimed on line 6e. **21**

22 Subtract line 21 from line 20. If line 21 is more than line 20, enter -0-
This is your **taxable income.**   ▶ **22**

Figure your tax, credits, and payments	**23**	Find the tax on the amount on line 22 Check if from: ☐ Tax Table (pages 62–67) or ☐ Form 8615 (see page 40). **23**

If you want the IRS to figure your tax, see the instructions for line 22 on page 39

24a Credit for child and dependent care expenses
Attach Schedule 2.   **24a**

b Credit for the elderly or the disabled
Attach Schedule 3.   **24b**

c Add lines 24a and 24b. These are your **total credits.**   **24c**

25 Subtract line 24c from line 23. If line 24c is more than line 23, enter -0-. **25**

26 Advance earned income credit payments from Form W-2.   **26**

27 Add lines 25 and 26. This is your **total tax.**   ▶ **27**

28a Total Federal income tax withheld If any tax is from Form(s) 1099, check here. ▶ ☐   **28a**

b 1994 estimated tax payments and amount applied from 1993 return.   **28b**

c Earned income credit. If required, attach Schedule EIC (see page 44).   **28c**
Nontaxable earned income:
amount ▶ _____ and type ▶ _____

d Add lines 28a, 28b, and 28c (don't include nontaxable earned income)
These are your **total payments.**   ▶ **28d**

Figure your refund or amount you owe	**29**	If line 28d is more than line 27, subtract line 27 from line 28d This is the amount you **overpaid.** **29**

30 Amount of line 29 you want **refunded to you.**   **30**

31 Amount of line 29 you want **applied to your 1995 estimated tax.**   **31**

32 If line 27 is more than line 28d, subtract line 28d from line 27 This is the **amount you owe.** For details on how to pay, including what to write on your payment, see page 52.   **32**

33 Estimated tax penalty (see page 52)
Also, include on line 32.   **33**

Sign your return

Under penalties of perjury, I declare that I have examined this return and accompanying schedules and statements, and to the best of my knowledge and belief, they are true, correct, and accurately list all amounts and sources of income I received during the tax year Declaration of preparer (other than the taxpayer) is based on all information of which the preparer has any knowledge

Your signature   Date   Your occupation

Keep a copy of this return for your records.

Spouse's signature If joint return, BOTH must sign   Date   Spouse's occupation

Paid preparer's use only

Preparer's signature ▶   Date   Check if self-employed ☐   Preparer's social security no.

Firm's name (or yours if self-employed) and address ▶   E.I. No.   ZIP code

♻ Printed on recycled paper   1994 Form 1040A page 2

Name _____ Date _____

34. Income Tax

Form 1040
Department of the Treasury—Internal Revenue Service
U.S. Individual Income Tax Return **1994** (5) IRS Use Only—Do not write or staple in this space.

For the year Jan. 1–Dec. 31, 1994, or other tax year beginning , 1994, ending , 19 OMB No. 1545-0074

Label
(See instructions on page 12.)

Use the IRS label Otherwise, please print or type

L A B E L H E R E

Your first name and initial | Last name | Your social security number

If a joint return, spouse's first name and initial | Last name | Spouse's social security number

Home address (number and street) If you have a P O box, see page 12 | Apt no

City, town or post office, state, and ZIP code If you have a foreign address, see page 12

For Privacy Act and Paperwork Reduction Act Notice, see page 4.

Presidential Election Campaign
(See page 12.)

Do you want $3 to go to this fund? . . . .
If a joint return, does your spouse want $3 to go to this fund? . . . . . .

Yes | No | Note: Checking "Yes" will not change your tax or reduce your refund.

Filing Status
(See page 12.)

Check only one box

1 Single
2 Married filing joint return (even if only one had income)
3 Married filing separate return. Enter spouse's social security no. above and full name here. ▶
4 Head of household (with qualifying person). (See page 13.) If the qualifying person is a child but not your dependent, enter this child's name here. ▶
5 Qualifying widow(er) with dependent child (year spouse died ▶ 19). (See page 13.)

Exemptions
(See page 13.)

6a Yourself. If your parent (or someone else) can claim you as a dependent on his or her tax return, do not check box 6a. But be sure to check the box on line 33b on page 2.
b Spouse
c Dependents:

(1) Name (first initial and last name)	(2) Check if under age 1	(3) If age 1 or older, dependent's social security number	(4) Dependent's relationship to you	(5) No. of months lived in your home in 1994

No. of boxes checked on 6a and 6b

No. of your children on 6c who:
• lived with you
• didn't live with you due to divorce or separation (see page 14)
Dependents on 6c not entered above

If more than six dependents, see page 14

d If your child didn't live with you but is claimed as your dependent under a pre-1985 agreement, check here ▶
e Total number of exemptions claimed

Add numbers entered on lines above ▶

Income

Attach Copy B of your Forms W-2, W-2G, and 1099-R here

If you did not get a W-2 see page 15

Enclose, but do not attach, any payment with your return

7 Wages, salaries, tips, etc. Attach Form(s) W-2 | 7
8a Taxable interest income (see page 15). Attach Schedule B if over $400 | 8a
b Tax-exempt interest (see page 16). DON'T include on line 8a | 8b
9 Dividend income. Attach Schedule B if over $400 | 9
10 Taxable refunds, credits, or offsets of state and local income taxes (see page 16) | 10
11 Alimony received | 11
12 Business income or (loss). Attach Schedule C or C-EZ | 12
13 Capital gain or (loss). If required, attach Schedule D (see page 16) | 13
14 Other gains or (losses). Attach Form 4797 | 14
15a Total IRA distributions | 15a | b Taxable amount (see page 17) | 15b
16a Total pensions and annuities | 16a | b Taxable amount (see page 17) | 16b
17 Rental real estate, royalties, partnerships, S corporations, trusts, etc. Attach Schedule E | 17
18 Farm income or (loss). Attach Schedule F | 18
19 Unemployment compensation (see page 18) | 19
20a Social security benefits | 20a | b Taxable amount (see page 18) | 20b
21 Other income. List type and amount—see page 18 | 21
22 Add the amounts in the far right column for lines 7 through 21. This is your total income ▶ | 22

Adjustments to Income

Caution: See instructions ▶

23a Your IRA deduction (see page 19) | 23a
b Spouse's IRA deduction (see page 19) | 23b
24 Moving expenses. Attach Form 3903 or 3903-F | 24
25 One-half of self-employment tax | 25
26 Self-employed health insurance deduction (see page 21) | 26
27 Keogh retirement plan and self-employed SEP deduction | 27
28 Penalty on early withdrawal of savings | 28
29 Alimony paid. Recipient's SSN ▶ | 29
30 Add lines 23a through 29. These are your total adjustments ▶ | 30

Adjusted Gross Income

31 Subtract line 30 from line 22. This is your adjusted gross income. If less than $25,296 and a child lived with you (less than $9,000 if a child didn't live with you), see "Earned Income Credit" on page 27 ▶ | 31

Cat. No. 11320B | Form **1040** (1994)

34. Income Tax

Form 1040 (1994)   Page 2

Tax Computation (See page 23)	32	Amount from line 31 (adjusted gross income)		32
	33a	Check if: ☐ You were 65 or older, ☐ Blind; ☐ Spouse was 65 or older, ☐ Blind. Add the number of boxes checked above and enter the total here . . . . ► 33a ☐		
	b	If your parent (or someone else) can claim you as a dependent, check here . ► 33b ☐		
	c	If you are married filing separately and your spouse itemizes deductions or you are a dual-status alien, see page 23 and check here . . . . . . ► 33c ☐		
	34	Enter the larger of your: Itemized deductions from Schedule A, line 29, OR Standard deduction shown below for your filing status. But if you checked any box on line 33a or b, go to page 23 to find your standard deduction. If you checked box 33c, your standard deduction is zero. • Single—$3,800 • Head of household—$5,600 • Married filing jointly or Qualifying widow(er)—$6,350 • Married filing separately—$3,175		34
	35	Subtract line 34 from line 32		35
If you want the IRS to figure your tax, see page 24	36	If line 32 is $83,850 or less, multiply $2,450 by the total number of exemptions claimed on line 6e. If line 32 is over $83,850, see the worksheet on page 24 for the amount to enter .		36
	37	Taxable income. Subtract line 36 from line 35. If line 36 is more than line 35, enter -0- .		37
	38	Tax. Check if from a ☐ Tax Table, b ☐ Tax Rate Schedules, c ☐ Capital Gain Tax Worksheet, or d ☐ Form 8615 (see page 24). Amount from Form(s) 8814 ► e |		38
	39	Additional taxes. Check if from a ☐ Form 4970 b ☐ Form 4972		39
	40	Add lines 38 and 39 . . . . ►		40
Credits (See page 24)	41	Credit for child and dependent care expenses. Attach Form 2441	41	
	42	Credit for the elderly or the disabled. Attach Schedule R .	42	
	43	Foreign tax credit. Attach Form 1116	43	
	44	Other credits (see page 25). Check if from a ☐ Form 3800 b ☐ Form 8396 c ☐ Form 8801 d ☐ Form (specify) _____	44	
	45	Add lines 41 through 44		45
	46	Subtract line 45 from line 40. If line 45 is more than line 40, enter -0- . . . ►		46
Other Taxes (See page 25)	47	Self-employment tax. Attach Schedule SE		47
	48	Alternative minimum tax. Attach Form 6251		48
	49	Recapture taxes. Check if from a ☐ Form 4255 b ☐ Form 8611 c ☐ Form 8828		49
	50	Social security and Medicare tax on tip income not reported to employer. Attach Form 4137		50
	51	Tax on qualified retirement plans, including IRAs. If required, attach Form 5329 . .		51
	52	Advance earned income credit payments from Form W-2		52
	53	Add lines 46 through 52. This is your total tax . . . . ►		53
Payments Attach Forms W-2, W-2G, and 1099-R on the front	54	Federal income tax withheld. If any is from Form(s) 1099, check ► ☐	54	
	55	1994 estimated tax payments and amount applied from 1993 return .	55	
	56	Earned income credit. If required, attach Schedule EIC (see page 27). Nontaxable earned income: amount ► | | and type ►	56	
	57	Amount paid with Form 4868 (extension request)	57	
	58	Excess social security and RRTA tax withheld (see page 32)	58	
	59	Other payments. Check if from a ☐ Form 2439 b ☐ Form 4136	59	
	60	Add lines 54 through 59. These are your total payments . . . . . . ►		60
Refund or Amount You Owe	61	If line 60 is more than line 53, subtract line 53 from line 60. This is the amount you OVERPAID. ►		61
	62	Amount of line 61 you want REFUNDED TO YOU . . . . ►		62
	63	Amount of line 61 you want APPLIED TO YOUR 1995 ESTIMATED TAX ►	63	
	64	If line 53 is more than line 60, subtract line 60 from line 53. This is the AMOUNT YOU OWE. For details on how to pay, including what to write on your payment, see page 32		64
	65	Estimated tax penalty (see page 33). Also include on line 64	65	

Sign Here
Keep a copy of this return for your records

Under penalties of perjury, I declare that I have examined this return and accompanying schedules and statements, and to the best of my knowledge and belief, they are true, correct, and complete. Declaration of preparer (other than taxpayer) is based on all information of which preparer has any knowledge.

Your signature	Date	Your occupation
Spouse's signature If a joint return BOTH must sign	Date	Spouse's occupation

Paid Preparer's Use Only

Preparer's signature	Date	Check if self-employed ☐	Preparer's social security no
Firm's name (or yours if self-employed) and address		E.I. No.	
		ZIP code	

Income Tax

Teacher Notes

Mathematical skills required:

addition, subtraction, and multiplication of decimals
multiplication with percents

New vocabulary:

adjusted gross income
adjustments to income
charitable contribution
deduction
exclusion
exemption
filing status
income tax withheld
refund
tax credit
taxable income

Related topics:

Income
Investing Money
Property Taxes
Sales Tax

Teaching suggestions:

1. Please note that tax tables and forms in this book may be out of date by the time you use them. After students have learned the *principles* taught here, you may want to show them current forms and tables.

2. Invite a representative of the Internal Revenue Service to speak to your class about the filing of tax forms.

3. Most students will not need to know about additional tax forms, such as Schedules C, D, and E. However, you might want to show them a selection of these forms to give them an idea of the complexity of some tax returns.

Chapter Sixteen

Insurance

Homeowner's
Life
Health and Medical
Automobile

35. Homeowner's

Homeowner's insurance is probably the simplest kind of insurance. Its purpose is to protect against the loss of or damage to your dwelling. Suppose your house burns down, your water pipes freeze and break, a neighbor is injured falling down your steps, or a tree blows over in a windstorm and destroys your roof. Homeowner's insurance will repay you a specific part of your losses in such cases. The annual premium that you pay depends primarily on the amount of insurance coverage you want for each type of damage that could be done to your home.

Some people need additional coverage beyond that provided in the normal policy. Suppose you kept some very expensive art or jewelry in your house. You would want to protect that art or jewelry against loss or theft. Property insurance is available to protect these expensive items also. The example below shows how the premium on a homeowner's policy is calculated.

● **Example:**

The Eterna Insurance Company charges a premium of 1.0456828% on the total value of a house for its Basic Homeowner's Policy. It also permits policyholders to pay their premiums annually, semi-annually, quarterly or monthly. It adds an extra charge for each of the last three of these plans, as follows:

Semiannually: add 2.3%;　*Quarterly:* add 4.5%;　*Monthly:* add 6.7%

What would be the annual, semiannual, quarterly, and monthly payments on a house valued at $89,500?

Solution:

The normal annual premium on this house, if paid all at once, would be:

Premium　= Rate × Value

$\quad\quad\quad$ = 1.0456828% × $89,500

$\quad\quad\quad$ = $935.89

If paid semiannually, an additional 2.3% is added to this amount:

Premium　= Basic rate + 2.3% × Basic rate

$\quad\quad\quad$ = $935.89 + 2.3% × $935.89

$\quad\quad\quad$ = $935.89 + $21.53 = $957.42

Paid twice a year, this would amount to: $957.42 ÷ 2 = $478.71. Similarly, the quarterly and monthly payments would be:

Quarterly premium　= $935.89 + 4.5% × $935.89 = $978.01

$\quad\quad\quad\quad\quad\quad\quad$ or $978.01 ÷ 4 = $244.50 each quarter

Monthly premium　= $935.89 + 6.7% × $935.89 = $998.59

$\quad\quad\quad\quad\quad\quad\quad$ or $998.59 ÷ 12 = $83.22 per month

35. Homeowner's

The Eterna Insurance Company charges a premium of 1.0456828% on the total value of a house for its Basic Homeowner's Policy. Policyholders may pay once a year, quarterly (2.3% additional charge) or monthly (6.7% additional charge). In addition, the company offers a Special Extended Coverage (SEC) for very valuable objects in a home, such as art or jewelry. The premium for SEC is 0.9008067% of the value of the insured goods. Use this information in answering the questions below.

1. What will be the annual premium for a Basic Homeowner's Policy on the Reisermans' house if the value of the house is currently $132,500?

   _____

2. The value of the Lengyles' house is now $120,500. What is the cost of insuring this house and paying on a quarterly basis?

   _____

3. Bonnie and Clyde Shapiro want to insure their home, worth $242,750 on today's market. How much will the insurance cost them if they pay their premium annually? If they pay quarterly?

   _____

4. What will be the cost of a Basic Homeowner's Policy on Betty MacDonald's house, assessed at $142,750? How much extra would she have to pay (total) if she pays her premiums monthly rather than annually?

   _____

5. Doug Watkoskey's house is worth $384,275. What will be the monthly premiums on this house if he gets a Basic Homeowner's Policy from Eterna?

   _____

6. The value of Regina's home is $85,500, but she also wants to insure $20,000 worth of art she keeps in the house. What will be her total annual premium for a Basic Homeowner's Policy that includes SEC?

   _____

7. Suppose Regina decides to pay for the policy described in Problem 6 on a quarterly or monthly basis. What would be her premium in each case?

   _____

8. Gregory has inherited a mansion from his grandfather. The value of the mansion is $475,000, and the home contains another $50,000 in valuable art. What would be the annual cost of insurance on the house and the art? What would be the monthly payments on this policy?

   _____

36. Life

Life insurance is an agreement between an individual who wants financial protection (the **insured**) and a company that is willing to provide that protection (the **insurer**). The agreement they make is called a **policy**. The insured agrees to pay the insurer a certain amount of money each year (the **premium**). In return, the insurer agrees to pay anyone the insured chooses (the **beneficiary**) if the insured dies. The amount of money to be paid in case of death is called the **face value** of the policy. After the insured has had a policy for a few years, it is possible to turn the policy back in for cash (in which case the policy ends) or to take a loan against the cash value of the policy.

Many kinds of insurance policies are available. **Term insurance** provides protection for brief periods of time, usually five or ten years. The insured pays premiums for this short period of time. The insurer provides insurance over this period of time. At the end of the five or ten years, the policy ends. It may be renewed, but there will be a new premium for the new policy. Term insurance is the least expensive form of insurance protection for a young family that needs heavy coverage while earnings are low.

A **straight** or **ordinary** policy is one in which the insured pays premiums as long as he or she is alive. A **limited payment life** policy is one in which the insured pays for some stated number of years, usually 20 or 30. At the end of that time, the insured no longer pays premiums, but is covered for the rest of her or his life.

An **endowment** policy is both a life insurance plan and a savings plan. At the end of some period of time (often 20 years), the insured stops paying premiums, the life insurance ends, and the insured gets back all the premiums paid plus a small amount of interest.

The premiums charged for each type of insurance policy are calculated by a company on the basis of many factors. These factors all help the company guess how long any particular person will live. The premium chart on page 192 shows the cost of various types of insurance policies with one company. You can use these charts with examples #1 and #2 below and in the practice problems dealing with premiums. The chart on page 193 shows the cash and loan value of various types of insurance policies. You can use this chart for the third example below and for practice problems dealing with cash and loan values.

- **Example 1:**

  What is the cost of a $20,000 ordinary life policy for a woman 25 years old?

  Solution:

  From the chart, the cost of $1000 of life insurance for a woman 25 years old is $17.36. So the cost of a $20,000 policy would be 20 times that amount: $20 \times \$17.36 = \$347.20$.

- **Example 2:**

  What is the cost of a $30,000 life insurance policy for a man 20 years old?

  Solution:

  The rates for men are 5% higher than the ones shown in the chart for women. So, the rates for a term policy for this man would be: $(5\% \times \$14.77) + \$14.77 = \$.74 + \$14.77 = \$15.51$. For a $30,000 policy, the premium would be: $30 \times \$15.51 = \$465.30$.

- **Example 3:**

  Patrina wants to borrow money against her $40,000 life insurance policy. She took out the policy at the age of 23 and is now 32 years old. How much could she borrow?

  (continued)

© 1983, 1996 Instructional Horizons. Produced and Distributed
by J. Weston Walch, Publisher, Portland, Maine 04104-0658   *191*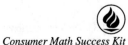

36. Life *(continued)*

Solution:

Look across the Table of Loan Values on page 193 until you come to Patrina's age, 23. Then read down until you find the number of years her policy has been in effect, 9 years. The entry here is $106.95. This means she can get $106.95 for each $1000 of insurance she holds, or, for $40,000: 40 × $106.95 = $4278.00.

Cost of Life Insurance—Typical Rates

Annual Life Insurance Rates—Female Lives*

(Rates are quoted per $1,000)

Age	Amount of Policy	Ordinary Life	20-Year Endowment	20-Year Limited Payment	10-Year Term
15	$ 2,000 up to $ 5,000	$17.06	$50.70	$26.55	----------
to	$ 5,001 up to $10,000	15.06	48.70	24.55	$ 5.98
19	$10,001 up to $25,000	13.56	47.20	23.05	4.98
	$25,001 up to $50,000	13.06	46.70	22.55	4.48
	$50,001 and over	12.86	46.50	22.35	4.28
20	$ 2,000 up to $ 5,000	18.77	50.99	30.33	----------
to	$ 5,001 up to $10,000	16.77	48.99	28.33	6.42
24	$10,001 up to $25,000	15.27	47.49	26.83	5.42
	$25,001 up to $50,000	14.77	46.99	26.33	4.92
	$50,001 and over	14.57	46.79	26.13	4.72
25	$ 2,000 up to $ 5,000	20.86	51.33	35.20	----------
to	$ 5,001 up to $10,000	18.86	49.33	33.20	6.86
29	$10,001 up to $25,000	17.36	47.83	31.70	5.86
	$25,001 up to $50,000	16.86	47.33	31.20	5.36
	$50,001 and over	16.66	47.13	31.00	5.16
30	$ 2,000 up to $ 5,000	23.48	51.90	41.60	----------
to	$ 5,001 up to $10,000	21.48	49.90	39.60	7.57
34	$10,001 up to $25,000	19.98	48.40	38.10	6.57
	$25,001 up to $50,000	19.48	47.90	37.60	6.07
	$50,001 and over	19.28	47.70	37.40	5.87
35	$ 2,000 up to $ 5,000	26.82	52.86	50.26	----------
to	$ 5,001 up to $10,000	24.82	50.86	48.26	8.92
39	$10,001 up to $25,000	23.32	49.36	46.76	7.92
	$25,001 up to $50,000	22.82	48.86	46.26	7.42
	$50,001 and over	22.62	48.66	46.06	7.22
40	$ 2,000 up to $ 5,000	31.29	54.59	62.87	----------
to	$ 5,001 up to $10,000	29.29	52.59	60.87	11.27
44	$10,001 up to $25,000	27.64	50.94	59.22	10.27
	$25,001 up to $50,000	27.14	50.44	58.72	9.77
	$50,001 and over	26.94	50.24	58.52	9.57

* Rates for males are 5% higher than those for females.

© 1983, 1996 Instructional Horizons. Produced and Distributed by J. Weston Walch, Publisher, Portland, Maine 04104-0658

Consumer Math Success Kit

36. Life

TABLE OF LOAN VALUES

CASH OR LOAN VALUE FOR $1000 OF FACE AMOUNT OF ORDINARY LIFE POLICY (TYPICAL RATES)

End of Year	Age 18	Age 19	Age 20	Age 21	Age 22	Age 23	Age 24	Age 25	Age 26	Age 27	Age 28	Age 29	Age 30	Age 31
3	$ .00	$ .99	$ 1.95	$ 2.94	$ 3.98	$ 5.06	$ 6.19	$ 7.36	$ 8.59	$ 9.86	$ 11.18	$ 12.58	$ 14.04	$ 15.59
4	14.15	15.49	16.88	18.33	19.83	21.40	23.04	24.74	26.52	28.37	30.31	32.35	34.49	36.74
5	28.48	30.23	32.06	33.96	35.94	38.00	40.15	42.39	44.72	47.17	49.72	52.41	55.22	58.19
6	43.05	45.22	47.49	49.84	52.30	54.86	57.52	60.29	63.20	66.23	69.40	72.73	76.24	79.92
7	57.86	60.46	63.16	65.98	68.91	71.97	75.14	78.46	81.93	85.56	89.36	93.34	97.53	101.92
8	72.90	75.93	79.09	82.37	85.78	89.33	93.03	96.90	100.94	105.16	109.58	114.22	119.09	124.22
9	88.20	91.66	95.26	99.00	102.89	106.95	111.18	115.60	120.21	125.03	130.07	135.36	140.93	146.78
10	103.73	107.63	111.67	115.88	120.26	124.82	129.58	134.55	139.73	145.15	150.82	156.78	163.04	169.62
11	119.50	123.83	128.33	133.01	137.88	142.95	148.24	153.76	159.52	165.54	171.84	178.46	185.41	192.72
12	135.52	140.28	145.23	150.38	155.75	161.33	167.15	173.22	179.55	186.18	193.12	200.40	208.05	216.10
13	151.77	156.97	162.38	168.01	173.86	179.96	186.30	192.93	199.85	207.08	214.65	222.60	230.95	239.75
14	168.26	173.91	179.78	185.88	192.22	198.83	205.71	212.89	220.39	228.23	236.44	245.06	254.12	263.66
15	184.99	191.09	197.41	203.99	210.82	217.94	225.36	233.10	241.18	249.63	258.48	267.78	277.55	287.84
16	201.96	208.50	215.28	222.23	229.66	237.30	245.25	253.55	262.22	271.28	280.78	290.75	301.23	312.78
17	219.16	226.15	233.39	240.92	248.75	256.90	265.39	274.24	283.50	293.18	303.32	313.97	325.18	336.99
18	236.60	244.03	251.73	259.74	268.06	276.73	285.75	295.18	305.02	315.31	326.11	337.45	349.38	361.98
19	254.27	262.14	270.31	278.79	287.61	296.80	306.36	316.35	326.78	337.70	349.15	361.18	373.86	387.24
20	272.17	280.49	289.11	298.08	307.39	317.10	327.21	337.76	348.78	360.33	372.44	385.18	398.60	412.78
At Age														
60	684.59	682.46	680.22	677.88	675.42	672.84	670.12	667.26	664.25	661.07	657.72	654.17	650.42	646.45
65	795.30	795.30	795.30	795.30	795.30	795.30	795.30	795.30	795.30	795.30	795.30	795.30	795.30	795.30

The values applying to this policy are those in the column headed with the age corresponding to the insuring age shown above, do not include the value of any dividend accumulations or additions which may be standing to the credit of this policy, and are for policies having no indebtedness.

© 1983, 1996 Instructional Horizons. Produced and Distributed by J. Weston Walch, Publisher, Portland, Maine 04104-0658

Consumer Math Success Kit

36. Life

The table on page 192 gives the annual premium rates for women for each $1000 worth of insurance for four different kinds of insurance policies. Men's rates are 5% higher. For quarterly payments, there is an extra charge of 2.5%. For monthly payments, there is an extra charge of 5.0%. The table on page 193 shows the loan and cash redemption values for various kinds of insurance policies for people at different ages who have held their policies for certain numbers of years. Use these tables for solving the problems below.

1. Rosa is now 17 years old. What will be the annual premium for a $5000 ordinary life insurance policy for her?

   _____

2. What will be the annual premium for a $10,000 20-year limited payment policy for Annette? She is now 20 years old.

   _____

3. Martin wants to know the cost of a $20,000 insurance policy taken out at the age of 16. Calculate the premium for each of the four kinds of insurance shown on page 192.

   _____

4. Delbert is now 17 years old. What would be the quarterly premium on a $30,000 20-year endowment policy for him?

   _____

5. Sandra wants to compare the annual, quarterly, and monthly premium rates for a $25,000 20-year limited payment life insurance policy. She is now 26 years old. What would each of these payments be?

   _____

6. Doris wants to borrow money on her $5000 ordinary life insurance policy which she purchased at the age of 18. She is now 29. How much money can she borrow on the policy?

   _____

7. Carmen holds a $50,000 insurance policy given to him by his aunt when he was 20. He is now 29. How much can he cash the policy in for?

   _____

8. Anne's plan is to buy a $50,000 insurance policy now and then cash it in at the age of 36. She is now 19 years old. What will be the cash value of the policy when she cashes it in?

   _____

37. Health and Medical

Medical expenses can be very costly today. Almost everyone needs insurance to protect against both common, everyday medical expenses and the less common, but very expensive "catastrophic" medical expenses. Many different medical insurance plans are available. Each one provides different kinds of protection ("coverage") and charges different premiums. Health and medical insurance plans are usually very complicated. You may need the advice of a professional in order to understand exactly how each one works. The chart on page 197 shows how one plan works. This plan has three parts:

1. *Basic Plan (BP)* provides limited coverage. It pays for the most common medical problems. It does not cover very serious situations. It includes a $50 deductible. This means the patient must pay the first $50 of any medical bill submitted under this plan.

2. *Major Medical (MM)* is designed to protect against the most serious, very expensive health problems. It picks up where the BP stops. The deductible under MM is $100 per year. For a person who has both BP and MM, only the $100 deductible applies. That means that for someone who has both BP and MM, the company pays all bills after the first $100 in any one year.

3. *Catastrophic Insurance Coverage (CIC)* pays for some costs that neither the BP nor MM covers. In many cases, the company you work for helps pay (or pays entirely) for BP and MM coverage. If you choose to have CIC, you pay the full premium on your own.

The example below shows how this medical plan would pay one set of medical bills.

● **Example:**

Rodney has been in the hospital for 38 days. His bill so far is as shown below. How much will the insurance company pay on this bill? How much will Rodney have to pay? Rodney has only Basic Plan coverage.

Hospital (room and services):	$ 12,482.23
X rays and lab exams:	$ 395.50
Drugs:	$ 422.28
Ambulance:	$ 35.00

Solution:

Refer to the chart on page 197 for the payments which can be made by insurance under each category.

Hospital: 100% of all charges; insurance pays $12,482.23

X rays and labs: 100% of all charges; insurance pays $395.50

Drugs: 20% of all charges = 20% × $422.28 = $84.46 (insurance)

Ambulance: $25 limit

Total paid by insurance: $12,482.23 + $395.50 + $84.46 + $25

$$= \$12,987.19 - \$50 \text{ deductible} = \$12,937.19$$

Total paid by Rodney = 80% × $422.28 (drugs) + $10 (ambulance)

$$+ \$50 \text{ (deductible)} = \$397.82$$

© 1983, 1996 Instructional Horizons. Produced and Distributed
by J. Weston Walch, Publisher, Portland, Maine 04104-0658   *195*   *Consumer Math Success Kit*

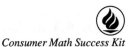

37. Health and Medical

- ## Extra Solved Example:

Leona was taken to the hospital on July 15, at which time she had surgery. She was released on August 29 and received the bill shown below. How much did her insurance pay? How much does Leona owe? Leona has both Basic Plan and Catastrophic Insurance Coverage, but no Major Medical.

Hospital:	$ 11,824.73
X rays and lab exams:	$ 895.42
Blood and plasma:	$ 340.00
Surgery:	$ 4,250.85
Drugs:	$ 503.08
Ambulance:	$ 52.50

Solution:

The chart below shows how much of the bill is paid by (1) Basic Plan, (2) Catastrophic Insurance Coverage, and (3) patient.

Item	Paid by BP	Paid by CIC	Paid by Patient
Hospital	100% ($11,824.73)	-0-	-0-
X rays and lab	100% ($895.42)	-0-	-0-
Blood and plasma	100% ($340.00)	-0-	-0-
Surgery	80% × $4250.85 = $3400.68	80% × ($4250.85 − $3400.68) = $680.14	$4250.85 − $3400.68 − $680.14 = $170.03
Drugs	20% × $503.08 = $100.62	-0-	80% × $503.08 = $402.46
Ambulance	$25.00	80% of ($52.50 − $25) = $22.00	$52.50 − $25.00 − $22.00 = $5.50

Total paid by insurance = $11,824.73 + $895.42 + $340.00 + $3400.68 + $100.62
+ $25.00 (BP) + $680.14 + $22.00 (CIC) − $50.00 (deductible)
= $17,238.59

Total paid by patient = $170.03 + $402.46 + $5.50 + $50.00 (deductible)
= $627.99

© 1983, 1996 Instructional Horizons. Produced and Distributed
by J. Weston Walch, Publisher, Portland, Maine 04104-0658   *196*

Consumer Math Success Kit

37. Health and Medical

Health and Medical Insurance Coverage

Service	Basic Plan (BP)	Major Medical (MM)	Catastrophic Coverage (CIC)
Doctor's services (includes medical doctors, dentists, psychologists, chiropractors, optometrists, etc., for outpatient services)	80% of all charges	-0-	80% of patient's share after BP payments
Hospital charges	100% for up to 120 days in a semiprivate room	80% of all charges after 120 days in a semiprivate room	80% of patient's share after MM payments
Surgery	80% of all charges	-0-	80% of patient's share after BP payments
X rays and lab examinations	100% of all charges	-0-	-0-
Ambulance	$25 per hospital visit	80% of all charges over $25	80% of patient's share after MM and BP payments
Drugs (prescription)	20% of all charges	80% of all charges	-0-
Blood and plasma	100% of all charges	-0-	-0-

Deductibles: $50 on any bill under BP; $100 per year under MM.

© 1983, 1996 Instructional Horizons. Produced and Distributed by J. Weston Walch, Publisher, Portland, Maine 04104-0658

Consumer Math Success Kit

37. Health and Medical

The table on page 197 explains the coverage provided by three types of health insurance policies. Refer to this table in solving the following problems.

1. Francine received a bill for $38.00 for a visit she made to her doctor's office. She has BP insurance. How much will her insurance company pay toward this bill? How much will she pay? This is her first claim of the year.

   _____

2. Vernon was charged $65.00 for an examination in his doctor's office. How much will Vernon's BP insurance policy pay toward this bill? How much will he have to pay? This is his first claim of the year.

   _____

3. As a result of her visit to the doctor's office, Elmira had to purchase prescription drugs that cost $36.00. Her office visit also cost her $75.00. What amount will Elmira's BP policy pay toward the total of these bills? How much will Elmira have to pay? This is Elmira's first claim of the year.

   _____

4. During his recent stay in the hospital, Ray had the following charges on his bill: Hospital (room and services for four days): $869.49; X rays and lab: $254.60; Drugs: $135.68. What will his BP policy pay toward these charges? How much will he have to pay? This is his first bill of the year.

   _____

5. The bill Winston received for a 15-day stay in the hospital contained the charges shown below. What part of the bill will the company pay? What part will he pay? This is his first claim of the year on his combined BP/CIC plan. Charges: Hospital (room and services): $4,589.02; X rays and lab: $698.72; Drugs: $449.75; Ambulance: $45.00; Blood and plasma: $245.00.

   _____

6. Danny was in the hospital for 19 days, during which time he received the services listed below. How much will his BP/CIC/MM plan pay for these charges? How much will he have to pay? This is his first claim on MM. Charges: Hospital (room and services): $7,854.10; X rays and lab: $2,785.30; Drugs: $850.00; Surgery: $2,756.39; Blood and plasma: $450.00; Ambulance: $95.00.

   _____

7. Arnella is very fortunate that she has complete BP/CIC/MM coverage because she just spent 145 days in the hospital. How much will she have to pay toward the following charges? This is her first claim on MM. Hospital (room and services): $45,968.02; $25,689.28 for first 120 days; X rays and lab: $5,056.23; Drugs: $4,040.03; Surgery: $6,512.27; Blood and plasma: $889.25; Ambulance: $75.00.

   _____

© 1983, 1996 Instructional Horizons. Produced and Distributed by J. Weston Walch, Publisher, Portland, Maine 04104-0658

Consumer Math Success Kit

38. Automobile

Car insurance provides two kinds of protection. The first is for damage you cause to some other person or to property owned by that person. This is called **liability insurance**. The second type is insurance against injury to you or to your own car. This coverage may include:

Medical: Covers bills for injuries to you and your passengers.

Uninsured motorist: Covers injuries to you and your passengers or damages to your car caused by someone driving without insurance.

Collision: Pays for damage to your own car. There is usually a **deductible** on collision insurance. This is the amount you pay for damages before the insurance company pays anything.

Comprehensive: Covers damage caused by storms, fire, theft, or causes other than accidents.

Towing: Pays for having your car towed in case of accidents or breakdowns.

Many factors are considered in setting the cost of car insurance. These may include age and make of car, age and sex of owner, city in which owner lives and car is kept, reasons for driving car (business or pleasure), and number of accidents involving car owner.

Car insurance differs a great deal from one state to another and from one company to another. The chart on page 200 shows how costs are calculated in one state. Use this chart in understanding the solved example below.

● **Example:**

Glenda has decided to take the insurance coverage on her car shown below. What will her annual premiums be for this coverage?

> *Liability:* 5/10/5
> *Medical:* $5000
> *Collision:* $200 deductible
> *Comprehensive:* $100 deductible

Solution:

The premium for each type of coverage is as follows:

Liability: 5/10/5 means coverage of $5000 (for any one person) and $10,000 (for all people hurt in one accident) and $5000 (for damage to another car). From the table on page 200, the premium for the 5/10 ($5000/$10,000) part is $102.80. Coverage for the /5 ($5000) part is $64.58.

Medical: Coverage for $5000 is $4

Collision: Coverage for $200 deductible is $95.50

Comprehensive: Coverage for $100 deductible is 183% × $95.50 = $174.77

> Glenda's total premium, then, = $102.80 + $64.58 + $4 + $95.50 + $174.77
> = $441.65

© 1983, 1996 Instructional Horizons. Produced and Distributed by J. Weston Walch, Publisher, Portland, Maine 04104-0658

Consumer Math Success Kit

38. Automobile

Automobile Insurance Rate Table

Type of Coverage	Limits	Premium
Liability: Bodily Injury	$5000/$10,000	$102.80 (basic)
	$10,000/$20,000	111% of basic premium
	$20,000/$40,000	114% of basic premium
	$25,000/$50,000	121% of basic premium
	$50,000/$100,000	132% of basic premium
	$100,000/$300,000	141% of basic premium
	$300,000/$500,000	150% of basic premium
Liability: Property Damage	$5000	$64.58 (basic)
	$10,000	111% of basic premium
	$20,000	114% of basic premium
	$25,000	121% of basic premium
	$50,000	132% of basic premium
	$100,000	141% of basic premium
	$300,000	150% of basic premium
Medical	$5000	$4.00 (basic)
	For each additional $1000	Add $0.95 to basic premium
Uninsured Motorist	$10,000/$20,000	Add $9.00 to basic premium
	$20,000/$40,000	Add $11.00 to basic premium
	$25,000/$50,000	Add $12.00 to basic premium
	$50,000/$100,000	Add $16.00 to basic premium
	$100,000/$300,000	Add $20.00 to basic premium
	$300,000/$500,000	Add $24.00 to basic premium
Collision	Basic rate: $200 deductible	$95.50
	Deductible = -0-	342% of basic rate
	Deductible = $100	183% of basic rate
	Deductible = $500	67% of basic rate
	Deductible = $1000	31% of basic rate
Comprehensive	Same rates as for collision	
Towing	$35.00	

200    *Consumer Math Success Kit*

Name _____ Date _____

38. Automobile

Refer to the table on page 200 for the premium rates for various types of automobile insurance in answering the following questions.

1. Armand has purchased a used car on which he wants to have liability insurance with limits of $5000/$10,000/$5000 (5/10/5). He has chosen not to take collision, comprehensive, or any other kind of insurance. How much will the annual premium on this insurance be?

_____

2. Claudette's insurance policy provides coverage of 10/20/10 for liability and deductibles of $200 each for collision and comprehensive coverage. She has no other type of insurance on her car. How much will her annual premium be on this policy?

_____

3. Yao's father has recommended the auto insurance listed below on his new car. What will be the annual premium on this kind of policy? Liability: 25/50/25; Medical: $25,000; Deductible: $100 on both collision and comprehensive; Uninsured motorist: 25/50.

_____

4. Jean wants to get complete insurance coverage and has selected the plan outlined below. What will be her annual premium on this policy? What will be her monthly premium if she has to pay 5.5% per annum interest charge in order to make monthly payments? Liability: 100/300/100; Medical: $10,000; Deductible: $500 in both collision and comprehensive; Uninsured motorist: 100/300.

_____

5. Lucie drives preschool children to the playground three times a week and wants auto insurance that will protect her to the maximum amount. Listed below are the conditions she has chosen for her policy. What will be her monthly premium payments if there is an extra charge of 6.4% per year for monthly payments? Liability: 300/500/300; Medical: $25,000; Deductible: $500 for both collision and comprehensive; Uninsured motorist: 300/500.

_____

Insurance

Teacher Notes

Mathematical skills required:

addition, multiplication, and division of decimals
multiplication of percents

New vocabulary:

beneficiary	insured	premium
cash value	insurer	property insurance
collision	liability	quarterly payment
comprehensive	limited payment life insurance	semiannual payment
coverage	loan value	straight insurance
deductible	medical coverage	term insurance
endowment life insurance	monthly payments	towing
face value	ordinary life insurance	uninsured motorist
homeowner's insurance	policy	

Related topics:

Budgets: Short-term Budgets
Estimating Answers

Teaching suggestions:

1. Have students identify the ways in which various types of insurance are important in *their* lives. Are they already covered by some form of health and medical insurance? Should they be? If they own some kind of vehicle, is it covered by insurance? What kind of coverage do they have? Do they own any property which should be covered by property insurance? Are they covered by any form of life insurance? Should they be? What types of life insurance are most appropriate for persons of different ages and different lifestyles? You might ask an insurance agent to talk to the class about questions such as these.

2. Discuss the advantages and disadvantages of using a life insurance policy as a savings plan and of borrowing money against one's life insurance policy.

3. Health and medical insurance is almost essential for everyone today. But the provisions of most policies are very complex. Invite a representative of a health and medical insurer to speak with the class about this type of coverage. Also invite a representative of a health maintenance organization (HMO), if there is one in your area, to describe the ways in which an HMO plan differs from more traditional health insurance.

4. Try to obtain sample health and medical bills from Blue Cross–Blue Shield or a similar company. Photocopy these bills and see if students can see how payments were determined for each.

CHAPTER SEVENTEEN
Interest

39. Interest

Interest is money paid for the privilege of using someone else's money. When you deposit your money in a savings account, the bank or credit union pays you interest on that money. The interest is a financial reward from the bank for using your money. If you borrow money from a bank, you pay the bank interest. The idea is the same: you are paying the bank for the privilege of using its money.

Most financial transactions involve interest at some point. Even if the interest charge is not obvious, it is probably present anyway. When you receive a credit card bill, for example, you are probably charged some interest. This is a payment to the credit card company for using their money at a store where you charged a purchase.

Interest charges sometimes have different names. The interest paid on a credit card bill or charge account may be called a **finance charge**. On some kinds of bank loans, the interest may be called the **discount rate**. By whatever name it is called, interest amounts to the same thing and is calculated in about the same way.

The amount of interest paid on something depends on four factors:

1. The amount of money on which the interest is paid. This is usually called the **principal**.

2. The **rate** at which the interest is paid (for example, 3% or 18%). Interest rates are usually given on a monthly or annual rate.

3. The **kind of interest** involved. **Simple interest** is paid only on the principal. **Compound interest** is paid on both principal and on interest already paid on that principal.

4. The length of **time** for which the interest is paid.

The relationship among these factors is sometimes given in a mathematical formula:

$$\text{Amount of interest} = \text{Principal} \times \text{Rate} \times \text{Time of loan}$$

or, $$i = p \times r \times t$$

If you know three of these factors, you can always calculate the fourth. Many times, for example, you want to know the interest rate on a loan. You can find that by solving the formula above for **rate**, or **r**:

$$r = \frac{i}{p \times t}$$

● **Example 1:**

What is the interest (simple) on a $100 loan at 5% for two years?

Solution:

$$i = p \times r \times t$$
$$i = \$100 \times 5\% \times 2 \text{ years}$$
$$i = \$10.00$$

(continued)

© 1983, 1996 Instructional Horizons. Produced and Distributed by J. Weston Walch, Publisher, Portland, Maine 04104-0658

Consumer Math Success Kit

39. Interest *(continued)*

- **Example 2:**

    What is the rate of simple interest on a savings account in which a $200 deposit made two years ago is now worth $222.20?

    Solution:

    $$r = \frac{i}{p \times t}$$

    $$r = \frac{\$22.20(222.20 - 200.00)}{\$200.00 \times 2 \text{ years}}$$

    $$r = 5.55\%$$

COMPOUND INTEREST

Solving problems with **compound interest** is a bit more complicated than problems with simple interest. The following example illustrates compound interest calculations.

- **Extra Solved Example 1:**

    A deposit of $100 is made in a savings account that pays 5% interest, compounded annually. How much will that account be worth in three years?

    Solution:

    You have to calculate the interest earned at the end of each "compounding period," in this case, each year.

Interest for year one	= Principal × Rate × Time
	= $100 × 5% per year × 1 year
	= $5
Amount in account at end of year one	= Principal + Interest earned
	= $100 + $5
	= $105
Interest for year two	= Principal × Rate × Time
	= $105 × 5% per year × 1 year
	= $5.25
Amount in account at end of year two	= Principal + Interest earned
	= $105 + $5.25
	= $110.25
Interest for year three	= Principal × Rate × Time
	= $110.25 × 5% per year × 1 year
	= $5.51
Amount in account at end of year three	= Principal + Interest earned
	= $110.25 + $5.51
	= $115.76

© 1983, 1996 Instructional Horizons. Produced and Distributed by J. Weston Walch, Publisher, Portland, Maine 04104-0658

Consumer Math Success Kit

Name _____ Date _____

39. Interest

1. Julian's savings account pays him 5% simple interest. How much interest will he earn on $100 deposited in this account for one year? What will be his balance in this account at the end of the year?

    _____

2. How much interest will Dorothy earn on $200 deposited in an account that pays $5\frac{3}{4}$% interest annually if she leaves the money in the account for one year?

    _____

3. The bank at which Shareko deposits his money pays $5\frac{1}{4}$% simple interest annually. How much interest will he earn on a deposit of $300.00 left in the account for six months? What will be his balance in the account at the end of this time?

    _____

4. Howard plans on leaving $625 in his savings account for 19 months. The account pays 5.7% simple interest annually. What will be the balance in his account at the end of this time?

    _____

5. Calculate the interest due to Gita on $100 left in an account that pays 5% compounded annually if the money is left in the account for one year.

    _____

6. One year ago Miriam deposited $400 in a savings account that pays 5% a year, compounded semi-annually. How much is her account worth today?

    _____

7. Seth deposited $250 in an account that pays 5.7% compounded quarterly. At the end of one year, how much interest has Seth earned on this deposit? What is the balance of his account?

    _____

8. Katherine would like to know how much interest she can earn if she deposits her income tax refund of $389.00 in an account that pays 5.4% compounded monthly. She wants to withdraw the money at the end of three months. What will be her balance at that time?

    _____

9. Rebecca's bank will pay her 5.7% annual interest, compounded daily, on her savings account. Calculate the amount of interest earned in one week in this account if Rebecca deposits $500 in the account.

    _____

39. Interest

INSTALLMENT PURCHASES

A common situation in which the consumer will have to pay interest is on installment purchases. An **installment purchase** is one in which you pay a small amount of the total purchase price at the beginning (this is the **down payment**), and the remaining part of the price in monthly installments. In addition to the balance due on the purchase price, a certain amount of interest is included in the monthly payments. The example below shows how to find the interest rate on an installment purchase.

● **Extra Solved Example 2:**

A jacket purchased on a three-month budget plan costs $35. Had you paid cash, the price would have been $31.50. How much interest did you pay on this purchase? What was the monthly interest rate? What was the annual interest rate?

Solution:

Amount of interest $= $ Total price paid $-$ Cash price
$= \$35.00 - \$31.50$
$= \$3.50$

Monthly interest rate $= \dfrac{\text{Amount of interest paid}}{\text{Cash price} \times \text{Number of months}} \times 100\%$

$= \dfrac{\$3.50}{\$31.50 \times 3 \text{ months}} \times 100\%$

$= 3.7\%$ per month

Annual interest rate $= 12 \times$ Monthly interest rate
$= 12 \times 3.7\%$
$= 44.4\%$

© 1983, 1996 Instructional Horizons. Produced and Distributed
by J. Weston Walch, Publisher, Portland, Maine 04104-0658

Consumer Math Success Kit

Name _____   Date _____

39. Interest

1. Murray has earned $12.00 in interest on $200 that he deposited in his savings account one year ago. What rate of interest was he paid on this account?

   _____

2. Four years ago, Grandmother Fletcher deposited $750 in an account for Doris. During that time, the money earned $180 in interest. What was the rate of simple interest paid on this account?

   _____

3. The credit union where Tino has a savings account will pay him $85.34 interest on a deposit of $735.67 left in the account for a period of two years. What rate of simple interest does the credit union pay?

   _____

4. Ericka's savings account shows a balance of $867.22 today. In the next three months, she will be able to earn $17.56 interest on this account. What annual rate of simple interest is paid on this account?

   _____

5. The FM stereo clock radio Sandra wants to buy will cost her $200 if she pays cash for it and $236 if she buys it on the 12-month installment plan. What rate of interest would she be paying on the installment plan?

   _____

6. The WalkPerson sound set that Jeremy wants to buy will cost $250 if he pays cash and $317.50 if he makes monthly payments over a period of 18 months. What rate of interest would he be paying under the installment plan?

   _____

7. The sport jacket that Leon wants to buy can be purchased for cash at $62.50 or on a monthly installment plan for $8.50 a month for eight months. What rate of interest would he be paying on the installment plan?

   _____

8. The new speakers Jennifer wants to buy for her stereo set cost $49.75 each. There are two speakers in the set. She can pay for these on the installment plan at the rate of $7.85 per month for 15 months. What is the rate of interest under the installment plan?

   _____

Consumer Math Success Kit Second Edition

Interest

Teacher Notes

Mathematical skills required:

multiplication and division of decimals and percents

New vocabulary:

compound interest
discount rate
finance charge
interest
principal
rate
simple interest

Related topics:

Bank Statements
Borrowing Money (all areas)
Checking Accounts
Credit (all areas)
Electronic Funds Transfer Systems
Investing Money (all areas)
Savings Accounts

Teaching suggestions:

1. This section is primarily a skill-building topic which will find application in many other topics in this book.

2. Have students list all of the purchases or expenses on which they have paid interest over the past six months. See if they can estimate the amount they have paid out in interest over that period of time.

3. Comparisons of simple versus compound interest are always valuable. Have students compare the amount of interest earned, for example, on two savings accounts, one paying $5\frac{1}{2}\%$ simple interest annually, and one paying $5\frac{1}{4}\%$ interest compounded monthly. At what point does the latter become a better savings investment than the former?

CHAPTER EIGHTEEN

Investing Money

Stocks
Bonds

40. Stocks

One way companies have of raising money is by selling stocks. **Stocks** are shares in a company. If you own stock in a company, you are actually a part owner in the company. Many people try to earn money by trading (buying and selling stocks) on the stock market. In order to understand stock transactions, there are two things you have to know about stocks: commission fees and stock market listings.

When you buy or sell stocks, you work through a **broker** who makes the actual transaction for you. You pay the broker a certain **commission** for this service. Table 5 on page 215 shows commission rates at one brokerage house.

Stock prices are listed in a somewhat unusual way. They are given in dollars and fractions of dollars. For example, a price of 8 $\frac{1}{8}$ for a stock means "8 and $\frac{1}{8}$ dollars." Since that is not the way we usually talk about prices, you must change this listing into more familiar dollars and cents. In this case:

$$\frac{1}{8} \text{ dollar} = 0.125 \text{ dollar, so that } 8\frac{1}{8} = \$8.13 \text{ (rounded off)}$$

Stock prices are usually listed in the business section of the daily newspaper. Table 6 on page 215 lists a few selected stocks taken from a typical daily newspaper. Look at the first entry in that table. This is the listing for Delta Airlines. Here is what the numbers listed for this stock mean:

$65\frac{1}{4}$	Highest price paid for the stock in the last 365 days
$39\frac{1}{2}$	Lowest price paid for the stock in the last 365 days
DeltaAir	Name of the stock
.20	Expected payment per share company will make to stockholders.
18	Price-to-earnings ratio; a measure used by investors to estimate the probable value of a stock
4952	Number of shares traded, in hundreds, on this day. In this example, $4952 \times 100 = 495,200$ were traded on the day in question
$60\frac{3}{4}$	Final trading price for the day
$-1\frac{1}{4}$	Net change in price from previous day to this day

● **Example:**

Four months ago, Patrick bought 100 shares of Fluor Corporation stock at $46\frac{3}{8}$. Yesterday he sold them at the price shown in Table 6. What was his profit or loss on this transaction?

Solution:

Purchase price	= 100 shares × \$46.375 ($46\frac{3}{8}$) per share = \$4637.50
Broker's commission	= \$2 + $\frac{3}{4}$% × \$4637.50
	= \$2 + \$34.78 = \$36.78
Cost to Patrick	= \$4637.50 + \$36.78 = \$4674.28
Sale price	= 100 shares × \$48.625 ($48\frac{5}{8}$) per share = \$4862.50
Broker's commission	= \$2 + $\frac{3}{4}$% × \$4862.50
	= \$2 + \$36.47 = \$38.47
Profit to Patrick	= \$4862.50 – \$38.47 = \$4824.03
	= \$4824.03 (profit) – \$4674.28 (cost)
	= \$149.75

Consumer Math Success Kit

40. Stocks

1. Cynthia has purchased 50 shares of Exxon stock at the price shown in Table 6. What was the cost of the stock itself? What was the broker's commission on the stock? What was the total cost to Cynthia?

    _____

2. SueAnne's father has suggested that she buy 100 shares of GTE stock this week. What will be the cost of this stock, broker's commission included?

    _____

3. Elizabeth's grandmother has given her 250 shares of General Dynamics (GenDyn) stock. What is the value of this stock today?

    _____

4. From the money he has been saving for over a year, Rudie has decided to buy 50 shares of Goodyear stock. With the broker's commission, what will this cost him?

    _____

5. With the $5,000 left to her by her great-aunt, Irene wants to purchase stock in the General Mills (GnMill) Company. How many shares of stock can she buy with this money? Do not consider the broker's commission, and remember that she can buy only an even number of shares.

    _____

6. What is the broker's commission on Irene's purchase, described in Problem 5?

    _____

7. One year after buying Exxon stock (Problem 1), Cynthia decides to sell all of her shares. The price of this stock has gone up 2 points. What is the value of the stock now? What is the broker's commission on this sale? How much money will Cynthia actually receive on this sale? What profit will she make overall on the sale?

    _____

8. When Rudie decides to sell his stock in Goodyear (Problem 4), the price of the stock is $35\,^7/_8$. What is the value of the stock now? What will the broker's commission be on this sale? How much will Rudie receive? How much did he make or lose on this stock?

    _____

© 1983, 1996 Instructional Horizons. Produced and Distributed
by J. Weston Walch, Publisher, Portland, Maine 04104-0658   *Consumer Math Success Kit*

40. Stocks

Table 5: Broker's Commissions

Total Amount of Transaction	Commission
Less than $200	$7
$200–$500	$5 + 2% of total amount of sale
$501–$1000	$3 + 1% of total amount of sale
$1001–$5000	$2 + $\frac{3}{4}$% of total amount of sale
$5001–$10,000	$\frac{1}{2}$% of total amount of sale
over $10,000	$\frac{1}{4}$% of total amount of sale

Table 6: Some Typical Stock Price Information[1]

$65\frac{1}{4}$	$39\frac{1}{2}$	DeltaAir	.20	18	4952	$60\frac{3}{4}$	$-1\frac{1}{4}$
$29\frac{1}{4}$	$23\frac{1}{2}$	Etown	2.04	14	35	$26\frac{3}{4}$	$-\frac{1}{8}$
$68\frac{1}{8}$	$56\frac{1}{8}$	Exxon	3.00	17	14841	68	$+\frac{3}{4}$
$64\frac{7}{8}$	47	FdHmLn	1.20	12	3228	63	$-\frac{1}{8}$
$18\frac{1}{8}$	$9\frac{3}{4}$	FidelFin	.28	16	108	$10\frac{1}{4}$	$+\frac{1}{8}$
$46\frac{5}{8}$	$26\frac{1}{2}$	FstUSA	.12	20	2056	$44\frac{1}{8}$	$-\frac{1}{4}$
$55\frac{5}{8}$	$41\frac{1}{4}$	Fluor	.60	20	1126	$48\frac{5}{8}$	$+\frac{1}{2}$
$32\frac{3}{4}$	$24\frac{3}{4}$	FordM	1.24	5	28099	$27\frac{1}{8}$	$+\frac{1}{8}$
$34\frac{7}{8}$	$29\frac{1}{2}$	GTE	1.88	13	13094	$34\frac{1}{4}$	— —
$48\frac{1}{4}$	38	GenDyn	1.50	13	1081	$46\frac{3}{4}$	$-\frac{3}{4}$
$64\frac{5}{8}$	$49\frac{3}{8}$	GnMill	1.88	23	3008	$59\frac{3}{8}$	$-1\frac{1}{8}$
$40\frac{5}{8}$	$31\frac{5}{8}$	Goodyear	1.00	10	5515	$37\frac{3}{8}$	$-\frac{3}{8}$

[1] The figures used here do not necessarily represent actual financial data for the companies listed.

© 1983, 1996 Instructional Horizons. Produced and Distributed by J. Weston Walch, Publisher, Portland, Maine 04104-0658

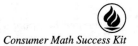
Consumer Math Success Kit

41. Bonds

Corporations and governmental bodies often raise money by selling bonds. A **bond** is really a request for a loan from an individual or a group to a company or a governmental agency that needs money. Like any other loan, a bond earns interest. Bonds are sold on markets, just as stocks are sold on a stock market. Table 7 on page 217 is a report on the bond market like one you might find in your own newspaper. Look at the first company listed on this chart, AltecC. Here is what each of the numbers listed for bond sales means:

$54\frac{1}{4}$	The highest price paid for the bonds during the last 365 days
$39\frac{3}{4}$	The lowest price paid for the bonds during the last 365 days
$6\frac{3}{4}$	The rate of interest paid on the bonds
08	The year in which the bonds mature (2008)
CCC & 14	The rating (CCC) and interest rate yield from the bonds, numbers that help a person decide if these bonds are a good investment or not
4	The number of bonds sold on this day, in thousands. In this case, there were $4 \times 1000 = 4000$ AltecC bonds sold
48	Final trading price for the day
$+2\frac{3}{8}$	The change in the bond price over the preceding day's price

When you buy or sell bonds, you work through a **broker** who makes the actual transaction for you. You pay the broker a certain **commission** for this service. You can use the commission rate chart, Table 5, page 215, to figure commissions for the problems in this section.

● **Example:**

Nadine purchased 500 bonds issued by the Zero Corporation (ZeroCp) last year when they were selling at $70\frac{1}{2}$. She has now decided to sell those bonds at yesterday's closing price (see Table 7). What is her profit or loss on this transaction?

Solution:

Purchase price	= 500 bonds × $70.50 ($70\frac{1}{2}$) per bond
	= $35,250.00
Broker's commission	= $\frac{1}{4}$% × $35,250.00 = $88.13
Total cost to Nadine	= $35,338.13
Price received	= 500 bonds × $77.25 ($77\frac{1}{4}$) per bond
	= $38,625.00
Broker's commission	= $\frac{1}{4}$% × $38,625.00 = $96.56
$38,625.00 – 96.56	= $38,528.44
Proceeds to Nadine	= $38,528.44
Profit on transaction	= $38,528.44 – $35,338.13 = $3190.31

© 1983, 1996 Instructional Horizons. Produced and Distributed
by J. Weston Walch, Publisher, Portland, Maine 04104-0658   216
Consumer Math Success Kit

41. Bonds

Table 7: Some Typical Bond Prices[2]

$54\frac{1}{4}$	$39\frac{3}{4}$	AltecC	$6\frac{3}{4}$	08	CCC	14	4	48	$+2\frac{3}{8}$
133	45	Condec	5	11	CCC	8.3	8	60	-5
149	$71\frac{1}{2}$	CrystO	$11\frac{3}{8}$	09	$--$	13	122	87	$+2$
101	$64\frac{1}{2}$	Digcn	$10\frac{1}{2}$	08	$--$	12.5	79	72	$-4\frac{1}{2}$
84	$73\frac{1}{2}$	FontA	$5\frac{1}{2}$	12	B	7.0	5	78	$-\frac{1}{8}$
$84\frac{1}{2}$	64	HornH	$11\frac{1}{2}$	05	$--$	14	74	$82\frac{1}{8}$	$-\frac{1}{4}$
$--$	56	McDono	6	05	BBB	9.4	12	64	$+6\frac{7}{8}$
$60\frac{3}{4}$	30	NVF Co	5	10	B	16	160	32	$-1\frac{1}{4}$
$--$	$72\frac{1}{8}$	ZeroCp	10	15	$--$	13	1	$77\frac{1}{4}$	$+\frac{5}{8}$

[2] The figures used here do not necessarily represent actual financial data for the companies listed.

41. Bonds

The information you need to solve the following problems is contained in Table 5, page 215, and Table 7, page 217.

1. Irwin has decided to buy 100 bonds issued by Digicon, Inc. (Digcn). What will these bonds cost him? What will be the broker's commission on this sale? What will be the total cost to Irwin?

   _____

2. Donna's uncle has given her 100 bonds issued by the Crystal Oil Corporation (CrystO). What are these bonds worth today?   _____

3. Suppose Donna had purchased the Crystal Oil bonds (Problem 2). What broker's commission would she have had to pay for these bonds? What would have been the total cost to her?

   _____

4. With the $2500 she inherited from her great-grandmother Andina, Natasha has decided to buy bonds issued by Horn and Hardart Corporation. (HornH). How many bonds can she buy? (She can buy only a whole number of bonds.)   _____

5. What broker's commission would Natasha have to pay on the purchase mentioned in Problem 4? What would be the total cost to her on this transaction?   _____

6. Penny has decided to purchase 1000 bonds issued by the Zero Corporation (ZeroCp). What will be her total cost for these bonds at the price listed in the table? Include the broker's commission in her total cost.   _____

7. One month after Irwin purchased Digicon bonds (Problem 1), they have increased in value by +1 point. If he sells the bonds now, how much money will he get for his 100 bonds? What will be the broker's commission on the bonds? How much profit will he actually make on this sale?

   _____

8. A year after receiving Crystal Oil bonds (Problem 2), Donna decides to sell the bonds. At the present time, they are listed at 84 $\frac{1}{2}$. Including the broker's commission, how much will Donna receive if she sells the bonds? What profit or loss will she make on this sale?

   _____

9. The current price of Zero Corporation bonds (Problem 6) is 81 $\frac{1}{8}$. If Penny sells her bonds now, at this price, what profit or loss will she make on the sale? Don't forget to include the broker's commission on this sale!

   _____

© 1983, 1996 Instructional Horizons. Produced and Distributed by J. Weston Walch, Publisher, Portland, Maine 04104-0658   *Consumer Math Success Kit*

Investing Money

Teacher Notes

Mathematical skills required:

conversion of fractions to decimals
multiplication of fractions, decimals, and whole numbers
multiplication of percents

New vocabulary:

bonds
broker
commission
investment
stock
transaction

Related topics:

Estimating Answers

Teaching suggestions:

1. Most daily newspapers carry stock and bond quotations in their financial pages every day. If you choose to go more deeply into this topic, those pages are an invaluable resource. Although these pages are fairly complex, students can quickly learn the information which is of most use to them at a beginner's level (i.e., the daily price of the stock or bond).

2. Invite an investment counselor to visit the class and give a simple introduction to stocks and bonds as investment opportunities. Special attention should be paid to the differences between these two and the advantages and disadvantages of each.

3. For many beginning investors, mutual funds are the best way to break into the market. Try to find a guest speaker who can describe a mutual fund and the advantages it provides to the first-time investor.

CHAPTER NINETEEN

Nutrition

42. Nutrition

Nutrition is the study of foods we eat and the way our bodies use those foods. Scientists have learned that certain types of food are essential to maintain good health. These foods are **carbohydrates, fats, proteins, vitamins,** and **minerals.** Certain minimum amounts of these foods are needed each day. These minimum amounts are known as the recommended dietary allowance (**RDA**). The table on page 228 shows the RDA for each food group for persons of different ages.

How do we know if we are eating properly? How can we tell if we are getting the RDA for each food group each day? Certain foods are especially high in each of the food groups. For example, meats and dairy products are especially good sources of fats. Meats, beans and nuts are good sources of proteins. You can tell how much of each nutrient group is contained in various foods by looking at a chart like the one on pages 226 and 227. The solved example below shows how to use the chart in finding out how nutritious a meal is.

One important function of foods is to provide our body with energy. The amount of energy provided by a food is measured in **calories.** A food that contains many calories can supply us with a lot of energy. It is important to get enough calories in the food we eat every day. But there is also a problem of getting too many calories. If we take in more calories than we can use in one day, our body stores the extra food. That is the most common way that people become overweight. The example below also shows how to measure calorie intake for one day.

● **Example:**

Sally kept a record of all the food she ate in a single day. That record is printed below. Tell why you think this would or would not be a good diet for this 13-year-old girl.

> *Diet:* 1 oz. sugar-covered cornflakes with one cup milk
>   and 2 tbsp. sugar
>   1 bag (about 20) potato chips
>   6 small fig bars
>   4 cola drinks
>   1 cup baked macaroni and cheese
>   1 piece apple pie

Solution:

Table 8 on page 224 shows the nutritional value of the food Sally ate on this day. The RDA's for each food group are also given. Sally is getting the correct amount of calories. But she is low in all other areas. She should think about changing her selection of foods to provide a diet higher in the essential five food groups.

                       Consumer Math Success Kit

42. Nutrition

Table 8: Solution to Solved Example

Item	Amount	Calories	Protein (g)	Calcium (mg)	Iron (mg)	Vitamin A (mg)	Thiamine (mg)	Riboflavin (mg)	Niacin (mg)	Ascorbic Acid (mg)
Cornflakes	1 oz	110	1	3	.3	-0-	12	.01	.5	0
Milk	1 cup	160	9	288	1	70	.08	42	1	2
Sugar	2 tbsp	90	-0-	-0-	tr*	-0-	-0-	-0-	-0-	-0-
Potato chips	30	345	3	24	1.2	tr*	12	.03	3.0	9
Fig bars	6	330	6	72	1.2	24	.06	.06	.6	tr*
Cola drinks	4 cups	380	-0-	-0-	-0-	-0-	-0-	-0-	-0-	-0-
Macaroni and cheese	1 cup	470	18	398	2.0	190	.22	44	2.0	tr*
Apple pie	1 piece	345	3	11	4	8	.03	.02	.5	1
Totals		2230	40	796	5.2	292	.63	.98	6.7	12
For comparison, RDA's =		2200	46	1200	18	800	11	1.3	15	50

*tr = trace

© 1983, 1996 Instructional Horizons. Produced and Distributed
by J. Weston Walch, Publisher, Portland, Maine 04104-0658

42. Nutrition

Refer to the tables on pages 226–228 in solving the following problems.

1. Danielle, a 15-year-old girl, reported the foods listed below for a single day in her life. Do you think this diet is nutritious or nonnutritious?

    Puffed wheat (3 oz), fortified, with 1 cup skim milk and 2 tbsp. sugar; 1 cup orange juice; 1 salad containing $\frac{1}{8}$ head lettuce, 1 stalk celery, 1 carrot, 1 tomato; 1 cup skim milk; 2 lean lamb chops; 1 cup long-grained rice; 1 cup cooked summer squash; 1 cup cola drink; 1 cup canned apricots.

    _____

    _____

    _____

    _____

2. Sam is a 15-year-old boy who reports eating the foods listed below on one day. Tell why you think his diet for this day is or is not healthful.

    1 cup fresh grapefruit juice; 5 oz. sugar-covered cornflakes with 6 tsp sugar and 1 cup whole milk; 1 cup coffee with 1 tsp. sugar and 1 tsp. cream; cheese omelet (3 eggs and 1 cup grated American cheese); 3 slices white bread with 3 pats butter; 2 apples; 2 cups cola drink; 2 pork chops; 2 baked potatoes with 4 pats butter and $\frac{1}{2}$ cup sour cream; 3 ears sweet corn; 2 pieces cherry pie; 2 scoops (slices) ice cream.

    _____

    _____

    _____

    _____

3. Wally, age 13, had the following foods during one day this week. Is this a nutritious diet for the day?

    1 cup orange juice; 2 eggs; 2 slices bacon; 1 slice whole wheat bread with 1 pat butter; 2 cups skim milk; sandwich of 2 oz. fresh ham with lettuce, tomato, and mayonnaise; 1 apple; 2 brownies; 2 cups skim milk; 1 chicken breast; 1 cup green beans (cooked); 1 cup egg noodles; 2 slices whole wheat bread with 1 pat butter; 2 cups skim milk; 1 piece cherry pie.

    _____

    _____

    _____

    _____

42. Nutrition

Table 9: Nutritive Values of Foods

Food	Amount	Calories	Protein (g)	Calcium (mg)	Iron (mg)	Vitamin A (mg)	Thiamine (mg)	Riboflavin (mg)	Niacin (mg)	Ascorbic Acid (mg)
Milk, whole	1 cup	160	9	288	0.1	70	0.08	0.42	0.1	2
Milk, skim	1 cup	90	tr*	298	0.1	2	0.10	0.44	0.2	2
Cream, coffee	1 tbsp †	30	tr*	15	tr*	26	tr*	0.02	tr*	tr*
Cream, sour	1 cup	490	7	235	1.0	372	0.55	0.48	6.0	22
Cheese, American	1 tbsp †°	30	2	52	0.1	18	tr*	0.03	tr*	-0-
Ice cream	1/8 qt	145	3	87	0.1	72	0.03	0.13	0.1	1
Eggs	1 cooked	110	7	51	1.1	135	0.05	0.18	tr*	-0-
Bacon	2 slices	100	5	2	0.5	-0-	0.08	0.05	0.8	—
Chicken, breast	1/2	155	25	9	1.3	14	0.04	0.17	11.2	—
Lamb chop	1 chop	400	25	10	1.5	—	0.14	0.25	5.6	—
Ham	3 oz	245	18	8	2.2	-0-	0.40	0.16	3.1	—
Pork chop	1 chop	260	16	8	2.2	-0-	0.63	0.18	3.8	—
Beans, green	1 cup	30	2	62	0.8	136	0.08	0.11	0.6	16
Carrots	1 whole, raw	20	1	18	0.4	1100	0.03	0.03	0.3	4
Celery	1 stalk	5	tr*	16	0.1	20	0.01	0.01	0.1	4
Lettuce	1 head	60	4	91	2.3	300	0.29	0.27	1.3	29
Potatoes, baked	1 potato	90	3	9	0.7	tr*	0.10	0.04	1.7	20
Potato chips	10 chips	115	1	8	0.4	tr*	0.04	0.01	1.0	3
Squash, summer	1 cup	30	2	52	0.8	164	0.10	0.16	1.6	21
Tomatoes, raw	1 tomato	35	2	20	0.8	270	0.10	0.06	1.0	34
Corn, sweet	1 ear	70	3	2	0.5	62	0.09	0.08	1.0	7

*tr = trace

†: Three teaspoons make one tablespoon.
°: There are 16 tablespoons in a cup.

© 1983, 1996 Instructional Horizons. Produced and Distributed by J. Weston Walch, Publisher, Portland, Maine 04104-0658

Consumer Math Success Kit

42. Nutrition

Table 9, p. 222 *(continued)*

Food	Amount	Calories	Protein (g)	Calcium (mg)	Iron (mg)	Vitamin A (mg)	Thiamine (mg)	Riboflavin (mg)	Niacin (mg)	Ascorbic Acid (mg)
Apples	1 apple	70	tr*	8	0.4	10	0.04	0.02	0.1	3
Apricots, canned	1 cup	220	2	28	0.8	902	0.05	0.06	0.9	10
Grapefruit juice	1 cup	95	1	22	0.5	4	0.09	0.04	0.4	92
Orange juice	1 cup	115	2	27	0.7	100	0.22	0.06	0.9	122
Bread, white	1 slice	60	2	19	0.6	tr*	0.06	0.05	0.6	tr*
Bread, whole wheat	1 slice	55	2	23	0.5	tr*	0.06	0.03	0.7	tr*
Brownies	1	95	1	8	0.4	8	0.04	0.02	0.1	tr*
Fig bars	1 bar	55	1	12	0.2	4	0.01	0.01	0.1	tr*
Corn flakes, sugar-coated	1 oz	110	1	3	0.3	-0-	0.12	0.01	0.5	-0-
Macaroni and cheese	1 cup	470	18	398	2.0	190	0.22	0.44	2.0	tr*
Noodles, egg	1 cup	200	7	16	1.4	22	0.23	0.14	1.8	-0-
Pie, apple	1 sector	345	3	11	0.4	8	0.03	0.02	0.5	1†
Pie, cherry	1 sector	355	4	19	0.4	118	0.03	0.03	0.6	1†
Rice, white	1 cup	185	3	17	1.5	-0-	0.19	0.01	1.6	-0-
Puffed wheat	1 oz	105	4	8	1.2	-0-	0.15	0.07	2.2	-0-
Butter	1 pat	50	tr*	1	-0-	46	---	---	---	-0-
Mayonnaise †	1 tbsp	65	tr*	2	tr*	6	tr*	tr*	tr*	---
Sugar †	1 tbsp	45	-0-	-0-	tr*	-0-	-0-	-0-	-0-	-0-
Cola beverage	1 cup	95	-0-	---	---	-0-	-0-	-0-	-0-	-0-

*tr = trace
†: Three teaspoons make one tablespoon.

Consumer Math Success Kit

42. Nutrition

Table 10: Recommended Daily Dietary Allowances (abridged)

	Age	Calories	Protein (g)	Calcium (mg)	Iron (mg)	Vitamin A (mg)	Thiamine (mg)	Riboflavin (mg)	Niacin (mg)	Ascorbic Acid (mg)
Males	11–14	2700	45	1200	18	1000	1.4	1.6	18	50
	15–18	2800	56	1200	18	1000	1.4	1.7	18	60
	19–22	2900	56	800	10	1000	1.5	1.7	19	60
	23–50	2700	56	800	10	1000	1.4	1.6	18	60
	51–75	2400	56	800	10	1000	1.2	1.4	16	60
Females	11–14	2200	46	1200	18	800	1.1	1.3	15	50
	12–18	2100	46	1200	18	800	1.1	1.3	14	60
	19–22	2100	44	800	18	800	1.1	1.3	14	60
	23–50	2000	44	800	18	800	1.0	1.2	13	60
	51–75	1800	44	800	10	800	1.0	1.2	13	60

© 1983, 1996 Instructional Horizons. Produced and Distributed
by J. Weston Walch, Publisher, Portland, Maine 04104-0658

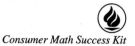

Consumer Math Success Kit

Nutrition

Teacher Notes

Mathematical skills required:

addition and multiplication of fractions, decimals, and whole numbers

New vocabulary:

ascorbic acid	nutrition
calcium	protein
calorie	recommended dietary allowance (RDA)
diet	riboflavin
food groups	thiamine
iron	vitamin A
niacin	

Related topics:

Budgets: Short-term Budgets

Eating Out

Estimating Answers

Grocery Shopping (all areas)

Recipes

Teaching suggestions:

1. This is one topic in which you should surely make use of students' experiences. Have them keep track of their complete diet for one week. Then have them do a complete analysis of the nutritional value of this diet, as is done in the solved example and practice problems here. The complete chart of nutritional value of foods can be found in almost any textbook on nutrition. The one on pages 226–227 was adapted from the U.S. Department of Agriculture's Home and Garden Bulletin No. 72.

2. Students should learn how to build nutritious diets making use of the four basic food groups. The home economics teacher, county extension agent, or some other specialist in this area would be a good resource person on this topic.

3. Pay special attention to the economics of nutritious diets also. That is, many combinations of foods will supply the necessary daily requirements, but some combinations are a good deal more or less expensive than others. This topic might be considered in conjunction with the activities on grocery shopping in this book (see Chapter 10).

CHAPTER TWENTY

Property Taxes

43. Property Taxes

A property tax is a tax charged on land, houses, commercial buildings and other "real" property owned by individuals and corporations. The amount of a property tax is determined by two factors: (1) the assessed value of the property and (2) the tax rate. The assessed value is the amount the government thinks your property is worth. Some cities and counties assess property at less than their market value (what you would get if you actually sold the property). They may choose 25%, 33%, 50%, or some other fraction to use when assessing property.

The property tax rate is determined by your local governmental body: city, town, county, or parish. It can be expressed in various ways. The most common systems are these:

1. *Percentage:* A 10% tax rate, for example, would mean that you pay a tax of 10% on the assessed value of your property.
2. *Millage:* A "mill" is an old unit of money worth 0.1 of 1¢ or one thousandth of a dollar. A rate of 10 mills means a tax of 10 mills for each $1 value of your property.
3. *Per thousand:* A rate of $15 per thousand means a tax of $15 on each $1000 of property value. The solved examples below illustrate all three types of tax rates.

● **Example 1:**

What is the annual property tax on the AuSable Machine Parts factory if the assessed value of the property is $148,342.16 and the tax rate is 4.83258%?

Solution:

$$\text{Property tax} = \text{Tax rate} \times \text{Assessed value}$$
$$= 4.83258\% \times \$148,342.16$$
$$= \$7168.75$$

● **Example 2:**

The home owned by Augustana diLorenzo is worth $84,350 on the market and is assessed at 30% of its market value. What is the annual property tax on this house if the current rate is 16.5 mills per $1 of assessed valuation?

Solution:

$$\text{Assessed value of house} = 30\% \times \text{Market value}$$
$$= 30\% \times \$84,350 = \$25,305$$
$$\text{Property tax} = .0165 \times \$25,305 = \$417.53$$

● **Example 3:**

Irma and Ed McCarthy own a farm whose market value is $228,150. The county taxes property at the rate of $3.25 per $1000 and property is assessed at 52.7% of market value. What is the McCarthy's tax bill this year?

Solution:

$$\text{Assessed value of farm} = 52.7\% \times \$228,150 = \$120,235.05$$
$$\text{Property tax} = \$3.25 \text{ per thousand} \times \$120.23505 \text{ thousands} = \$390.76$$

43. Property Taxes

1. The Kurtas' home is assessed at $154,500. The tax rate in their town is 5.325% of the assessed valuation. What will be the amount of the Kurtas' tax bill this year?

   _____

2. David and Roberta Harrington own a home which has an assessed valuation of $128,325. Their town taxes property at a rate of $2.75 per $1000. What is the Harringtons' tax bill this year?

   _____

3. Maxine Trapeeze owns a condominium which has a market value of $125,000 and is assessed at 32% of its market value. The tax rate in Maxine's town is 4.62359%. What is Ms. Trapeeze's property tax this year?

   _____

4. You are in the market for a new house, and you have narrowed your choices down to two properties. Both houses have the same market value: $142,500. But the houses are in different towns where the tax rates are different. In the first town, the house is assessed at 30% of its market value and taxed at the rate of 6.5972% of assessed value. In the second town, the house is assessed at 23% of its market value and taxed at the rate of 19.6 mills per $1. What would be the property tax on each house?

   _____

5. The Rialdos own a summer cottage on Gull Lake worth $128,000 on the market. The cottage is assessed at 28% of its value and taxed at 2.65729% of its assessed value. What is the property tax on this property?

   _____

6. Mrs. Wentworth owns two hardware stores in two different towns. The first has a market value of $269,750 and is assessed at 50% of its market value. The tax rate in this town is $4.25 per $1000. The second store is valued at $252,950 and is assessed at 45% of its market value. The tax rate in this town is 4.265 mills per $1. What is the total tax Mrs. Wentworth has to pay for these two stores?

   _____

7. Dave Farrell has decided to build a new garage next to his house. The new garage will increase the value of his property from $178,900 to $183,250. If this property is assessed at 48% of its market value and the tax rate is $2.85 per $1000, by how much will this year's property tax increase because of the new garage?

   _____

© 1983, 1996 Instructional Horizons. Produced and Distributed
by J. Weston Walch, Publisher, Portland, Maine 04104-0658   234   *Consumer Math Success Kit*

Property Taxes

Teacher Notes

Mathematical skills required:

multiplication of decimals and percents

New vocabulary:

assessed valuation
millage
percentage tax rate
per $1000 tax rate
property tax
tax rate

Related topics:

Budgets: Short-term Budgets
Estimating Answers

Teaching suggestions:

1. Have students find out the rate at which property is assessed in your community and the current tax rate. Use these figures to calculate the property tax on certain fictional properties in the community.

2. Tax rates on commercial property are sometimes different from those on residential property. Discuss with students the reasons that this might be so and whether this is a good idea or not.

CHAPTER TWENTY-ONE
Recipes

44. Recipes

How much mathematics do you need to prepare a good meal? Probably not very much. A good recipe and some experience is about all you need. But there are exceptions to that rule. The major exception comes when you have to cook for more or fewer people than your recipe is written for. Perhaps you are planning dinner for 16 people. And you have decided to use your favorite pasta recipe. But that recipe is written for *six* people! Then what do you do? Here is the point at which mathematics can be very important.

One method for solving this problem is to use a **conversion factor**. Two steps are involved in the method:

Step 1: Determine a conversion factor (CF) that will make a recipe originally written for "x" people suitable for "y" people. That conversion factor can be expressed mathematically as:

$$CF = \frac{\text{number of people to be served}}{\text{number of people named in recipe}} = \frac{x}{y}$$

Step 2: Multiply the amount of each ingredient in the given recipe by the conversion factor (CF) determined above.

The following example shows how to use this method.

● **Example:**

The recipe below is designed for four people. What quantities should be used for a party of eight people?

$\frac{1}{2}$ cup Indonesian soy sauce	$\frac{1}{2}$ cup ground roasted peanuts
1 teaspoon ground hot red pepper	1 clove garlic, minced
$\frac{3}{4}$ cup hot water	juice of 1 lemon
$\frac{1}{3}$ cup peanut butter	3 pound leg of lamb

Solution:

Step 1: Number of people to be served = y = 8

Number of people named in recipe = x = 4

$$CF = \frac{8}{4} = 2$$

Step 2: Multiply each part of the recipe by the CF:

Soy sauce: $\frac{1}{2}$ cup × 2   = 1 cup
Red pepper: 1 tsp × 2   = 2 tsp
Hot water: $\frac{3}{4}$ cup × 2   = $1\frac{1}{2}$ cups
Peanut butter: $\frac{1}{3}$ cup × 2   = $\frac{2}{3}$ cup
Peanuts: $\frac{1}{2}$ cup × 2   = 1 cup
Garlic: 1 clove × 2   = 2 cloves
Lemon: 1 × 2   = 2
Lamb: 3 lbs × 2   = 6 lbs

© 1983, 1996 Instructional Horizons. Produced and Distributed by J. Weston Walch, Publisher, Portland, Maine 04104-0658

Consumer Math Success Kit

44. Recipes

1. Aunt Flora's recipe for tuna salad sandwiches is given below. The recipe is written for four sandwiches, but you need to make eight. Change the recipe accordingly.

   1 can tuna $\frac{1}{2}$ cup mayonnaise
   $\frac{1}{4}$ cup chopped celery $\frac{1}{4}$ teaspoon salt

   _____

   _____

2. The Barringers have a traditional family recipe for meatloaf that serves eight people. Now that the children are gone, Mrs. Barringer usually makes the same dish for four people. Adjust the recipe below so that it will serve four people, rather than eight.

   4 cups chopped beef   4 tbsp parsley
   $1\frac{2}{3}$ cup chopped onion $1\frac{1}{3}$ cup water
   $\frac{1}{2}$ cup shortening $\frac{1}{2}$ tsp salt
   4 cups chopped potatoes $\frac{1}{2}$ tsp pepper

   _____

   _____

   _____

   _____

3. Cindy has found a wonderful recipe for poached fish, but it serves only two people. She will have to serve six. How should the following ingredients be changed?

   1 medium onion   1 tsp salt
   1 bay leaf   1 lb fish filets
   1 tsp paprika   3 sprigs parsley
   3 slices lemon   1 tsp pepper

   _____

   _____

   _____

   _____

(continued)

© 1983, 1996 Instructional Horizons. Produced and Distributed
by J. Weston Walch, Publisher, Portland, Maine 04104-0658   240   *Consumer Math Success Kit*

44. Recipes (continued)

4. The following omelet recipe from the *Just for Two* cookbook must be corrected in order to serve five people. What changes are necessary in the ingredients?

4 eggs   2 tbsp chopped onion
$\frac{1}{8}$ tsp pepper $\frac{1}{4}$ tsp salt
$\frac{1}{4}$ cup water   1 tbsp butter

_____

_____

_____

5. Andy usually makes a two-layer birthday cake but has decided to make his next one a three-layer cake. How should the two-layer recipe given below be adjusted to make a three-layer cake?

1 pkg cream cheese   1 tbsp milk
1 tsp vanilla   2 $\frac{1}{2}$ cups confectioner's sugar

_____

_____

6. Annette likes the coleslaw recipe below from the *Cooking for a Crowd* cookbook. But she is serving only eight people. How should this recipe for 20 people be adjusted?

10 cups chopped cabbage   1 $\frac{1}{2}$ tsp caraway seed
$\frac{1}{2}$ cup chopped onion   1 $\frac{1}{4}$ cup sour cream
$\frac{1}{2}$ cup mayonnaise   1 tsp dry mustard
1 tsp salt

_____

_____

_____

7. The recipe for french-fried onion rings below will serve three people, but there will be ten at your dinner party. Adjust the recipe accordingly.

1 large onion $\frac{1}{4}$ tsp salt
$\frac{3}{4}$ tsp baking powder $\frac{1}{2}$ cup flour
$\frac{2}{3}$ cup milk $\frac{1}{2}$ tsp pepper

_____

_____

_____

     Consumer Math Success Kit

Recipes

Teacher Notes

Mathematical skills required:

multiplication and division of whole numbers and fractions

New vocabulary:

Related topics:

Estimating Answers

Teaching suggestions:

1. Invite students to bring their favorite recipe to class. Then have them revise that recipe so that it will serve a larger or smaller number of people. If any students in the class are also taking home economics courses at the same time, work in these two subjects may be correlated.

2. Some of the mathematical answers obtained in this section do not necessarily make good culinary sense. For example, if one bay leaf is needed to spice a meal for three people, it probably is *not* necessary to use two bay leaves when that recipe is adjusted for six people. Also, the mathematical calculations used in these problems often produces results that don't make much sense in the kitchen. It is uncommon to find "$\frac{1}{5}$ tsp" or "$\frac{6}{7}$ cup" measures. In such cases, a cook would round the mathematical answer off to some value which most closely corresponds to the cooking utensils which are commonly available (probably $\frac{1}{4}$ tsp and 1 cup in the above examples). The answers given for this topic are mathematically correct but will need to be corrected for "common sense" considerations in a few instances.

CHAPTER TWENTY-TWO
Sales Tax

45. Sales Tax

A sales tax is charged by nearly every state and by some cities in the United States. The tax rate varies a great deal from less than 1% to 10% or more. The tax is charged on all purchases in some states and only on certain purchases in others. The following examples illustrate some situations in which sales tax must be determined.

- **Example 1:**

Verella has decided to purchase a new rotary mower that sells for $189.95. She lives in a state where the sales tax is 6.5% on all items. How much sales tax will she have to pay on the mower? What will be the full price of the mower with tax?

Solution:

Sales tax	$= 6.5\% \times$ Price of mower
	$= 6.5\% \times \$189.95 = \$12.35$
Full price, including tax	$=$ Price of mower $+$ Sales tax
	$= \$189.95 + \$12.35$
	$= \$202.30$

- **Example 2:**

Restaurant meals in a particular state are taxed at the rate of 8%. What is the tax on the meal described below? What is the total cost of the meal, tax included?

2 hamburgers @ $1.39   1 french fries @ 99¢
3 milkshakes @ $1.09   1 onion rings @ $1.35
2 bacon-lettuce-tomato sandwiches @ $1.79

Solution:

Cost of meal $= 2 \times \$1.39 + \$.99 + (3 \times \$1.09) + (2 \times \$1.79) + \$1.35$
$= \$11.97$

Sales tax $= 8\% \times$ Cost of meal
$= 8\% \times \$11.97 = \$.96$

Total price of meal $= \$11.97 + \$.96$
$= \$12.93$

- **Example 3:**

All of the items listed below are subject to a 4.5% state sales tax. What is the tax and total cost of these items? 4 shirts @ $9.95; 1 jacket @ $10.99; 6 T-shirts @ $1.39; 2 pr socks @ $1.95; 1 pr trousers @ $15.99.

Solution:

Cost of goods $= 4 \times \$9.95 + \$10.99 + (2 \times \$1.95) + (6 \times \$1.39) + \$15.99 = \$79.02$

Tax on this sale $= 4.5\% \times \$79.02 = \$3.56$

Total price of goods $= \$79.02 + \$3.56 = \$82.58$

Name _____ Date _____

45. Sales Tax

1. In his last visit to the SunShine Flower Shop, Felix bought 1 philodendron plant @ $2.99, 1 jade plant @ $4.99, and 1 spider plant @ $1.50. The sales tax rate in this state is 3%. What was the tax and total cost of Felix's purchase?

_____

2. Barbara keeps track of her grocery purchases with a hand-calculator. When she has finished buying, she notices that her total is $25.15. At the rate of 5%, what sales tax will she have to add to this subtotal? What is the total cost of her groceries?

_____

3. Before leaving for a day at the beach, Wanda purchases the items listed below at the corner store. The sales tax in her state is 6.5%. How much sales tax must she pay on this purchase, and what is her total bill at the store? 2 rolls of film @ $1.19 each; 1 bottle sunscreen @ $4.25; 1 beach ball @ $1.79; 2 batteries @ two for $1.99.

_____

4. The restaurant meals tax in a certain state is 4%. What will be the total bill for the meal that the Farnuzzi family has ordered? 1 antipasto @ $3.95; 1 lasagna dinner @ $5.95; 1 veal cutlet dinner @ $6.95; 1 manicotti dinner @ $6.50; 2 coffees @ 50¢ ea.; 1 milk @ 50¢; 1 birthday cake @ $3.00.

_____

5. The four children in the Durant family have decided to chip in and buy a rowboat for their parents. The cost of the rowboat is $124.95 and the state sales tax is 6%. How much will each of the children have to pay toward the cost of the boat?

_____

6. Serena and Jill want to buy a new television set. They live on the border of Massachusetts, which has a 5% sales tax, and New Hampshire, which has no sales tax. The price of the set is $295 in Massachusetts and $299.95 in New Hampshire. In which state will it be cheaper to buy the set?

_____

7. Paula's father has reminded her that it's time to paint the house. He sends her to the store with the following list of items to purchase. What will be the cost of these items, the sales tax, and the total bill? The sales tax in this state is 4.5%. 3 pkg. sandpaper @ 75¢; two 4" paint brushes @ $2.29; 10 gal. of purple house paint @ $7.99; 2 gal. of green trim paint @ $8.25.

_____

246   *Consumer Math Success Kit*

Sales Tax

Teacher Notes

Mathematical skills required:

multiplication by percents

New vocabulary:

sales tax

Related topics:

Eating Out
Grocery Shopping (all areas)
Home Care (all areas)

Teaching suggestions:

1. The daily newspaper provides many opportunities for practicing this skill. Students may be assigned certain topics and/or items in the newspaper on which to calculate sales tax. For example, they might be instructed to do some imaginary grocery shopping from food prices listed in the paper and then to calculate the sales tax on this list.

2. A few cities and other municipalities have local sales tax also. If you live near such a municipality, show how two sales taxes may be figured on the same purchase.

CHAPTER TWENTY-THREE

<u>Savings Accounts</u>

46. Savings Accounts

A **savings account** is a method for putting aside money from time to time in a bank, credit union, or other financial institution. While the money is in the account, it also draws interest. After a period of time, the money you take out of the account includes both the money you originally put in (the **principal**) and the **interest** the bank has paid to you. The amount of interest you earn in a savings account depends on a number of factors including: (1) the **amount of money** you put into the account (the principal); (2) the **rate of interest** paid by the bank or other institution; (3) the **length of time** the money is in the account; (4) the **type of interest** paid (simple or compound); and (5) the **kind of savings account** you have. Today, there are many kinds of savings accounts available. They differ from each other primarily on the basis of the rate of interest paid, the minimum deposit required, and the length of time you are required to leave your money in the account. The following example illustrates a common type of savings account.

● **Example:**

Arthur Weems deposits his savings in a regular savings account at Carmen's Credit Union. The account pays 6.4%, compounded quarterly, on the lowest balance during the quarter. From this information and the record of transactions below, determine the quarterly interest payments and Arthur's balance at the end of the year.

January 1; balance:	$ 285.80	July 31; deposit:	$ 150.00
January 30; deposit:	$ 100.00	August 16; deposit:	$ 300.00
March 3; deposit:	$ 250.00	September 8; deposit:	$ 275.00
March 28; deposit:	$ 300.00	September 21; withdrawal:	$1950.00
May 9; deposit:	$ 150.00	October 30; deposit:	$ 250.00
June 8; deposit:	$ 85.00	November 21; deposit:	$ 175.00
July 3; deposit:	$ 450.00	December 27; deposit:	$ 200.00

Solution:

First quarter (1/1–3/31); Lowest balance = $285.80 (1/1)
Interest = 6.4% × $285.80 × $\frac{1}{4}$ year = $4.57
Balance: 3/31 = $935.80 + $4.57 = $940.37

Second quarter (4/1–6/30); Lowest balance = $940.37 (4/1)
Interest = 6.4% × $940.37 × $\frac{1}{4}$ year = $15.05
Balance: 6/30 = $1175.37 + $15.05 = $1190.42

Third quarter (7/1–9/30); Lowest balance = $415.42 (9/21)
Interest = 6.4% × $415.42 × $\frac{1}{4}$ year = $6.65
Balance: 9/30 = $415.42 + $6.65 = $422.07

Fourth quarter (10/1–12/31); Lowest balance = $422.07 (10/1)
Interest = 6.4% × $422.07 × $\frac{1}{4}$ year = $6.75
Balance: 12/31 = $1047.07 + $6.75 = $1053.82

46. Savings Accounts

1. Edna opens a savings account with $15 on March 1. The account pays 6% simple interest. How much will she have in her account one year later?

   _____

2. Luis has saved $25 from his paper route. He deposits the money in an account that pays $5\frac{1}{2}$% simple interest per year. How much will he have in his account six months later? One year later?

   _____

3. Fortunella opens a savings account with the Gold and Silver Bank on January 1 with a deposit of $35. The bank pays $5\frac{3}{4}$% simple interest per year. How much will the account be worth April 1? July 1? October 1?

   _____

4. The savings account that Rosa has at the Gold and Silver Bank pays $5\frac{1}{2}$% interest, compounded quarterly. If she deposits $50 on June 1, how much will she have in her account three months later? Six months later? One year later?

   _____

5. Melissa has $100 to deposit in a savings account. She can put it either in an account that pays 6.2% simple interest or $5\frac{1}{4}$% compound interest (compounded quarterly). What balance will her account show at the end of one year in each of these two accounts?

   _____

6. How much interest will Ross earn if he deposits $250 in a savings account that pays $5\frac{1}{2}$% interest, compounded monthly? Answer this question for the following time periods: After one month? After two months? After three months?

   _____

7. Veronica is trying to decide whether to deposit $500 in (a) an account that pays 6.5% simple interest, (b) an account that pays $5\frac{1}{2}$% interest, compounded semiannually, or (c) an account that pays $5\frac{1}{4}$% interest, compounded quarterly. At the end of one year, which account will yield the most interest for her?

   _____

8. Tony earns $15 a week for two months on his paper route. At the end of that time, he invests one quarter of those earnings in a savings account at the Gold and Silver Bank. The bank pays 5.3218% annual interest, compounded monthly. How much money will he have in his account after one month? After three months?

   _____

Savings Accounts

Teacher Notes

Mathematical skills required:

addition, subtraction, and multiplication of decimals
multiplication of percents

New vocabulary:

compound interest
interest
lowest balance
principal
rate of interest
savings account
simple interest

Related topics:

Bank Statements
Checking Accounts
Estimating Answers
Interest

Teaching suggestions:

1. Begin with problems on simple interest in this section until students have developed the idea of what simple interest is all about. Then, move to problems dealing with compound interest. There are relatively few savings accounts that pay simple interest any longer, so the informed consumer should know something about the way compound interest works.

2. Calculations involving compound interest, particularly over extended time periods, can be tiresome. However, such calculations can be performed and carried over within most hand-calculators. A student should be able to determine compound interest for a number of time periods without writing down any intermediary answers. When students have developed this skill, you might ask them to extend the period of time for which compound interest is determined in problems such as Practice Problem 8.

3. Many banks today pay interest, of whatever kind, on the minimum balance in an account over a period of time. This makes it necessary to be very careful about recording deposits and withdrawals in the proper order. Use the solved example to show why this is so. Ask students to calculate the interest on this account if the final balance for the month, rather than the lowest balance, is used to determine the interest paid.

Chapter Twenty-four
Telephone Bills

47. Telephone Bills

Rates for telephone service can be very complicated. Perhaps you have only standard service and make no long-distance calls. If so, you probably pay only a basic rate, and your bills are simple. But that is not what "telephone service" means for most people. It's more likely that you have various special kinds of service ("call waiting," "transfer calls," etc.). Each of these services adds to your monthly bill. And, of course, long-distance calls add even more. Page 258 lists the costs for many kinds of service offered by one telephone company. Use the rates shown there to calculate the monthly telephone bills described in the solved examples below.

● **Example 1:**

Alonso Johnson has basic service only. His long-distance calls for the month are listed below. From this information and the chart on page 258, calculate his telephone bill for the month.

Long-distance calls: $.95; $.68; $1.85; $4.89; $.98

Solution:

Bill = Basic service + Long-distance charges

Long-distance charges = $.95 + $.68 + $1.85 + $4.89 + $.98 = $9.35

Bill = $18.22 + $9.35 = $27.57

● **Example 2:**

Miranda has statewide service, call-waiting service, and an unlisted telephone number. Her long-distance calls for the month are listed below. Calculate Miranda's telephone bill for the month.

Long-distance charges: $8.75; $.45; $3.88; $7.29; $1.87; $1.13; $1.82;
$2.33; $.45; $1.87; $.45; $1.09

Solution:

Total bill = Sum of all charges + Long-distance charges

Total of long distance charges = $8.75 + $.45 + $3.88 + $7.29 + $1.87 + $1.13 + $1.82
$$+ \$2.33 + \$.45 + \$1.87 + \$.45 + \$1.09$$
$$= \$31.38$$

Total bill = $38.80 + (see Table 11, page 258, for extra charges) $2.70
$$+ \$1.28 + \$31.38$$
$$= \$74.16$$

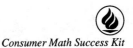

Consumer Math Success Kit

47. Telephone Bills

Shown below are the telephone charges for various types of service in this community.

Table 11: Telephone Charges

Basic monthly service:	$18.22
Countywide service:	$27.90
Statewide service:	$38.80
Unlisted number:	$1.28 per month service charge
Call-waiting service:	$2.70 per month
Call-forwarding service:	$2.70 per month
Three-way calling service:	$3.30 per month
Speed calling (8 numbers):	$2.20 per month
(30 numbers):	$4.30 per month
Additional listing:	$1.25 per telephone per month
Temporary suspension of service:	$4.90 per month

         Consumer Math Success Kit

Name _____ Date _____

47. Telephone Bills

Charges for telephone services are listed on page 258.

1. Willie Blankken has basic monthly telephone service. Last month, he made two long-distance calls, amounting to $7.82. What will his telephone bill be this month?

   _____

2. Chester Baker's telephone service includes countywide service and call-forwarding. In addition, he made two long-distance calls last month, amounting to $1.32 and $2.07. What will Chester's telephone bill be this month?

   _____

3. Determine Fecadu Bahtu's telephone bill for a month in which he made the long-distance calls shown below. In addition, he has countywide service, three-way calling, and call-waiting service. Long-distance calls: $3.09; $2.58; $2.23; $4.56.

   _____

4. In addition to her statewide service, Rosalie Brown has the following special telephone services: speed calling (30 numbers) and an unlisted number. Her long-distance calls for the month are as follows: $8.95; $4.57; $1.07. What is her telephone bill for the month?

   _____

5. Elaine Rio's babysitting service has been very successful, and she makes use of many of the special services the telephone company has to offer. Calculate her bill for one month in which she had the following services and charges: countywide service, call waiting, call forwarding, speed calling (eight numbers), and two additional listings. Her long-distance calls for the month were as follows: $14.87; $10.95; $9.04; $8.23; $4.58; $3.95; $5.67; $10.07; $23.63; $9.67; $8.31; $11.00.

   _____

Telephone Bills

Teacher Notes

Mathematical skills required:

addition of decimals

New vocabulary:

basic rate
(various types of special services)

Related topics:

Budgets: Short-term Budgets
Estimating Answers
Excise Tax
Housing

Teaching suggestions:

1. Charges for various types of telephone services vary widely from state to state and community to community. You probably should include some problem solving in this area that makes use of rates in your own community. These are often listed in the front section of the telephone directory. Most telephone companies are very happy to provide speakers to classes on the use and economics of telephone service.

2. The problems in this section do not ask for excise tax charges on the bills given, but that information could also be required of students as they solve these problems.

CHAPTER TWENTY-FIVE

Travel

Taxis
Automobile Expenses
Other Motorized Vehicles
Bus and Train

48. Taxis

Taxicabs normally charge in one of two ways. They may charge a flat fee for certain trips. For example, a ride from the train station to the airport might cost $12.00. A second type of charge for riding in a cab involves a "beginning rate" and then an additional charge for each fraction of a mile (or kilometer). For example, a cab company might charge 90¢ for the first $\frac{1}{10}$ of a mile and then 10¢ for each $\frac{1}{10}$ mile thereafter. Another company's rates might be $1.20 for the first $\frac{1}{9}$ mile and then 20¢ for each $\frac{1}{9}$ mile thereafter. It helps the consumer to know what these rates are before getting into the cab. This way you can estimate the cost of your ride ahead of time.

● **Example #1:**

Rates for the Richards Cab Company are:

> 75¢ for the first $\frac{1}{8}$ mile and
> 15¢ for each $\frac{1}{8}$ mile thereafter.

What would be the cost of a five-mile ride in a Richards cab?

Solution:

A convenient way to solve this problem is to convert the distance traveled into eighths of a mile:

$$5 \times \frac{8}{8} = \frac{40}{8}$$

The initial or "step-in" rate for the first $\frac{1}{8}$ mile is $.75.

That leaves $\frac{39}{8}$ ($\frac{40}{8} - \frac{1}{8}$) miles to go at 15¢ per $\frac{1}{8}$ mile, or $39 \times 15¢ = \$5.85$.

The total charge, then, is $.75 + $5.85 = $6.60.

● **Example 2:**

The total driving distance from 5th Avenue and 48th Street to LaGuardia Airport is 25.2 kilometers. Rates with the Moderno Cab Company are $1.10 for the first .1 km and 12¢ for each additional kilometer. What is the cost of the cab ride? The passenger also pays $1.25 in tolls and will tip the driver 15% of the fare. What is the total cost of the ride?

Solution:

Total distance traveled in tenths of kilometer = $25.2 \div .1 = 252$ tenths of a kilometer
Fare is divided as: "step-in" charge + tenths of kilometer

Cost   = first 0.1 km + 251 more
             = $1.10 + $0.12 (251)
             = $1.10 + $30.12 = $31.22

Add tolls   = $31.22 + $1.25 = $32.47

Add tip   = 15% × $32.47 = $4.87

Total   = Fare + Tip
             = $32.47 + $4.87 = $37.34

Consumer Math Success Kit

48. Taxis

Map of Sunnybrook

	Hawkins	Wentworth	Driscoll	Buena Vista	Wheatley	Gessup	Haines
East Blvd.							
Sixth							
Fifth							
Main							
Third							
Second							
First							

East View Stadium: 5 1/8 mi

Centerville : 4.6 km

Airport: 4 1/4 mi

Blue Oak Park: 3 5/8 mi

Each block = 1/4 mi or .4 km

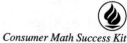

Consumer Math Success Kit

Practice Problems

48. Taxis

Look at the map of Sunnybrook on page 264. Each block in this city is exactly $\frac{1}{4}$ mile (or .4 km) wide and $\frac{1}{4}$ mile (or .4 km) long. Use this map to determine the taxi fares for each of the following trips. There are three taxi companies in town. The rates charged by each are as follows:

Bluebird Taxi (BT): 75¢ for first $\frac{1}{8}$ mile; 15¢ for each $\frac{1}{8}$ mile thereafter.

Marchetti Brothers (MB): $1.10 for first $\frac{1}{4}$ mile; $.25 for each $\frac{1}{4}$ mile thereafter.

O'Brien's Cabs (OC): $.85 for first 0.1 km; 15¢ for each 0.1 km thereafter.

1. What is the fare in the Bluebird Taxi (BT) from Haines and First to Haines and Fifth?

   _____

2. What is the fare in a Marchetti Brothers cab (MB) from Driscoll and Fifth to Buena Vista and Third?

   _____

3. What is the fare in an O'Brien's cab (OC) for a ride from Second and Hawkins to Gessup and Fifth?

   _____

4. What is the fare in a BT cab from Wheatley and First to Wentworth and East Blvd.?

   _____

5. What is the fare in an MB cab from Third and Driscoll to Sixth and Wheatley?

   _____

6. What is the fare in an OC from Second and Wentworth to Sixth and Haines?

   _____

7. What is the fare in a BT cab from Wentworth and Sixth to Blue Oak Park?

   _____

8. What is the fare in an MB cab from the airport to East View Stadium?

   _____

9. What is the fare in an OC from First and Hawkins to Centerville?

   _____

© 1983, 1996 Instructional Horizons. Produced and Distributed
by J. Weston Walch, Publisher, Portland, Maine 04104-0658

Consumer Math Success Kit

49. Automobile Expenses

Many expenses are involved in owning and operating a car. Among these are the following:

1. Cost of gasoline and oil.

2. Maintenance: Tune-ups, oil changes, lubrications, etc.

3. Repairs: Replacement and repair of worn and defective parts.

4. Depreciation: Loss in value because of car's growing older.

5. Insurance.

These costs differ widely from vehicle to vehicle depending on factors such as size of car, age of car, efficiency of operation, and so forth. The tables on pages 269 and 270 list some typical values for the items listed above. Refer to these values in the solved examples that follow.

● **Example:**

What is the cost of gasoline and oil for operating Irene's subcompact car in a year when it was driven 6000 miles?

Solution:

Cost of gasoline	= Number of gallons used × Cost per gallon
Number of gallons	= Distance traveled ÷ Fuel efficiency
	= 6000 miles ÷ 30 miles per gallon
	= 200
Cost of gasoline	= 200 gallons × $1.29 per gallon
	= $258.00
Cost of oil	= Number of quarts used × Cost per quart
Number of quarts	= Distance traveled ÷ Miles per quart
	= 6000 miles ÷ 1000 miles per quart
	= 6 quarts
Cost of oil	= 6 quarts × $1.19 per quart
	= $7.14
Cost of gasoline + oil	= $258.00 + $7.14 = $265.14

49. Automobile Expenses

● **Extra Solved Example:**

Rick Haynes drives his compact car about 8,000 miles per year as a messenger for the Speed-O Company. The company pays him 15¢ a mile for his travel expenses. Based on his actual operating costs (pages 269 and 270), did he make or lose money on his travel budget? What travel allowance would allow him just to break even? The value of his car is now $3,250.

Solution:

The tables on pages 269 and 270 list seven expenses to be considered:

1. Fuel costs = Number of gallons × Cost per gallon

    Number of gallons = 8000 miles ÷ 26 miles per gallon = 307.7 gallons

    Cost of gasoline = 307.7 gallons × $1.45 per gallon = $446.17

2. Oil costs = Number of quarts × Cost per quart

    Number of quarts = 8000 miles ÷ 2500 miles per quart = 3.2 quarts

    Cost of oil = 4 quarts × $1.19 per quart = $4.76

3. Tune-up costs = $29.88

4. Lube and oil change = $11.88

5. Repairs = $325.00

6. Depreciation = 16.2% × Value of car

    = 16.2% × $3250

    = $526.50

7. Insurance = 14.5% × Value of car

    = 14.5% × $3250

    = $471.25

Total of all expenses = $446.17 + $4.76 + $29.88 + $11.88 + $325.00 + $526.50 + $471.25
    = $1815.44

Cost of operation per mile = $1815.44 ÷ 8,000 miles
    = 22.7¢ per mile

The result is that Rick is paid only about two thirds the actual costs of driving his car. He would have to receive 22.7¢ a mile to cover his actual driving expenses.

49. Automobile Expenses

The information you need for solving the following problems is found on pages 269–270.

1. Bernie drives his subcompact car about 5000 miles per year. How much gas will he use in an average year? how much oil?   _____

2. Candy has purchased a compact car. What will it cost her for gasoline and oil to drive this car 4,000 miles this year?   _____

3. The intermediate car Warren has just bought will probably be driven 10,000 miles in the next year. How much will Warren have to spend on gasoline and oil for the car during this time?

   _____

4. The subcompact car M.J. drives runs about 15,000 km per year. What will be the cost of gasoline and oil for the car during the year?   _____

5. Domenico wants to know the annual fuel and oil costs for three kinds of cars—a subcompact, a compact, and an intermediate—if each car is to be driven a total of 24,000 miles this year.

   Subcompact: _____

   Compact: _____

   Intermediate: _____

6. Virien knows that she normally drives 25,000 km per year. What would be the cost of gasoline and oil for each one of the three kinds of cars mentioned in Problem 5?

   Subcompact: _____

   Compact: _____

   Intermediate: _____

7. Anthony is trying to estimate the costs of driving his subcompact car for the coming year. He wants to include the costs of gasoline, oil, tune-ups (one per year), and lube and oil change (one per year). He expects to drive 8,000 miles. What costs should he plan on?

   _____

8. If Anthony were to buy an intermediate car, what would be the costs of operating this car for one year? Include the same costs as those mentioned in Problem 7 for 12,000 miles of driving.

   _____

(continued)

49. Automobile Expenses
(continued)

9. Laura wants to know the total estimated cost of driving her intermediate car a total of 12,500 miles in the coming year. At the beginning of the year, the estimated value of her car was $4200.

_____

10. A compact car will be driven 27,500 miles in the coming year. Its current estimated value is $5250. What are the total estimated costs for this car?

_____

11. Virgil's older model subcompact car is expected to have about three more years of good driving left. Its current value is $450. What expenses can Virgil expect for this car in the coming 12 months? He expects to drive the car about 35,000 km.

_____

12. What are the total estimated driving expenses for a car that will have to go 42,500 miles in the coming year? Answer this question for the three cars listed below:

Subcompact: Current value: $525.   _____

Compact: Current value: $4675.   _____

Intermediate: Current value: $6895.   _____

Table 12: Some Typical Fuel and Oil Costs

Gasoline:	Regular:	$1.29 per gallon or 34.1¢ per liter
	Special:	$1.45 per gallon or 38.4¢ per liter
	Super:	$1.59 per gallon or 42.1¢ per liter
Oil:		$1.19 per quart or $1.25 per liter

49. Automobile Expenses

Table 13: Vehicle Maintenance, Operating, and Repair Information*

Type of Vehicle	Number of Cylinders	Fuel Used	Fuel Efficiency	Oil Efficiency	Tune-up Costs	Lube and Oil Change	Repairs	Depreciation	Insurance
Moped		gasoline (regular)	135 mpg 57 km/L	1 qt/4000 mi 1 L/6500 km	$12.50	$8.50	$65.00	12% of value	11.9% of value
Motorbike		gasoline (regular)	110 mpg 47 km/L	1 qt/3000 mi 1 L/4800 km	$14.50	$9.50	$75.00	15% of value	12.8% of value
Motorcycle		gasoline (regular)	95 mpg 40 km/L	1 qt/2000 mi 1 L/3200 km	$16.50	$9.50	$100.00	22% of value	14.2% of value
Subcompact car	4	gasoline (regular)	30 mpg 13 km/L	1 qt/1000 mi 1 L/1500 km	$24.88	$11.88	$225.00	11.7% of value	12.9% of value
Compact car	6	gasoline (special)	26 mpg 11 km/L	1 qt/2500 mi 1 L/4000 km	$29.88	$11.88	$325.00	16.2% of value	14.5% of value
Intermediate car	8	gasoline (special or super)	34 mpg 15 km/L	1 qt/5000 mi 1 L/8000 km	$39.98	$11.88	$250.00	21.8% of value	18.0% of value

*The data in this table have been **invented** for the purposes of this exercise and do not necessarily reflect the costs of vehicles actually in use at the time of this publication.

Consumer Math Success Kit

50. Other Motorized Vehicles

Many people today choose to drive motorized vehicles other than automobiles. Motorcycles, motorbikes, and mopeds are all popular. Calculating the cost of operating one of these vehicles involves seven factors:

1. Cost of gasoline
2. Cost of oil
3. Cost of tune-ups
4. Cost of lubrication and oil changes
5. Cost of repairs
6. Depreciation
7. Cost of insurance

These factors differ a great deal depending on the type of vehicle being considered, the age of the vehicle, the condition it is in, and so forth. The charts on pages 269 and 270 give you some average values for all of the factors listed above. These values are used in the example below.

● **Example:**

Florence intends to buy a new motorcycle to travel back and forth to school. If she drives the motorcycle 25,000 kilometers in one year, what will be the total costs for all of the factors listed above? The current value of the motorcycle is $3870.00.

Solution:

Cost of gasoline = Number of liters used × Cost per liter

Number of liters used = Distance traveled ÷ Fuel efficiency
= 25,000 kilometers ÷ 40 kilometers per liter
= 625 liters

Cost of gasoline = 625 liters × 34.1¢ per liter
= $213.13

Cost of oil = Number of liters used × Cost per liter

Number of liters = Distance traveled ÷ Oil efficiency
= 25,000 kilometers ÷ 3200 kilometers per liter
= 7.8 liters

Cost of oil = 8 liters × $1.25 per liter = $10.00

Tune-up costs = $16.50

Lube and oil costs = $9.50

Repairs = $100.00

Depreciation = 22% of value
= 22% × $3870 = $851.40

Insurance = 14.2% × $3870 = $549.54

Total of all costs = $213.13 + $10.00 + $16.50 + $9.50
+ $100.00 + $851.40 + $549.54 = $1750.07

© 1983, 1996 Instructional Horizons. Produced and Distributed
by J. Weston Walch, Publisher, Portland, Maine 04104-0658   *Consumer Math Success Kit*

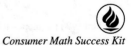

Name _____   Date _____

50. Other Motorized Vehicles

The information needed to solve the following problems is found on pages 269 and 270.

1. Cheryl has just purchased a new motorbike. She expects to ride the motorbike about 1,000 miles in the next year. What will be the fuel and oil costs for the motorbike over this period of time?

   _____

2. Maurice expects to drive his motorcycle about 5,000 miles during the next year. Estimate the cost of fuel and oil for the motorcycle for the year.

   _____

3. Danielle expects to drive her moped a total of 4,000 km during the next six months. What will be the cost of fuel and oil for this number of kilometers?

   _____

4. How much will it cost to purchase gasoline and oil for a motorcycle that will be used to drive 7,500 miles?

   _____

5. Sofia's motorcycle is currently valued at $2,450. Estimate the total costs of driving this motorcycle a distance of 5,000 miles in the next 12 months.

   _____

6. Yee's moped cost him $350. He expects to use it to drive back and forth to school and to work a distance of about 21,500 km in the next 12 months. How much should he set aside for all expenses connected with the moped over this period of time?

   _____

7. The motorbike Corean is considering buying will cost $1,995. If she drives it a total of 8,950 km during the next year, what will be the total operating costs for this motorbike?

   _____

© 1983, 1996 Instructional Horizons. Produced and Distributed
by J. Weston Walch, Publisher, Portland, Maine 04104-0658   272   *Consumer Math Success Kit*

51. Bus and Train

Calculating the cost of travel by bus or train is usually not a problem for consumers. Fares are very simple to figure out. What *does* present a problem for bus or train travel is reading schedules. This problem exists because it is easy to forget that one hour contains 60 minutes. Therefore, many people get confused when they try to figure out how long it will take to get from one place to another by bus or train. The example below goes into detail about calculating the time needed for a trip by bus.

● **Example:**

Bus #988 leaves Jabez Corner at 11:33 A.M. and arrives at Queen Ann Corner at 1:08 P.M. How long will this trip take?

Solution:

In general, it is always true that

Elapsed time for a trip = Arrival time – Departure time

But notice that you cannot solve this problem quite as easily as all that. If you simply substitute times in this equation, you get:

Elapsed time = 1:08 P.M. – 11:33 A.M.

That is, you would be subtracting a large number from a smaller one!

The problem is that we start counting over again at 1 P.M. One o'clock is really **13 hours** after midnight. One way to take care of this problem is to use a 24-hour clock, as the military forces do. All "P.M." times become 12+ the time. So, 1:08 P.M. on the 24-hour clock is really 1308. Morning times stay as they are so that 11:33 A.M. is still 1133. Now we can go back to the subtraction problem above:

Elapsed time = 1308 – 1133

But this will still not give the right answer because we have forgotten that each hour contains 60 minutes. It is better to write the above equation as:

Elapsed time = 13 hours 8 minutes – 11 hours 33 minutes

We can subtract 11 hours from 13 hours, but not 33 minutes from 8 minutes. The way to handle this is to change one hour in the "13 hours" to 60 minutes. Then we can write:

Elapsed time = 13 hours   8 minutes = 12 hours 68 minutes

– 11 hours 33 minutes – 11 hours 33 minutes

Now we can go ahead and subtract. The answer we get is 1 hour 35 minutes, which is the time it takes to make this bus trip.

51. Bus and Train

Bus Schedules

Use the bus schedules on page 275 to follow the example below.

● **Extra Solved Example:**

Konrad plans to take the bus on Monday from Jabez Corner to Queen Ann Corner. How much time will this trip take on each of these buses: 122, 124, and 126?

Solution:

Elapsed time = Arrival time − Departure time

For bus #122:

Elapsed time = 10:03 A.M. − 9:10 A.M.

```
= 10 hours  03 minutes
−  9 hours  10 minutes
=  9 hours  63 minutes
−  9 hours  10 minutes
=          53 minutes
```

For bus #124:

Elapsed time = 11:33 A.M. − 10:40 A.M.

```
= 11 hours  33 minutes
− 10 hours  40 minutes
= 10 hours  93 minutes
− 10 hours  40 minutes
=          53 minutes
```

For bus #126:

Elapsed time = 1:33 P.M. − 12:40 P.M.
= 1333 − 1240 (24-hour clock times)

```
= 13 hours  33 minutes
− 12 hours  40 minutes
= 12 hours  93 minutes
− 12 hours  40 minutes
=          53 minutes
```

The same time is needed for all three trips.

51. Bus and Train

Bus Schedules

BOSTON—QUEEN ANN CORNER—
NORWELL—HANOVER—PEMBROKE—DUXBURY—KINGSTON—PLYMOUTH CENTER

Trip Numbers 2455		MONDAY-FRIDAY								READ DOWN								SATURDAY				SUNDAY & HOLIDAYS				READ DOWN	
		101	103	105	401	107	109	111	113	115	117	119	121	123	125	127	247	129	131	135	271	273	279	283	137	285	299	207
		AM	AM	PM	PM	PM	PM	PM	PM	PM	PM	PM	PM	PM	PM	PM	PM	AM	PM	PM	PM	PM	AM	AM	PM	AM	PM	PM

PLYMOUTH CENTER—KINGSTON—
DUXBURY—PEMBROKE—HANOVER—NORWELL—QUEEN ANN COR.—BOSTON

Trip Numbers 2455		MONDAY-FRIDAY								READ DOWN							SATURDAY					SUNDAY AND HOLIDAYS					READ DOWN
		100	102	104	106	108	110	112	114	116	118	218	122	124	126	128	130	250	252	254	150	152	156	276	278	280	282	288	164
		AM	AM	AM	AM	AM	AM	AM	AM	AM	AM	AM	AM	AM	PM	PM	PM	From Hy. PM	From Hy.	From Hy.	AM	AM	From Hy. PM	From Hy. PM	From Hy. PM	From Hy. PM	From Hy. PM	From Hy. PM

Consumer Math Success Kit

51. Bus and Train

Bus Schedules

Use the bus schedules on page 275 to solve the following problems.

1. Each night after work, Italo takes the #123 bus from South Station Terminal to his home, near Tura's Pharmacy, Kingston. How long would this trip normally take?

   _____

2. In getting to work, Italo takes the #114 bus. How long does this trip take?

   _____

3. When Fern visits her friend Alice, she takes bus #247, leaving from Queen Ann Corner. Alice lives in North Plymouth. How long will this bus ride take?

   _____

4. After spending the day together, Fern and Alice visit their friend Maureen, who lives at the Tarklin Apartments in Duxbury. Then the three of them take Bus #128 back to Queen Ann Corner. How long does the ride back take them?

   _____

5. Shirley lives in Plymouth Center and takes the bus to work every morning to the Greyhound Terminal in Boston. She must leave for work between 7:00 and 8:00 A.M. Which bus(es) will get her to Boston in the least time?

   _____

6. Renata wants to take a bus from Hanover Mall to North Plymouth to make her doctor's appointment. She can leave any time after noon, but must be in North Plymouth before 5:00 P.M. Which bus(es) will get her there most quickly?

   _____

Consumer Math Success Kit

51. Bus and Train

Train Schedules

Use the train schedules on page 274 to follow the example below.

● **Extra Solved Example:**

Which of the following is the fastest train from Toronto to Montreal: #60, #44, #64, #66, #56, #58?

Solution:

As always, the elapsed time is the difference between the time the train leaves and the time it reaches its destination.

Elapsed time = Arrival time − Departure time

For Train #60:   Elapsed time = 1135 − 0710

= 11 hours 35 minutes
− 7 hours 10 minutes
= 4 hours 25 minutes

For Train #44:   Elapsed time = 1510 − 0900

= 15 hours 10 minutes
− 9 hours 00 minutes
= 6 hours 10 minutes

For Train #64:   Elapsed time = 1740 − 1300

= 17 hours 40 minutes
− 13 hours 00 minutes
= 4 hours 40 minutes

For Train #66:   Elapsed time = 2010 − 1545

= 20 hours 10 minutes
− 15 hours 45 minutes
= 19 hours 70 minutes
− 15 hours 45 minutes
= 4 hours 25 minutes

For Train #56:   Elapsed time = 2210 − 1630

= 22 hours 10 minutes
− 16 hours 30 minutes
= 21 hours 70 minutes
− 16 hours 30 minutes
= 5 hours 40 minutes

(continued)

         Consumer Math Success Kit

51. Bus and Train (continued)

For Train #58:   Elapsed time   = 0730 – 2335

Notice the special problem here. The train leaves just before midnight and arrives the next morning. We can express the times best in the following way:

$$
\begin{aligned}
\text{Elapsed time} \ &= \quad 7 \text{ hours } 30 \text{ minutes} \\
&- \underline{23 \text{ hours } 35 \text{ minutes}} \\
&= \quad 7 \text{ hours} + 24 \text{ hours later } 30 \text{ minutes} \\
&- \underline{22 \text{ hours} \qquad\qquad\quad 35 \text{ minutes}} \\
&= 31 \text{ hours } 30 \text{ minutes} \\
&- \underline{23 \text{ hours } 35 \text{ minutes}} \\
&= 30 \text{ hours } 90 \text{ minutes} \\
&- \underline{22 \text{ hours } 35 \text{ minutes}} \\
&= \quad 7 \text{ hours } 55 \text{ minutes}
\end{aligned}
$$

From these calculations we can see that the fastest trains are #60 and #66. Both take 4 hours and 25 minutes for the trip. The slowest train is the overnighter, #58, which takes 7 hours and 55 minutes.

Train Schedules/Via Rail

TORONTO – BELLEVILLE – KINGSTON – BROCKVILLE – MONTRÉAL

km	Mi	Eastern Time / Heure de l Est		RAPIDO 60 Ex Sun Sauf dim	CAPITAL 44 Daily Quot	RAPIDO 62 Daily Quot	RAPIDO 64 Daily Quot	RAPIDO 66 Daily Quot	BONA-VENTURE 56 Daily Quot	RAPIDO 46 Daily Quot	RAPIDO 68 Ex Sat Sauf sam	ONTARIAN 656 Ex Sat Sauf sam	CAVALIER 58 Daily Quot
0	0	Toronto, Ont	Dp	Y 07 10	09 00	L 10 45	M 13 00	R 15 45	16 30	E 17 10	S 17 50	20 10	23 35
21	13	Guildwood		O 07 26	09 21	A 11 05	13 17	E 16 01	16 51	X 17 30	I 18 10	20 28	23 59
51	32	Oshawa		R K	09 39			N 17 10		E C	M	20 47	00 22
101	63	Port Hope				S		A			C O	21 16	01 00
113	70	Cobourg			10 16	A	14 01	I 17 50			E	21 25	01 12
163	101	Trenton Jct				L		S 18 17				21 52	
182	113	Belleville			10 54	L	14 35	S 18 35				22 06	02 06
217	135	Napanee			11 14	E		A				22 27	
254	158	Kingston		09 15	11 42	13 07	15 15	N 17 50	19 20	19 35	20 05	22 55	03 02
290	180	Gananoque			12 03			C					
335	208	Brockville	Ar		12 30			E	20 02	20 31			03 55

					LAKE-SHORE 54 Daily Quot								
335	208	Brockville	Dp		13 00				20 04				04 40
354	220	Prescott			13 15								
428	266	Cornwall, Ont			13 55		16 36		20 56		21 31		06 00
476	296	Coteau Qué											06 29
520	323	Dorval (CN)		11 15	14 45	15 25	17 20	19 50	21 45		22 25		07 05
539	335	Montréal Qué (Central Stn / Gare Centrale)	Ar	11 35	15 10	15 50	17 40	20 10	22 10		22 50		07 30

51. Bus and Train

Train Schedules/Amtrak

SCHEDULES IN EFFECT
Boston-Providence-Springfield-Hartford-New Haven-New York-Newark-Trenton-Philadelphia-Wilmington-Baltimore-Washington

km	Mi	Station	67 The Night Owl (Daily)	169 The Patriot (Ex Su)	151 The Shoreliner (Ex Su)	95 The Colonial (Daily)	99E Metroliner Service (Ex Sa)	155 The Shoreliner (Su only)	19 The Crescent (Daily)	117 Metroliner Service (Ex Sa)	409 Conn. Valley Service (Daily)	173 The Merchants Limited (Daily)	Metroliner Service (Ex Su)	177 The Yankee Clipper (Daily)	143 The Mount Vernon (Su Only)	189 The Mount Vernon (Ex Su)	419 Conn. Valley Service (Ex Su)	183 The Benjamin Franklin (Daily)	421 Conn. Valley Service (Daily)	167 The Bay State (Daily)
0	0	Boston, MA – South Sta (ET) Dp	10 15P	5 53A	7 00A	7 50A		9 00A				9 40A		2 40P				4 50P		6 00P
19	12	Route 128, MA	10 33P	6 11A	7 18A	8 08A		9 18A				9 58A		2 58P				R 5 08P		6 18P
70	44	Providence, RI	11 09P	6 51A	7 54A	8 46A		9 54A				10 36A		3 34P				5 44P		6 54P
92	57	East Greenwich, RI				9 15A												6 00P		
114	71	Kingston, RI	11 38P	7 20A								11 06A		4 03P				6 13P		7 21P
141	88	Westerly, RI	11 54P	7 35A								11 21A		4 18P				6 28P		
155	96	Mystic, CT (Mystic Seaport)		7 45A										4 28P				6 38P		
171	106	New London, CT	12 19A	8 00A	8 57A	9 52A		10 54A				11 45A	E	4 43P				6 52P		7 57P
199	124	Old Saybrook, CT (Valley R R)	12 39A	8 19A		10 11A						12 04P	X	5 02P				7 11P		
158	98	Springfield, MA									11 09A		P		5 10P		6 11P		7 14P	
171	106	Enfield, CT (Thompsonville)									11 21A		R				6 23P		7 26P	
182	113	Windsor Locks, CT									11 31A		E		5 32P		6 33P		7 36P	
189	117	Windsor, CT									11 37A		S				6 39P		7 42P	
199	124	Hartford, CT									11 49A		S		5 50P		6 51P		7 54P	
216	134	Berlin, CT (New Britain)									12 01P				6 02P		7 03P		8 06P	
228	142	Meriden, CT									12 12P				6 13P		7 14P		8 17P	
238	148	Wallingford, CT									12 22P				6 23P		7 24P		8 27P	
247	153	North Haven, CT (Hamden)									12 31P						7 33P		8 36P	
258	160	New Haven, CT Ar	1 15A	8 55A	9 53A	10 48A		11 47A			12 43P	12 43P		5 40P	6 45P		7 45P	7 45P	8 48P	
252	157	New Haven, CT Dp	1 30A	9 05A	10 03A	10 58A		11 57A				12 53P		5 50P	6 55P		7 55P	7 55P	8 58P	
260	174	Bridgeport, CT	1 52A									1 15P		6 12P	7 15P			8 15P		
315	196	Stamford, CT	2 21A	9 54A		11 47A						1 44P		6 43P	7 43P			8 45P		9 47P
330	205	Rye, NY										1 58P						8 57P		
373	232	New York, NY – Penn Sta Ar	3 17A	10 50A	11 45A	12 45P		1 35P				2 50P		7 45P	7 55P	9 00P		9 45P		10 46P
373	232	New York, NY – Penn Sta Dp	3 47A	11 00A	12 01P	12 55P	1 30P		2 00P	2 30P		3 00P	3 30P	8 00P	8 00P	9 00P		10 00P		

51. Bus and Train

Train Schedules

The train schedules you need to solve these problems are on pages 278 and 279.

1. José wants to travel from Boston to New Haven on Amtrak train #169. How long will the trip take?

   _____

2. Veronica lives in Providence. She plans on visiting her Uncle Jerome in New London. If she takes Amtrak train #193, how long will this trip take her?

   _____

3. Jean-Paul intends to take the VIA Rail train from Cobourg to Cornwall. He wants to leave Cobourg as soon after 1:00 P.M. as possible. Which train should he take, and how long will the trip take him?

   _____

4. Eleanora has to get from Boston to New York City by Amtrak train. She can leave any time after 2:00 P.M. and before 7:00 P.M. Which trains could she take? Which train would take the least time for this trip?

   _____

5. Bernard gets out of work in Providence at 5:00 P.M. He wants to leave for New London as soon after that as possible. How many Amtrak trains could he take that same evening? How long would the trip to New London be on this train (or these trains)?

   _____

6. Mr. Leveille must take the VIA Rail train from Toronto to Montreal twice a week. He can leave any time after noon. Which train makes the fastest time between these two cities?

   _____

7. Bonnie Sue would like to take the Amtrak train from Old Saybrook to Rye some morning next week. Do any trains make this connection? If so, how long will the trip take?

   _____

8. Maurice would like to take a morning VIA Rail train from Kingston to Brockville. He would prefer to travel by the Rapido train, if possible. Is that possible? What train(s) could he take? How long will the trip be?

   _____

Travel

Teacher Notes

Mathematical skills required:

> addition, subtraction, multiplication, and division of whole numbers, fractions, and decimals
> understanding and use of 24-hour clock

New vocabulary:

> beginning rate (taxi)
> fuel efficiency
> maintenance costs
> depreciation
> step-in rate (taxi)
> elapsed time
> 24-hour clock

Related topics:

> Estimating Answers
> Insurance: Automobile
> Vacation Planning

Teaching suggestions:

1. Find out the rates for taxi service in your own town. Have students determine the cost of taking a taxi between certain points in the community.

2. Bus and train schedules for your own area are probably available at local terminals or from local transportation companies. Travel agents may be able to supply these schedules also. Have students use these local timetables to determine the time required for travel between various local and nearby locations using bus and/or train.

3. You may want students to consider the alternatives of traveling from one place to another by various types of transportation. That is, what is the relative time and cost involved in going from your community to New York City (or Chicago or Los Angeles or Houston) by train or bus? Students can suggest factors which would help a person decide among these possibilities.

CHAPTER TWENTY-SIX

Utility Bills:
Gas, Electric, and Water

52. Gas, Electric, and Water

Charges for these three services are determined in much the same way. A meter installed in your house or apartment measures the quantity of gas, electricity, or water you use. Then, your bill is calculated by multiplying the amount used by a rate determined by the company. That is,

Your cost = Units used × Cost per unit

For electricity, the quantity used is measured in kilowatt-hours (kwh). For gas and water, the unit is cubic feet (cu ft).

Calculating your bill can be more complicated than this. Sometimes the rate a company charges for gas, water, or electricity depends on how much is used. The more a customer uses, the smaller the rate. Rates for businesses and industries may be different from residential rates.

● **Example: Gas Charges**

The gas meter in the D'Angelos' apartment has four dials that read as shown below. What quantity of gas do these dials represent? If the dials read 4430 last month, what quantity of gas did the D'Angelos use this month? Use the rate chart on page 288 to determine the cost of gas for the D'Angelos this month.

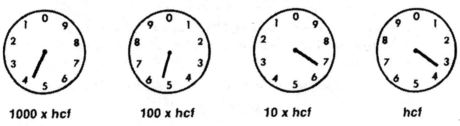

1000 x hcf   100 x hcf   10 x hcf   hcf

Solution: Gas Charges

Check first to be sure that you know how to read each dial. Notice that some read in one direction (clockwise) and others in the opposite direction (counterclockwise). The one at the far right, for example, reads in the same direction as a clock. The hand is pointing between the 3 and the 4. This means it has passed the "3" marker and is on its way to the "4" marker. You should record a "3" for this dial.

The next dial to the left reads in the reverse direction, that is, counterclockwise. In this case, the hand is between "6" and "7." You should record a "6" for this dial. Similarly, the readings on the next two dials, from right to left, are "5" and "4." The meter reading for this month is 4563 hundred cubic feet (or 4563 hcf). The cost of this gas can be calculated by multiplying the amount of gas used by the price of the gas, per hundred cubic feet. Or:

Cost of gas = (4563 hcf – 4430 hcf) × Cost per hcf

But notice for the cost of gas, you must **add** a special "adjustment rate" of $.4344 to every "regular rate" listed on the chart. So, for 133 hcf of gas used, the actual rate is $.228 + $.4344 per hcf = $.6624 per hcf. So,

Cost of gas = 133 hcf × $.6624 per hcf

= $88.09

52. Gas, Electric, and Water

● **Extra Solved Example: Electric Rates**

Shown below are the dials on Robert Wyrocki's electric meter at the end of the month of July. The meter reading at the beginning of the month was 5989 kwh (kilowatt hours). From this information and the rate chart on page 288, determine Robert's electric bill for the month.

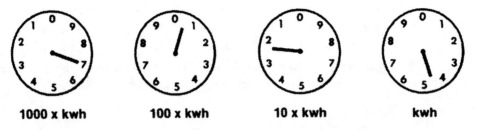

| 1000 x kwh | 100 x kwh | 10 x kwh | kwh |

Solution: Electric Rates

The reading on the dials shown above is 7024. This means that the amount of electricity used during the month is 7024 – 5989 kwh or 1035 kwh. The cost of this electricity is:

Cost of electricity = Amount used × Rate per kwh

To determine the rate, notice that in addition to all "regular" charges, there is a "fuel adjustment charge" of 2.92100¢ per kwh. Since Robert used more than 1000 kwh, his total rate is:

$$\text{Rate per kwh} = \text{Regular rate} + \text{Fuel adjustment}$$
$$= 5.35\text{¢} + 2.921\text{¢}$$
$$= 8.271\text{¢}$$

and,

$$\text{Cost of electricity} = 1035 \text{ kwh} \times 8.271\text{¢ per kwh}$$
$$= \$85.60$$

Consumer Math Success Kit

52. Gas, Electric, and Water

- **Extra Solved Example: Water and Sewer Charges**

   Shown below are the dials on MarJo Henken's water meter at the end of September. The meter reading three months earlier was 179.8 hcf (hundred cubic feet). The rates for water and sewer use are given on page 288. From this information, calculate the water and sewer bill MarJo will have to pay this quarter.

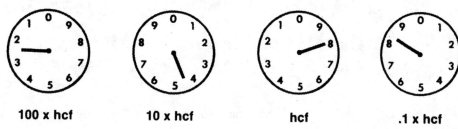

| 100 x hcf | 10 x hcf | hcf | .1 x hcf |

Solution: Water and Sewer Charges

   The reading on the dials shown above is 248.8 hcf. This means that the total amount of water used in MarJo's apartment this quarter was

$$\text{Amount of water used} = \text{Month end reading} - \text{Month beginning reading}$$
$$= 248.8 \text{ hcf} - 179.8 \text{ hcf}$$
$$= 69 \text{ hcf}$$

Notice that there are two charges made on this bill. One is for the water used and the other for the sewer use. So, the charges for the quarter are:

$$\text{Water use} = 69 \text{ hcf} \times 74¢ \text{ per hcf}$$
$$= \$51.06$$

$$\text{Sewer use} = 69 \text{ hcf} \times 41¢ \text{ per hcf}$$
$$= \$28.29$$

$$\text{Total bill} = \$51.06 + \$28.29$$
$$= \$79.35$$

But notice also that there is a discount if the bill is paid within 14 days. The discount applies to water, but not sewer, charges. So, the discounted bill amounts to:

$$\text{Discounted bill} = (\text{Water charges} - 10\%) + \text{Sewer charges}$$
$$= (\$51.06 - 10\% \times \$51.06) + \$28.29$$
$$= (\$51.06 - \$5.11) + \$28.29$$
$$= \$45.95 + \$28.29$$
$$= \$74.24$$

Consumer Math Success Kit

52. Gas, Electric, and Water

- ### Gas

  Charges are assessed in the following way.[1]

If you used more than	but less than	you pay
0 hcf	9 hcf	$.418 per hcf
9 hcf	15 hcf	$.332 per hcf
15 hcf	50 hcf	$.269 per hcf
50 hcf	125 hcf	$.241 per hcf
125 hcf	- - - - - -	$.228 per hcf

  In addition, add $.4344 per hcf to *all* above rates for the cost of "gas adjustment."

- ### Electric

  Electric rates vary depending on the kind of consumer using the electricity (residential, religious, governmental, commercial, industrial, etc.) and on the kind of electricity provided (high- or low-tension service). The chart below shows the rates for only one kind of service.[2]

If you used more than	but less than	you pay
0 kwh	10 kwh	$3.00
10 kwh	1000 kwh	5.85¢ per kwh
1000 kwh	- - - - - -	5.35¢ per kwh

  In addition, add 2.92100¢ per kwh to *all* above rates for the cost of "fuel adjustment."

- ### Water and Sewer

  Water and sewer rates are the same for any quantity of water used. In this community, they are:

  Water: 74¢ per hundred cubic feet

  Sewer: 41¢ per hundred cubic feet

  Discount on water (but not sewer) charges paid within 14 days is 10%.

---

[1]*The symbol "hcf" stands for "hundred cubic feet."*
[2]*The symbol "kwh" stands for "kilowatt-hours of electrical power."*

© 1983, 1996 Instructional Horizons. Produced and Distributed
by J. Weston Walch, Publisher, Portland, Maine 04104-0658   288   *Consumer Math Success Kit*

52. Gas, Electric, and Water

1. Shown below are meter readings for the Alonzos' gas meter over a period of four months. From this information and the rate chart on page 288, calculate their bills for these four months.

Meter reading, August 1: 4563 hcf

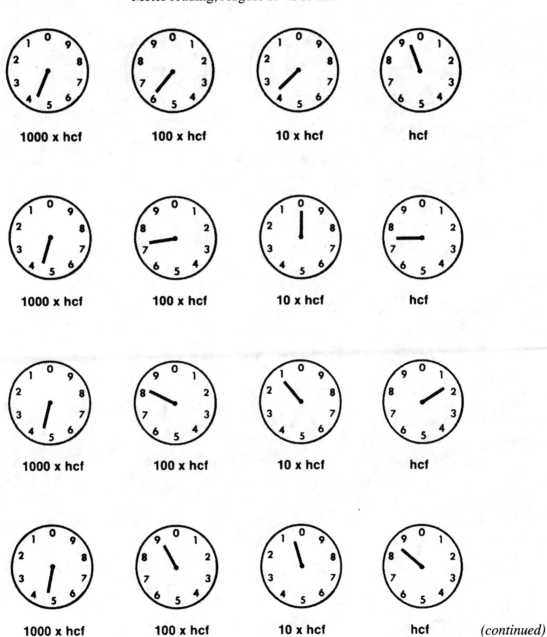

1000 x hcf	100 x hcf	10 x hcf	hcf
1000 x hcf	100 x hcf	10 x hcf	hcf
1000 x hcf	100 x hcf	10 x hcf	hcf
1000 x hcf	100 x hcf	10 x hcf	hcf

(continued)

Consumer Math Success Kit Second Edition

52. Gas, Electric, and Water *(continued)*

2. Shown below are meter readings for the Johannsons' electric meter over a period of four months. From this information and the rate chart on page 288, calculate their bills for these four months.

Meter reading, March 1: 7024

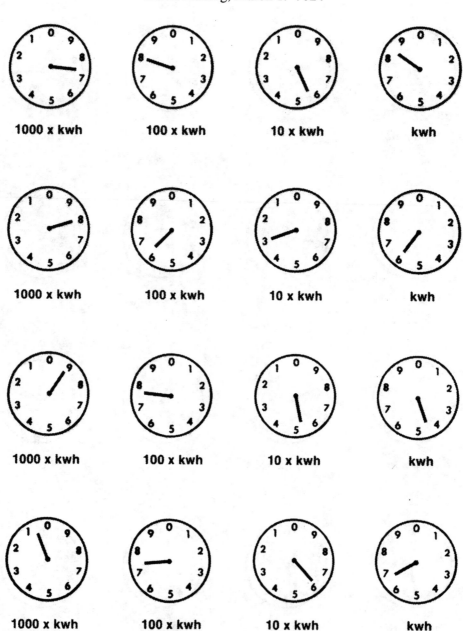

(continued)

Name _____ Date _____

Practice Problems (I)   Utility Bills

52. Gas, Electric, and Water *(continued)*

3. Shown below are meter readings for the Chows' water meter over a period of one year (one reading every three months). From this information and the rate chart on page 288, calculate their quarterly water bills.

Meter reading, June 30: 248.8 hcf

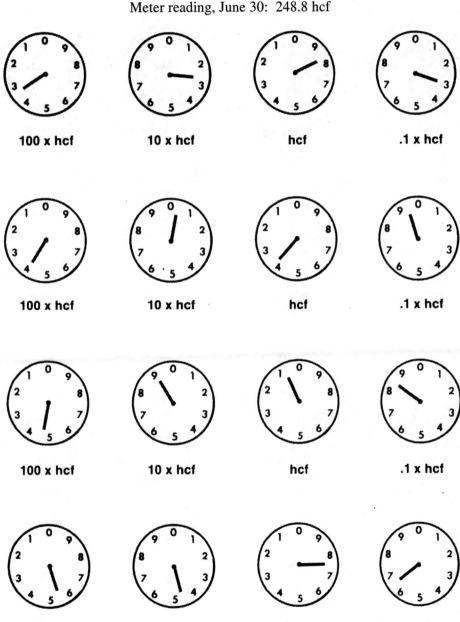

100 x hcf   10 x hcf   hcf   .1 x hcf

100 x hcf   10 x hcf   hcf   .1 x hcf

100 x hcf   10 x hcf   hcf   .1 x hcf

100 x hcf   10 x hcf   hcf   .1 x hcf

Consumer Math Success Kit Second Edition

52. Gas, Electric, and Water

1. Shown below are meter readings for the Alonzos' gas meter over a period of four months. From this information and the rate chart on page 288, calculate their bills for these four months.

Meter reading, December 1: 4908 hcf

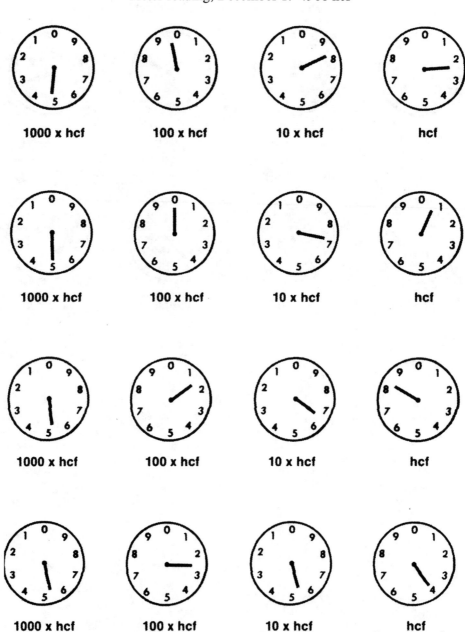

<table>
<tr><td>1000 x hcf</td><td>100 x hcf</td><td>10 x hcf</td><td>hcf</td></tr>
</table>

(continued)

52. Gas, Electric, and Water *(continued)*

2. Shown below are meter readings for the Johannsons' electric meter over a period of four months. From this information and the rate chart on page 288, calculate their bills for these four months.

Meter reading, July 1: 0766

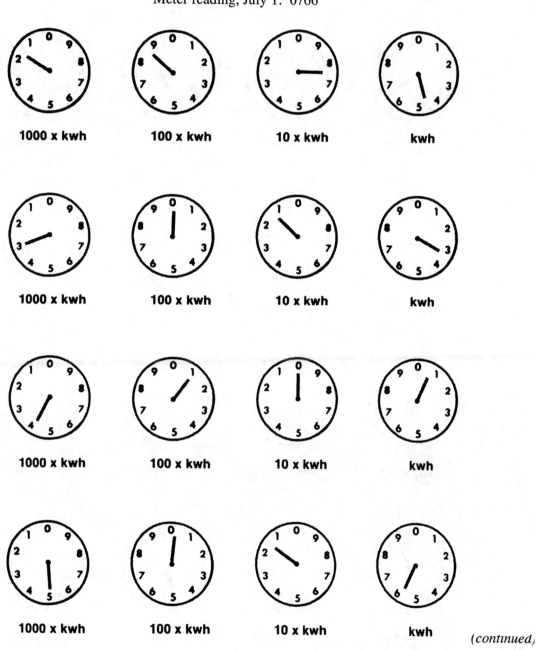

| 1000 x kwh | 100 x kwh | 10 x kwh | kwh |

| 1000 x kwh | 100 x kwh | 10 x kwh | kwh |

| 1000 x kwh | 100 x kwh | 10 x kwh | kwh |

| 1000 x kwh | 100 x kwh | 10 x kwh | kwh |

(continued)

© 1983, 1996 Instructional Horizons. Produced and Distributed by J. Weston Walch, Publisher, Portland, Maine 04104-0658

Consumer Math Success Kit Second Edition

52. Gas, Electric, and Water (continued)

3. Shown below are meter readings for the Chows' water meter over a period of one year (one reading every three months). From this information and the rate chart on page 288, calculate their quarterly water bills.

Meter reading, June 30: 5476 hcf

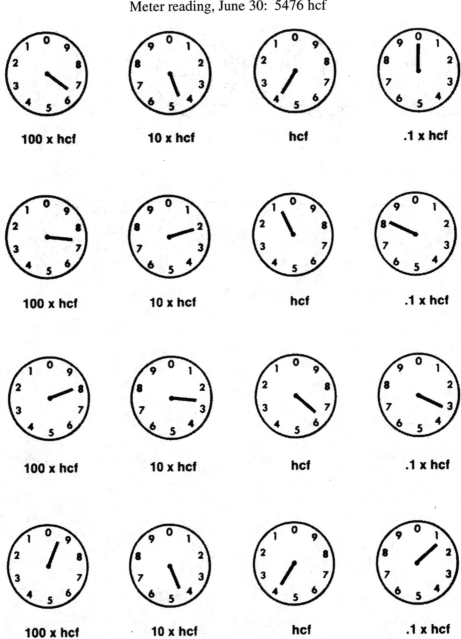

Utility Bills

Teacher Notes

Mathematical skills required:

> subtraction of whole numbers
> multiplication of decimals

New vocabulary:

> adjustment rate
> fuel adjustment
> hundred cubic feet (hcf)
> kilowatt-hour (kwh)
> meter reading rate (cost per kwh or hcf)

Related topics:

> Budgets: Short-term
> Heating Costs
> Housing

Teaching suggestions:

1. Nearly every student will have access to a gas, electric, and/or water meter in his or her own residence. Ask students to make a drawing of their own meters. Have them indicate the location of the hands on the meters at different times for one week. Have them calculate the amount of gas, electricity, or water used during this week.

2. Obtain rate charts for gas, electric, and/or water use in your own community. Often, these rates are printed on the back of a monthly bill. Using these rates, students should be able to calculate the cost of gas, electricity, and/or water from their results above.

3. Discuss the practice of allowing different rates for gas, electricity, and water for (1) different types of users (i.e., residential, religious, commercial, industrial, etc.) and (2) different levels of use. What are the advantages, disadvantages, and consequences of this policy for the company involved and for the general community?

Chapter Twenty-Seven
Vacation Planning

53. Vacation Planning

Did you ever think of a vacation as a mathematical problem? You may be planning a boat cruise around the world or a three-day camping trip. But there are certain mathematical questions that have to be answered for every vacation trip. These include such problems as the costs of:

1. *Travel:* Getting to and from the place you have chosen for a vacation.

2. *Housing:* Paying for a place to live at the vacation site.

3. *Meals:* Eating while you are going to and from the vacation site and while you are there.

4. *Incidental expenses:* Entertainment, sight-seeing tours, souvenir purchases, laundry, and the like.

The solved problem below shows how mathematics is involved in the planning of one vacation.

● **Example:**

Joy, Andrea, and Violet are planning a two-week camping trip to Northern Ontario. Listed below are their anticipated expenses. Determine the cost of the trip for each person.

Travel: Bus from Windsor to Timmos: $62.80 per person, one way, with 10% discount for round-trip. Hike to campsite.

Housing: Purchase of tent and camping equipment: $250.00 total cost.

Meals: Purchase of groceries: $6 per day total cost.

Incidental expenses: $2 per day per person.

Solution:

The calculations are shown below for each individual.

Travel: Cost of round-trip bus fare = $62.80 \times 2 - 10\% \times (\$62.80 \times 2)$
$$= \$125.60 - \$12.56$$
$$= \$113.04 \text{ per person}$$

Housing: Cost per person = Total cost ÷ 3
$$= \$250.00 \div 3$$
$$= \$83.33 \text{ per person}$$

Meals = Total cost for 14 days ÷ 3
$$= \$6 \text{ per day} \times 14 \text{ days} \div 3$$
$$= \$84.00 \div 3$$
$$= \$28.00 \text{ per person}$$

Incidental expenses = Cost per day × Number of days
$$= \$2 \text{ per day} \times 14 \text{ days}$$
$$= \$28 \text{ per person}$$

Total cost per person = $113.04 + $83.33 + $28.00 + $28.00
$$= \$252.37$$

© 1983, 1996 Instructional Horizons. Produced and Distributed
by J. Weston Walch, Publisher, Portland, Maine 04104-0658

Consumer Math Success Kit

53. Vacation Planning

● **Extra Solved Example:**

Andy and Tony live in Denver. They are planning to visit Houston for one week. They are planning to travel by air and stay at Arthur's Economy Motel in downtown Houston. Their estimated expenses for the trip are listed below. From this information, calculate the probable cost of this trip for each person.

> Airfare, Denver-Houston-Denver: $138.00 per person, one way.
>
> Arthur's Economy Motel: $34.50 per day for two persons + 6.5% tax.
>
> Meals: $12 per person per day.
>
> Incidental expenses: $10 per person per day.

(Assume that Andy and Tony will be gone eight full days and seven nights.)

Solution:

1. Travel costs (per person)
   - = One-way airfare × 2 (for round-trip)
   - = $138.00 × 2
   - = $276.00

2. Housing costs (for both)
   Tax
   - = Cost of room + Tax
   - = 6.5% × $34.50
   - = 0.065 × $34.50
   - = $2.24

   Daily cost
   - = $34.50 + $2.24
   - = $36.74

   Cost per week
   - = Daily cost × 7 days
   - = $36.74 × 7
   - = $257.18

   Cost for each person
   - = Total cost ÷ 2
   - = $257.18 ÷ 2
   - = $128.59

3. Meals (per person)
   - = Cost per day × Number of days
   - = $12 × 8
   - = $96

4. Incidental expenses (per person)
   - = Cost per day × Number of days
   - = $10 × 8
   - = $80

Total cost per person = Travel + Housing + Meals + Incidentals
   = $276.00 + $128.59 + $96.00 + $80.00
   = $580.59

© 1983, 1996 Instructional Horizons. Produced and Distributed
by J. Weston Walch, Publisher, Portland, Maine 04104-0658   *300*

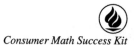

Consumer Math Success Kit

53. Vacation Planning

1. Christie and Judy are planning a vacation at Yellowstone National Park. The one-way bus fare to Yellowstone from their hometown is $120.00 per person. Their camping fees will be $7.00 per night for the campsite. They will be gone eight nights. What will be the cost for each person for this trip (travel and housing only)?

   _____

2. The Maguires are planning a four-day/three-night trip to New York City. The train fare will be $37.25 per person each way, and the hotel room will cost $65.50 per night. Besides Mr. and Mrs. Maguire, there are three children in the family, all of whom pay full train fares. What will be the cost of transportation and housing for this vacation?

   _____

3. Bob and Pierre are planning a five-day/four-night camping trip at Ketchikan Lake. The one-way bus fare from their hometown is $49.50, but there is a 10% discount for round-trip tickets. Their campsite will cost $9.50 per night. They estimate that they will have to spend a total of $8.00 per day on food, and they want to have another $2.50 each for incidental expenses. How much will this vacation cost each person?

   _____

4. The four children in the Foster family have decided to treat their parents to a vacation in New Orleans. The whole family will fly from their hometown and stay five days (four nights) in a hotel in New Orleans. The one-way airfare is $98.00 for each person. The hotel will cost $82.25 per night. Meals will probably cost about $45.00 per day, and incidentals will come to another $10 per person per day. What will be the total cost of the trip? What will be the cost to each of the four children paying for the trip?

   _____

5. The Sedovic family has been watching for travel bargains in planning their vacation. They have found a flight to Pittsburgh that will cost $59.00 one way for each adult member and 25% off this price for each child in the family. The hotel they have chosen charges $28.50 per night plus $5.50 for each child. Their meals will probably cost $6.75 per person per day, and they have decided to keep incidentals to no more than $5 per person per day. There are two adults and three children in this family. How much will a seven-day, six-night vacation to Pittsburgh cost at these prices?

   _____

Vacation Planning

Teacher Notes

Mathematical skills required:

addition, multiplication, and division of whole numbers and decimals
multiplication of decimals

New vocabulary:

anticipated expenses
housing costs
incidentals
meal expenses

Related topics:

Budgets: Long- and Short-term Budgets
Eating Out
Estimating Answers
Travel (all areas)

Teaching suggestions:

1. This topic provides an excellent opportunity for students to use their mathematical skills in a real-life situation. Ask them to think about a vacation they would like very much to take and that would probably be within their financial means (or those of the family). Then have them estimate the costs for travel, housing, meals, and incidental expenses for this vacation. They may want to consider the costs of alternative ways of doing the vacation (car vs. train; hotel vs. camping, etc.).

2. Invite a local travel agent to talk to the class about options in vacation planning. He or she will know a great deal about ways to cut costs in planning for vacations. Some of the special offers, like those mentioned in Problems 3 and 5 (page 301), can offer substantial savings, but are not always easy to find out about. After the agent's presentation, students may be asked to calculate the costs of certain "special" vacations about which the agent has talked.

Answers to Practice Problems

1. Bank Statements, p. 4:

1. Checkbook: $223.85 + $0.79 − $2.45 = $222.19
   Statement: $227.19 + $25.00 − $30.00 = $222.19
2. Checkbook: $307.87 + $1.19 − $3.15 = $305.91
   Statement: $304.11 + $32.50 − $30.70 = $305.91
3. Checkbook: $45.98 + $1.83 − $6.05 = $41.76
   Statement: $282.19 + $50.00 − $290.43 = $41.76
4. Checkbook: $389.32 + $0.79 − $2.75 = $387.36
   Statement: $434.30 + $252.92 − $299.86 = $387.36

2. Borrowing Money: Promissory Notes, p. 10:

1. $40
2. $37.50
3. $114; $614
4. $1741.88
5. $4851; $5202; $5553

6. a. $80
   b. $96
   c. $28.25
   d. $666
   e. $1019.25

3. Borrowing Money: Short-term Loans, p. 12:

1. $141.98; $283.95; $425.93
2. $177.75; $4322.25
3. $492.71; $7.29; $485.42; $14.58; $478.12; $21.88
4. $50.63; 13.5%
5. $10.70; 7.6%

6. a. $991.25; $8.75
   b. $1942; $57.99
   c. $2438.12; $61.88
   d. $4889.17; 13.3%
   e. $78.38; 11.4%

4. Borrowing Money: Collateral Loans, p. 14:

1. $206.43
2. a. $8.61; $1008.61
   b. $19.20; $1019.20
   c. $46.48; $1546.48
   d. $75.04; $2325.04
   e. $126.12; $1876.12
   f. $275.35; $3775.35
   g. $130.12; $2130.12
   h. 10.8%; $2142.20
   i. 13.4%; $282.39
   j. 11/22; $111.04

5. Borrowing Money: Installment Loans (I), p. 16:

1. Month 1: $97.22 + $42.79 = $140.01
   Month 2: $97.22 + $41.60 = $138.82
   Month 3: $97.22 + $40.41 = $137.63
   Month 4: $97.22 + $39.22 = $136.44
   Month 5: $97.22 + $38.03 = $135.25
   Month 6: $97.22 + $36.84 = $134.06

2. Month 1: $135.42 + $81.79 = $217.21
   Month 2: $135.42 + $80.09 = $215.51
   Month 3: $135.42 + $78.38 = $213.80
   Month 4: $135.42 + $76.68 = $212.10
   Month 5: $135.42 + $74.98 = $210.40
   Month 6: $135.42 + $73.27 = $208.69

3. a. Month 1: $104.17 + $20.42 = $124.59
      Month 2: $104.17 + $19.57 = $123.74
      Month 3: $104.17 + $18.72 = $122.89

   b. Month 1: $83.33 + $16.38 = $99.71
      Month 2: $83.33 + $15.47 = $98.80
      Month 3: $83.33 + $14.56 = $97.89

   c. Month 1: $116.67 + $17.21 = $133.88
      Month 2: $116.67 + $16.06 = $132.73
      Month 3: $116.67 + $14.91 = $131.58

   d. Month 1: $79.17 + $8.55 = $87.72
      Month 2: $79.17 + $7.84 = $87.01
      Month 3: $79.17 + $7.12 = $86.29

   e. Month 1: $83.33 + $6.19 = $89.52
      Month 2: $83.33 + $5.50 = $88.83
      Month 3: $83.33 + $4.81 = $88.14

4. Month 1: $69.44 + $18.85 = $88.29
   Month 2: $69.44 + $17.81 = $87.25
   Month 3: $69.44 + $16.76 = $86.20
   Month 4: $69.44 + $15.71 = $85.15

5. Month 1: $43.75 + $13.56 = $57.31
   Month 2: $43.75 + $13.00 = $56.75
   Month 3: $43.75 + $12.43 = $56.18
   Month 4: $43.75 + $11.87 = $55.62

6. Borrowing Money: Installment Loans (II), p. 18:

1. a. $57.83; b. $144.58; c. $289.17

2. a. $120.00; $93.33
   b. $30.00; $88.33
   c. $180.00; $363.33
   d. $595.00; $341.25
   e. $121.50; $31.75
   f. $85.25; $52.94
   g. $147.00; $357.83
   h. $37.80; $48.48
   i. $139.69; $59.31
   j. $642.60; $41.51

3. 16.2%

4. 12.8%

5. a. 13.4%; b. 14.1%; c. 10.9%

7. **Borrowing Money: Mortgage Loans, p. 20:**

   1. Month 1: Interest $495.83; Principal: $14.72
      Month 2: Interest $495.69; Principal: $14.86
      Month 3: Interest $495.54; Principal: $15.01

   2. Month 1: Interest $573.75; Principal: $18.65
      Month 2: Interest $573.50; Principal: $18.90
      Month 3: Interest $573.24; Principal: $19.16

   3. Month 1: Interest $1727.00; Principal: $15.80
      Month 2: Interest $1726.79; Principal: $16.01
      Month 3: Interest $1726.58; Principal: $16.22

   4. Mortgage amount: $31,800
      Month 1: Interest: $378.95; Principal: $16.85
      Month 2: Interest: $378.75; Principal: $17.05
      Month 3: Interest: $378.55; Principal: $17.25
      Month 4: Interest: $378.34; Principal: $17.46
      Month 5: Interest: $378.13; Principal: $17.67
      Month 6: Interest: $377.92; Principal: $17.88

   5. Mortgage amount: $85,875
      Month 1: Interest: $1,238.03; Principal: $27.47
      Month 2: Interest: $1,237.64; Principal: $27.86
      Month 3: Interest: $1,237.23; Principal: $28.27
      Month 4: Interest: $1,236.83; Principal: $28.67
      Month 5: Interest: $1,236.41; Principal: $29.09
      Month 6: Interest: $1,235.99; Principal: $29.51

8. **Budgets: Long-term Budgets, pp. 26–27:**

   1. $500; $50
   2. $433.33
   3. $570
   4. $123.50
   5. $35.42 per year for 12 years
   6. Washing machine: $52.86 for 7 years; Refrigerator: $82.86 for 7 years; Television set: $69.44 for 9 years; Electric range: $42.50 for 10 years
   7. Refrigerator: $82.86 per year; $6.90 per month
      Washing machine: $52.86; $4.40. Dryer: $50.00; $4.17
      Sewing machine: $15.23; $1.27
   8. Saving $4000 per year, it will take just over 11 years; saving $7000 per year, it will take just over 6 years.

9. **Budgets: Short-term Budgets, pp. 29–30:**

   1. Food: $411.74   Housing: $137.25
      Clothing: $490.17   Automobile expenses: $235.28

2. Food: $329.47   Recreation: $62.76
    Housing: $392.23   Gifts: $47.07
    Clothing: $109.82   Insurance: $78.45
    Personal care: $31.38   Taxes: $141.20
    Medical care: $78.45   Savings: $47.07
    Automobile expenses: $188.27   Other: $62.76

3. Spent more than average on personal care; automobile expenses; recreation; gifts; and savings. Spent less than average on food; housing; medical care; insurance; and other expenses. An "average" distribution of their $2,457.68 income would have been (in same order as table):
    Food: $516.11   Recreation: $98.31
    Housing: $614.42   Gifts: $73.73
    Clothing: $172.04   Insurance: $122.88
    Personal care: $49.15   Taxes: $221.19
    Medical care: $122.88   Savings: $73.73
    Automobile expenses: $294.92   Other: $98.31

4. Monthly income: $2,632.97; budgeted items (in same order as in table):
    Food: $552.92   Recreation: $210.64
    Housing: $526.59   Gifts: $78.99
    Clothing: $184.31   Insurance: $131.65
    Personal care: $157.98   Taxes: $263.30
    Medical care: $131.65   Savings: $131.65
    Automobile expenses: $157.98   Other: $105.32

5. Incomes (maximum to minimum): $3840.00; $3200.00; $2560.00
    Budgets (maximum to minimum in each category):
    Purchase of equipment: $691.20; $576.00; $460.80
    Purchase of supplies: $844.80; $704.00; $563.20
    Repairs: $576.00; $480.00; $384.00
    Advertising: $384.00; $320.00; $256.00
    Taxes: $460.80; $384.00; $307.20
    Other expenses: $230.40; $192.00; $153.60
    Profit: $652.80; $544.00; $435.20.

10. Checking Accounts (I), p. 36:

1. $604.20;   2. $399.92;   3. $177.55;   4. $226.06

10. Checking Accounts (II), p. 37:

1. $189.06;   2. $546.43;   3. $175.12;   4. $485.06

10. Checking Accounts (III), p. 38:

1. $1520.20;   2. $592.45;   3. $1536.95

11. Credit: Retail Store Charge Accounts, pp. 44–45:

1. Previous balance: $140.41
   New charges: $146.06
   Payments: $50.00
   Finance charge: $1.36
   New balance: $237.83
   Minimum payment due: $35.67

2. Previous balance: $237.83
   New charges: $96.35
   Payments: $40.00
   Finance charge: $2.97
   New balance: $297.15
   Minimum payment due: $44.57

3. Previous balance: $376.10
   New charges: $121.55
   Payments: $93.50
   Finance charge: $4.24
   New balance: $408.39
   Minimum payment due: $61.26

4. Previous balance: $429.67
   New charges: $218.98
   Payments: $50.00
   Finance charge: $5.70
   New balance: $604.35
   Minimum payment due: $90.65

5. Previous balance: $506.37
   New charges: $188.31
   Payments: $150.00
   Finance charge: $5.35
   New balance: $550.03
   Minimum payment due: $82.50

12. Credit: Installment Buying, p. 47:

1. $675; 25%
2. $550.02; 19.8%
3. $59.38; 11.1%
4. $20.00; 20.8%
5. $410; 19.4%
6. 11%; $110.63
7. $415.52; 11.1%
8. 3.5%; $940.08

13. Credit: Budget Accounts, p. 49:

1. $34.83
2. $69.67
3. $85.83
4. $103.73
5. $112.61
6. 12.7%; 1.06%
7. 14.9%; 1.24%
8. 14.7%; 1.22%; $5.51

14. Credit: Credit, Charge, and Bank Cards, pp. 51–52:

1. Finance charge: $0.49
   New balance: $170.73
   Minimum payment due: $20.00

2. Finance charge: $2.26
   New balance: $251.14
   Minimum payment due: $20.00

3. Finance charge: $3.47
   New balance: $608.06
   Minimum payment due: $32.50

4. Finance charge: $21.03
   New balance: $1933.41
   Minimum payment due: $103.34

15. Eating Out, p. 59:

1. $4.60
2. $7.70; $.31; $8.01
3. $15.45; $.62; $16.07
4. $16.35; $.65; $17.00
5. $27.70; $1.52; $29.22; $5.54; $34.76
6. $26.15; $1.31; $27.46; $2.62; $30.08; $6.02

16. Electronic Funds Transfer Systems, p. 64:

1. Interest paid: $1.60
   Charges: $0.06
   Balance: $336.26

2. Interest paid: $0.96
   Charges: $0.12
   Balance: $437.10

3. Interest paid: $2.18
   Charges: $0.12
   Balance: $424.16

4. Interest paid: $1.16
   Charges: $0.18
   Balance: $324.71

17. Estimating Answers, p. 70:

(*Note:* In any of these problems, other estimates are possible.)

1. $14; $36
2. $18; $2
3. $5
4. 2 m^3
5. $58
6. $66; $4
7. $11; $4
8. $13.20
9. two cans; $48
10. $94; $6

18. Excise Tax, p. 76:

1. $3.34; $70.82
2. $93.00
3. Yes ($195.64)
4. $265.38
5. $121.56
6. $79.99
7. $236.00
8. $335.01
9. Total cost of ticket: $350.00; yes, she has enough.
10. $37.54
11. $0.88
12. $1.21; $2.02

19. Grocery Shopping: Finding the Cost, p. 82:

1. $4.57; $0.43
2. $10.09; $4.91
3. $6.63
4. Yes ($21.60; $1.08; $22.68; change: $2.32)
5. $22.00; $0.66; $22.66
6. $24.75; $1.24; $25.99; $4.01

20. Grocery Shopping: Unit Pricing, p. 84:

1. $2.00 per pound
2. $1.25 per box
3. $1.67 per pound
4. $0.21 per apple
5. $0.40; $0.40; $0.45 (per pound)
6. $1.50; $1.40; $1.20 (per pound)
7. $0.33; $0.30; $0.28 (per can)
8. $1.70; $1.50; $1.40 (per pound)
9. 8.2¢; 8.7¢; 8.9¢ (per ounce)
10. $1.78; $1.19; $0.93 (per kilogram)
11. $3.16; $3.14; $0.84 (per kilogram)
12. 24.3¢; 21.8¢; 17.9¢ (per ounce)

21. Grocery Shopping: Discount Food Stores, p. 86:

1. $3.87; $3.27; $3.03
2. $16.59; $14.69; $13.71
3. $23.78; $20.74; $19.29
4. $18.09; $15.78; $14.80
5. $26.73; $24.22; $21.74
6. $37.44; $32.15; $29.62

22. **Grocery Shopping: Sales, p. 88:**

    1. $18.48; $17.98; $17.58
    2. $12.91; $12.83; $12.53
    3. $29.31; $26.70; $24.92
    4. $29.52; $27.01; $26.18
    5. $22.76; $20.43; $19.40
    6. $23.28; $21.55; $20.86

23. **Grocery Shopping: Discount Coupons, p. 91:**

    1. $13.69; $11.54; $10.71
    2. $20.61; $16.31; $18.09
    3. $5.32; $3.22; $3.20
    4. $24.59; $19.18; $21.51
    5. $51.68; $44.18; $44.02
    6. $23.89; $16.01; $18.52

24. **Heating Costs, p. 98:**

    1. $169.82
    2. $186.00
    3. $200.48
    4. $211.18
    5. $407.79
    6. $661.57
    7. 799.2 gallons; $718.48
    8. 4206.5 liters; $954.88

25. **Home Care: Painting, pp. 106–107:**

    1. 2 pints
    2. 2 pints; $9.90
    3. 1 gallon; $18.95
    4. 838 ft^2; 3 gallons; $56.85
    5. 1950 ft^2; 7 gallons; $174.65
    6. 1865.36 ft^2; 10 gallons (for two coats); $217.90

    7. a. 112 ft^2; $23.90
        b. 150 ft^2; $35.85
        c. 112.5 ft^2; $23.90
        d. 107.25 ft^2; $23.90
        e. 75 ft^2; $23.90
        f. 150.37 ft^2; $35.85

    8. a. 177 ft^2; $47.50
        b. 761.3 ft^2; $166.25
        c. 152.05 ft^2; $47.50
        d. 416.9 ft^2; $95.00

26. **Home Care: Wallpapering, p. 109:**

    1. 320 ft^2; 11 rolls; $175.45
    2. 468 ft^2; 16 rolls; $255.20
    3. 368 ft^2; 13 rolls; $233.35
    4. 325.94 ft^2; 10 rolls; $199.90
    5. 485 ft^2; 17 rolls; $271.83

    6. a. 292 ft^2; 10 rolls; $139.50
        b. 252 ft^2; 9 rolls; $89.55
        c. 320.94 ft^2; 11 rolls; $175.45
        d. 256.94 ft^2; 9 rolls; $152.55
        e. 324.44 ft^2; 11 rolls; $252.45

27. **Home Care: Yard Work, p. 111:**

    1. 3200 ft^2; 8 boxes; $111.60
    2. 6000 ft^2; 10 boxes; $269.50
    3. 802.58 ft^2; 3 boxes; $59.97
    4. 748.96 ft^2; 3 bottles; $47.85

    5. a. 340 ft^2; 2 bags; $53.90; 1 bag; $37.25
        b. 1200 ft^2; 4 bags; $107.80; 1 bag; $37.25
        c. 660 ft^2; 3 bags; $80.85; 1 bag; $37.25
        d. 1094.32 ft^2; 4 bags; $107.80; 1 bag; $37.25
        e. 1128.51 ft^2; 4 bags; $107.80; 1 bag; $37.25

28. Home Care: Patios and Driveways (I), p. 113:

1. 1670 ft^2; 5 bags; $92.50
2. 112 ft^2; 504 bricks; $141.12
3. 112 blocks; $54.88
4. 56 ft^3; 2 bags; $17.14
5. 128.58 ft^2; 129 blocks @ $63.21; 3 bags @ $25.71; Total cost: $89.41
6. 115.68 m^2; 4 cans; $131.96; 3856 bricks; $1349.60; 5 bags; $129.25

28. Home Care: Patios and Driveways (II), p. 114:

1. 700 ft^2; 3 cans; $73.50
2. 647.50 ft^2; 2 cans; $49.00
3. 66.5 ft^2; 5 rolls; $319.95
4. 233.1 ft^2; 16 rolls; $1023.84
5. For each court: 1248 m^2; 9 cans material; $269.55; 3 cans paint; $97.50
   Total cost: $367.05   For six courts: $2202.30
   (Answer will differ slightly if total area of courts is taken first.)

29. Home Care: Carpentry, pp. 116–117:

1. 48 ft^2; 48 board feet; $52.32
2. 195 ft^2; 195 board feet; $154.05
3. 187.68 ft^2; $219.59
4. a. $364.50   c. $253.60
   b. $358.36   d. $354.80

30. Housing, p. 122:

1. $375.00; $187.50
2. $316.67; $116.67
3. $320.38; $116.50
4. $261.35
5. $27,308.50; $106,000
6. $54,250.00; $211,200
7. $21,638.00; $120,487.50

31. Income: Wages, p. 128:

1. $403.00
2. $330.00; $245.53
3. $310.00; $264.80
4. $602.00; $462.61
5. $1209.30; $922.55

32. Income: Salaries, p. 130:

1. $788.46; $565.64
2. $701.92; $508.50
3. $876.62; $650.07
4. $1172.29; $840.06
5. $765.24; $572.26

33. Income: Commissions, p. 132:

1. $200.00
2. $439.78
3. $278.69
4. $938.81; $866.99
5. $3577.77
6. no; no
7. $573.13; $507.29
8. $267.42

34. Income Tax, p. 178:

1. Income tax: $1511.00;
   Refund: $1393.35

2. Income tax: $3865.00;
   Refund: $179.36

3. Income tax: $1826.00;
   Refund: $863.91

4. Income tax: $3963.00;
   Owes: $320.83

5. Income tax: $3361.00;
   Refund: $2461.13

6. Income tax: $3179.00
   Refund: $3730.02

35. Insurance: Homeowners, p. 190:

1. $1385.53

2. $1289.03 (annual); $322.26 (per quarter)

3. $2538.39; (one annual payment); $2596.77 (total annual charge if premium is paid quarterly); $649.19 (per quarter)

4. $1492.71; $100.01 (extra)

5. $357.29 per month

6. $1074.22

7. $274.73 (per quarter); $95.52 (per month)

8. $5417.39 (annual); $481.70 (monthly)

36. Insurance: Life, p. 194:

1. $85.30

2. $283.30

3. $284.80; $991.20; $484.00; $104.60

4. $377.00

5. $792.50; $203.08; $69.34

6. $597.50

7. $4763.00

8. $11,307.50

37. Insurance: Health and Medical, p. 198:

1. Company: -0-; Patient: $38.00

2. Company: $2.00; Patient: $13 + $50 = $63

3. Company: $67.20 – $50.00 = $17.20;
   Patient: $43.80 + $50.00 = $93.80

4. Company: $1151.23 – $50.00 = $1101.23;
   Patient: $108.54 + $50.00 = $158.54

5. Company: $5663.69 – $50.00 = $5613.69;
   Patient: $363.80 + $50.00 = $413.80

6. Company: $14,677.73 – $100 = $14,577.73;
   Patient:$113.06 + $100.00 = $213.06

7. Company: $61,467.16 – $100.00 = $61,367.16;
   Patient: $1073.64 + $100.00 = $1173.64

38. Insurance: Automobile, p. 201:

1. $167.38

2. $376.79

3. $587.06

4. $392.74 (annually); $34.53 (monthly)

5. $426.05 (annually); $37.77 (monthly)

39. Interest (I), p. 207:

1. $5.00; $105.00
2. $11.50
3. $7.88; $307.88
4. $681.41
5. $5.00
6. $420.25
7. $14.55; $264.55
8. $394.28
9. $500.56

39. Interest (II), p. 209:

1. 6%
2. 6%
3. 5.8%
4. 8.1%
5. 18% (annually); 1.5% (monthly)
6. 18% (annually); 1.5% (monthly)
7. 13.2% (annually); 1.1% (monthly)
8. 14.7% (annually); 1.23% (monthly)

40. Investing Money: Stocks, p. 214:

1. $3400.00 (cost of stock); $27.50 (broker's commission); $3427.50 (total cost)
2. $3452.69
3. $11,687.50
4. $1884.77
5. 84 shares
6. $39.41
7. $3500.00 (current value); $28.25 (broker's commission); $3471.75 (net to Cynthia); $44.25 (profit)
8. $1793.75 (current value); $15.45 (broker's commission); $1778.30 (net to Rudie); $106.47 (loss)

41. Investing Money: Bonds, p. 218:

1. $7200.00; $36.00; $7236.00
2. $8700.00
3. $43.50; $8743.50
4. 30
5. $20.48; $2484.23
6. $77,250.00; $193.13; $77,443.13
7. $7300.00; $36.50; $27.50
8. $8450.00; $42.25; $8407.75; $292.25 (loss)
9. $81,125.00; $202.81; $80,922.19; $3479.06

42. Nutrition, p. 225:

Tables for these three problems follow on pages 313, 314, and 315.

43. Property Taxes, p. 234:

1. $8227.13
2. $325.89
3. $1849.44
4. $2820.30 and $642.39
5. $952.37
6. $573.22 plus $485.47, for a total tax of $1058.69
7. $5.95

44. Recipes, pp. 240–241:

1. 2 cans tuna; $\frac{1}{2}$ cup chopped celery; 1 cup mayonnaise; $\frac{1}{2}$ tsp salt

2. 2 cups chopped beef; $\frac{5}{6}$ cup chopped onion; $\frac{1}{4}$ cup shortening; 2 cups chopped potatoes; 2 tbsp parsley; $\frac{2}{3}$ cup water; $\frac{1}{4}$ tsp salt; $\frac{1}{4}$ tsp pepper

3. 3 onions; 3 bay leaves; 3 tsp paprika; 9 slices lemon; 3 tsp salt; 3 lbs fish filets; 9 sprigs parsley; 3 tsp pepper

4. 10 eggs; $\frac{5}{16}$ tsp pepper; $\frac{5}{8}$ cup water; 5 tbsp chopped onion; $\frac{5}{8}$ tsp salt; $2\frac{1}{2}$ tbsp butter

5. $1\frac{1}{2}$ pkg cream cheese; $1\frac{1}{2}$ tsp vanilla; $1\frac{1}{2}$ tbsp milk; $3\frac{3}{4}$ cups confectioner's sugar

6. 4 cups chopped cabbage; $\frac{1}{2}$ cup sour cream; $\frac{2}{5}$ tsp salt; $\frac{3}{5}$ tsp caraway seed; $\frac{1}{5}$ cup chopped onion; $\frac{1}{5}$ cup mayonnaise; $\frac{2}{5}$ tsp dry mustard

7. 3 or 4 onions; $2\frac{1}{2}$ tsp baking powder; $2\frac{1}{5}$ cups milk; $\frac{5}{6}$ tsp salt; $1\frac{2}{3}$ cups flour; $1\frac{2}{3}$ tsp pepper

45. Sales Tax, p. 246:

1. $9.48 + $.28 = $9.76

2. $1.26; $26.41

3. $10.41 + $0.68 = $11.09

4. $27.85 + $1.11 = $28.96

5. $33.11

6. Massachusetts: $309.75; New Hampshire: $299.95

7. $103.23 + $4.65 = $107.88

(continued on page 317)

Table 42: Nutrition—Solution, Practice Problem 1

Food	Amount	Calories	Protein (g)	Calcium (mg)	Iron (mg)	Vitamin A (mg)	Thiamine (mg)	Riboflavin (mg)	Niacin (mg)	Ascorbic Acid (mg)
Puffed wheat	3 oz	315	12	24	3.6	–0–	.45	.21	6.6	–0–
Skim milk	2 cups	180	tr*	596	.2	4	.20	.88	.4	4
Sugar	2 tbsp	90	–0–	–0–	tr*	–0–	–0–	–0–	–0–	–0–
Orange juice	1 cup	115	2	27	.7	100	.22	.06	.9	122
Lettuce	⅛ head	7.5	.5	11.4	.29	37.5	.04	.03	.16	3.6
Celery	1 stalk	5	tr*	16	.1	20	.01	.01	.1	4
Carrot	1	20	1	18	.4	1100	.03	.03	.3	4
Tomato	1	35	2	20	.8	270	.10	.06	1.0	34
Lamb chops	2	800	50	20	3.0	–0–	.28	.50	11.2	–0–
Rice	1 cup	185	3	17	1.5	–0–	.19	.01	1.6	–0–
Squash	1 cup	30	2	52	.8	164	.10	.16	1.6	21
Cola	1 cup	95	–0–	–0–	–0–	–0–	–0–	–0–	–0–	–0–
Apricots	1 cup	220	2	28	.8	902	.05	.06	.9	10
Totals		2097.5	74.5	829.4	12.2	2597.5	1.67	2.01	24.76	202.6
For comparison, RDA's =		2100	46	1200	18	800	1.1	1.3	14	60

*tr = trace

Table 42: Nutrition—Solution, Practice Problem 2

Food	Amount	Calories	Protein (g)	Calcium (mg)	Iron (mg)	Vitamin A (mg)	Thiamine (mg)	Riboflavin (mg)	Niacin (mg)	Ascorbic Acid (mg)
Fresh grapefruit juice	1 cup	95	1	22	.5	4	.09	.04	.4	92
Sugar-coated cornflakes	5 oz	550	5	15	1.5	-0-	.60	.05	2.5	-0-
Sugar	7 tsp	105	-0-	-0-	tr*	-0-	-0-	-0-	-0-	-0-
Cream	1 tsp	10	tr*	5	tr*	8.7	tr*	tr*	tr*	tr*
Whole milk	1 cup	160	9	288	0.1	70	0.08	0.42	0.1	2
Coffee (black)	1 cup	-0-	-0-	-0-	-0-	-0-	-0-	-0-	-0-	-0-
Eggs (scrambled)	3	330	21	153	3.3	405	.15	.54	tr*	-0-
American cheese	1 cup	480	32	832	1.6	288	tr*	.48	tr*	-0-
White bread	3 slices	180	6	57	1.8	tr*	.18	.15	1.8	tr*
Butter	7 pats	350	---	7	-0-	322	---	---	---	-0-
Apples	2	140	tr*	16	.8	20	.08	.04	.2	6
Cola	2 cups	190	-0-	---	---	-0-	-0-	-0-	-0-	-0-
Pork chops	2	520	32	16	4.4	-0-	1.26	.36	7.6	40
Baked potatoes	2	180	6	18	1.4	tr*	.20	.08	3.4	11
Sour cream	½ cup	245	3.5	118	.5	186	.28	.24	3.0	11
Sweet corn	3 ears	210	9	6	1.5	186	.27	.24	3.0	21
Cherry pie	2 pieces	710	8	38	.8	236	.06	.06	1.2	2
Ice cream	2 slices†	290	6	174	.2	144	.06	.26	.2	2
Totals		4745	138.5	1765	18.4	1869.7	3.31	2.96	23.4	176
For comparison, RDA's =		2800	56	1200	18	1000	1.4	1.7	18	60

*tr = trace
†1 slice - 1/8 quart

Table 42: Nutrition—Solution, Practice Problem 3

Food	Amount	Calories	Protein (g)	Calcium (mg)	Iron (mg)	Vitamin A (mg)	Thiamine (mg)	Riboflavin (mg)	Niacin (mg)	Ascorbic Acid (mg)
Orange juice	1 cup	115	2	27	.7	100	.22	.06	.9	122
Eggs	2	220	14	102	2.2	270	.1	.36	tr*	-0-
Bacon	2 slices	100	5	2	.5	-0-	.08	.05	.8	-0-
Bread, whole wheat	5 slices	275	10	115	2.5	tr*	.3	.15	3.5	tr*
Butter	2 pats	100	tr*	2	-0-	92	-0-	-0-	-0-	-0-
Skim milk	6 cups	540	tr*	1788	.6	12	.6	2.64	1.2	12
Ham	2 oz	164	12	5	1.5	-0-	.27	.11	2.1	-0-
Lettuce	⅛ head	7.5	.5	11.4	.3	38	.04	.03	.16	3.6
Tomato	½	17.5	1	10	.40	135	.05	.03	.5	17
Mayonnaise	1 tbsp	65	tr*	2	tr*	6	tr*	tr*	tr*	-0-
Apple	1	70	tr*	8	.4	10	.04	.02	.1	3
Brownies	2	190	2	16	.8	16	.08	.04	.2	tr*
Chicken	1 breast	310	50	18	2.6	28	.08	.34	22.4	-0-
Beans	1 cup	30	2	62	.8	136	.08	.11	.6	16
Noodles	1 cup	200	7	16	1.4	22	.23	.14	1.8	-0-
Pie	1 slice	355	4	19	.4	118	.03	.03	.6	1
Totals		2759	109.5	2203.4	15.1	983	2.20	4.11	34.86	174.6
For comparison, RDA's =		2700	45	1200	18	1000	1.4	1.6	18	50

*tr = trace

46. **Savings Accounts, p. 252:**

1. $15.90
2. $25.69; $26.38
3. $35.50; $36.00; $36.51
4. $50.69; $51.39; $52.82

5. $106.20; $105.35
6. $251.15; $252.30; $253.46
7. $532.50; $527.88; $526.77
8. $30.13; $30.27; $30.40

47. **Telephone Bills, p. 259:**

1. $26.04;   2. $33.99;   3. $46.36;   4. $58.47;   5. $157.97

48. **Travel: Taxis, p. 265:**

1. $1.80
2. $1.60
3. $5.50

4. $3.30
5. $2.10
6. $6.10

7. $7.65
8. $12.48
9. $14.80

49. **Travel: Automobile Expenses, pp. 268-269:**

1. 166.67 gallons; 5 quarts
2. $223.08 + $2.38 = $225.46
3. $426.47 + $2.38 = $428.85
4. $393.46 + $12.50 = $405.96
5. Subcompact: $1032.00 + $28.56 = $1060.56
   Compact: $1338.46 + $11.90 = $1350.36
   Intermediate: $1023.53 + $5.95 = $1029.48
6. Subcompact: $655.77 + $21.25 = $677.02
   Compact: $872.72 + $8.75 = $881.47
   Intermediate: $640.00 + $5.00 = $645.00
7. $344.00 + $9.52 + $24.88 + $11.88 = $390.28
8. $511.76 + $3.57 + $39.98 + $11.88 = $567.19
9. Answers are arranged in same order as items in Table 13, page 270:
   $533.09 + $3.57 + $39.98 + $11.88 + $250.00 + $915.60 + $756.00 = $2510.12
10. $1533.65 + $13.09 + $29.88 + $11.88 + $325.00 + $850.50 + $761.25 = $3525.25
11. $918.07 + $30.00 + $24.88 + $11.88 + $225.00 + $52.65 + $58.05 = $1320.53
12. Subcompact: $1827.50 + $51.17 + $24.88 + $11.88 + $225.00 + $61.43 +
    $67.73 = $2269.59
    Compact: $2370.19 + $20.23 + $29.88 + $11.88 + $325.00 + $757.35 +
    $677.88 = $4192.41
    Intermediate: $1812.50 + $10.71 + $39.98 + $11.88 + $250.00 + $1503.11 +
    $1241.10 = $4869.28

50. Travel: Other Motorized Vehicles, p. 272:

1. $11.73; $1.19; $12.92
2. $67.89; $3.57; $71.46
3. $23.93; $1.25; $25.18
4. $101.85; $4.76; $106.61
5. $67.89 + $3.57 + $16.50 + $9.50 + $100.00 + $539.00 + $347.90 = $1084.36
6. $128.62 + $5.00 + $12.50 + $8.50 + $65.00 + $42.00 + $41.65 = $303.27
7. $64.94 + $2.50 + $14.50 + $9.50 + $75.00 + $299.25 + $255.36 = $721.05

51. Travel: Bus Schedules, p. 276:

1. 40 min
2. 60 min
3. 40 min
4. 28 min
5. 1 hr 19 min for both #112 and #118
6. Both #105 and #107: 31 min

51. Travel: Train Schedules, p. 280:

1. 3hr 2 min
2. 1 hr 8 min
3. #64: 2 hr 35 min
4. #157: 4 hr 46 min
5. #193: 1 hr 8 min; #157: 1 hr 3 min
6. #66: 4 hr 25 min
7. No
8. No; #44: 48 min

52. Utility Bills: Gas, Electric, and Water (I), pp. 289–291:

1. $51.33; $45.93; $70.24; $65.51
2. $73.15; $68.24; $92.47; $83.70
3. $58.83 + $32.60 = $91.43 ($85.55); $55.94 + $31.41 = $87.35 ($81.76); $64.31 + $35.61 = $99.92 ($93.49); $42.03 + $23.29 = $65.32 ($61.12)

52. Utility Bills: Gas, Electric, and Water (II), pp. 292-294:

1. $49.98; $59.44; $66.19; $58.08
2. $91.64; $94.21; $89.91; $80.25
3. $71.34 + $39.52 = $110.86 ($103.73); $56.83 + $31.49 = $88.32 ($82.64); $78.07 + $43.26 = $121.33 ($113.53); $87.17 + $48.30 = $135.47 ($126.75)

53. Vacation Planning, p. 301:

1. $268.00;   2. $569.00; $3. $140.60;   4. $507.50;   5. $1182.75